INDUSTRIAL ELECTRONICS
Devices, Circuits and Applications

Edward F. Driscoll

Professor, Electronics
Fitchburg State College
Fitchburg, Mass. 01420

american technical society · chicago, 60637

Preface

Electronics is becoming increasingly important in operation and control of industrial equipment and processes. Electronics adds greatly to the precision, repeatability and reliability of processes and products. As modern technology expands, the number of industrial applications is expected to multiply.

The purpose of this industrial electronics text is to help meet the ever-increasing needs of technicians and other industrial personnel. The level of content is suitable for technical institutes, community colleges, secondary industrial curricula and industrial training programs. The subject matter is presented in a non-mathematical, descriptive format rather than in a mathematical, quantitative manner. It is intended for the technician rather than for the engineer. A mathematics background is not required. However, knowledge of elementary electricity and electronics is a prerequisite.

The field of industrial electronics has expanded so rapidly in recent years that no single text could cover all areas. In this book the material presented is divided into six *Units,* each covering a broad range of topics as shown in the *General Contents* which is an index of the *Units* and the *Sections* in each *Unit.* In addition, each *Unit* contains its own individual *Contents,* listing all topics covered in each of its Sections. Also, each *Unit* has its own *List of Illustrations,* its own *Laboratory Procedures* Section, its own set of *Review Questions* and *Answers to Review Questions.* With this arrangement, information can be located easily while each *Unit* or area of study remains independent of the others.

The general plan of the text consists of: (1) discussions and illustrations of industrial electronic devices, their construction, characteristics, advantages, disadvantages and applications; (2) a set of laboratory experiences which provide "hands-on" opportunities for observation and study of operating characteristics and applications of a variety of these devices. Although the text materials are arranged in a certain sequence, each *Unit* stands alone, with no one *Unit* prerequisite to another. Consequently, any convenient sequence may be followed.

To obtain maximum benefit from these materials a good procedure to follow might be: study and discussion of the text, followed by the related laboratory work. The lab work will provide worthwhile experiences with basic device operation and representative applications.

The author expresses his appreciation to the various manufacturers of electrical and electronic devices and equipment who provided photographs and data for inclusion in the text.

Edward F. Driscoll

iii

General Contents

UNIT 1

On-Off
Switching Devices

Unit 1

Contents

Unit 1

Unit 1

List of Illustrations

Unit 1

Unit 1

Unit 1

section 1

Introduction

On-off control of electric circuits is an important aspect of all phases of industrial electronics. Devices used for such control may be grouped into three main divisions: switches, relays, and circuit breakers. Although these devices have many applications in electronics, they are really electromechanical. True electronic switching such as used in computer circuits is in another category and is described in other Units of this book, especially Unit 3, *Power Tubes and Solid-State Controls.*

Certain devices may be listed in more than one category. For example, one multiple-contact switching device shown in some catalogs as a *stepping relay* is shown in other catalogs as a *stepping switch.* Also, the *reed switch,* which is actuated by a magnet or an energized coil, can be found listed as a switch or as a relay. In this book, stepping and reed devices will be considered as relays. Switches and relays are alike in their

1

on-off or making and breaking action. Circuit breakers are special normally-closed switches which are automatically opened as a result of electrical overload and which can be manually reset.

Making and Breaking Action

In many switching operations consideration must be given to the making-and-breaking sequence. In some situations it is desirable to make one circuit connection before breaking another. This is illustrated in Fig. 1, showing a make-before-break sequence. In view (A), line A is connected to line C. In view (B), actuation of the switch connects line C to line B. In view (C), further actuation disconnects line C from line A.

To disconnect a line from one circuit

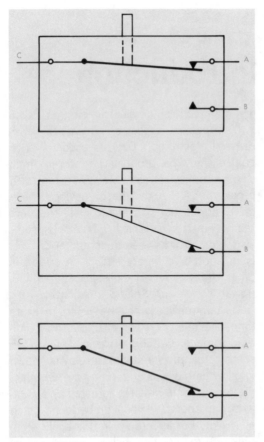

Fig. 1. *SPDT make-before-break (Form D) switch.*

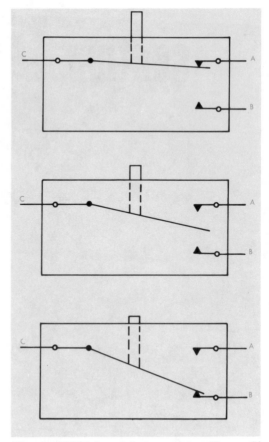

Fig. 2. *SPDT break-before-make (Form C) switch.*

before connecting it to another, a break-before-make switch is used. This is shown in Fig. 2. In view (A), line C is connected to line A. In view (B), actuation of the switch disconnects line C from line A and then connects it to line B, as shown in view (C).

Fig. 3 shows a number of accepted contact forms for switches and relays. In addition to those illustrated, a number of other forms are available.

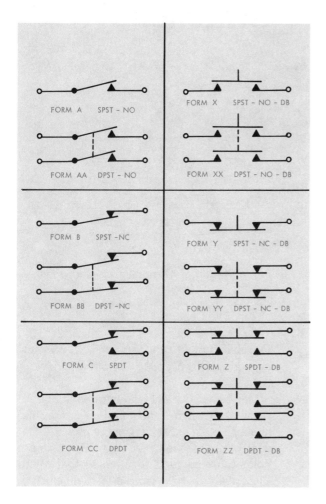

Fig. 3. *Basic contact forms.*

Unit 1

section 2 Switches

There are a number of types and forms of switches used in on-off control of electric circuits. They may be classified according to mode of operation, construction, or function, such as: manual, precision, limit, mercury, pressure, temperature, liquid level, etc.

Manual Switches

There are several forms of manual switches, such as: pushbutton, toggle, rotary, slide, knife and key. Some are simple two-contact switches; others have several sets of contacts. Some make momentary contact; others maintain contact.

Momentary contact is shown in Fig. 4. When the actuating member is pushed (by pushbutton or toggle lever) or turned (by rotating a knob) the movable contact is transferred from the normally-closed (NC) contact to the normally-open (NO) contact, as shown in view (B). When released, the

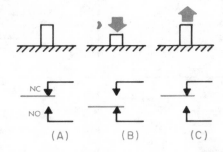

Fig. 4. *Action of momentary-contact manual switch.*

movable contact returns to the NC contact by spring-return action, as shown in view (C).

Maintained contact is illustrated in Fig. 5. When the switch is actuated, the movable contact is transferred from contact 1 to contact 2, as shown in view (B). A latch holds these contacts together so that when the actuator is released they remain closed,

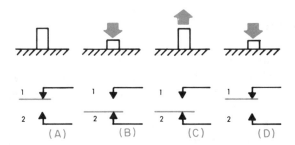

Fig. 5. *Action of maintained-contact manual switch.*

as shown in view (C). A second application of force to the actuator releases the latch, and the movable contact returns to contact 1, as shown in view (D).

Toggle Switches. Toggle switches are available in two kinds of action: maintained and momentary, with two or three operating positions. A two-position, single-pole, single-throw (SPST) toggle switch with maintained action is shown in Fig. 6.

Pressure on the actuator in one direction connects the switch contacts together, as shown in view (A). They remain connected until pressure is applied to the actuator to disconnect them, as shown in view (B). If a spring mechanism is added to the switch it becomes an SPST momentary-action device, as shown in Fig. 7. Here, actuation overcomes the spring tension and the contacts are connected. When pressure on the actu-

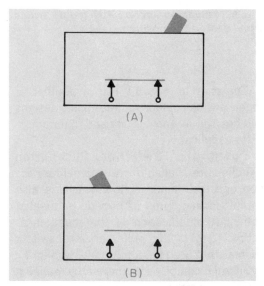

Fig. 6. *Maintained-contact SPST toggle switch.*

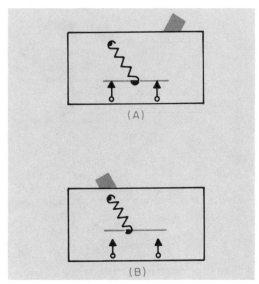

Fig. 7. *Momentary-contact SPST toggle switch.*

ator is removed, the contact connection is broken by the spring-return mechanism, as shown in view (B).

A single-pole, double-throw (SPDT) maintained-action toggle switch is illustrated in Fig. 8. An SPDT switch with a "center off" position is shown in Fig. 9. With maintained action, this switch is set manually to the center-off position. With momentary action, this is accomplished by a spring-return mechanism.

A two-position toggle switch, having normally-open (NO) and normally-closed (NC) contacts, is shown in Fig. 10. In view (A) the common terminal C is connected to the NC contact by a spring-loaded mechanism. Operation of the actuator overcomes the spring force and connects terminal C to the NO contact, as shown in view (B). This connection is maintained as long as pressure is applied to the actuator. Release of the actuator allows the spring mechanism to return terminal C to the NC contact.

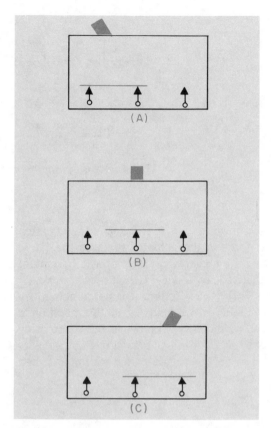

Fig. 9. *Maintained-action SPDT toggle switch with "center-off" position.*

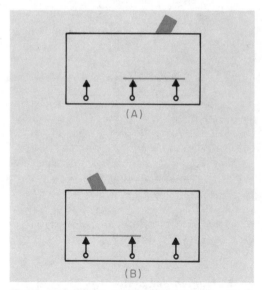

Fig. 8. *Maintained-action SPDT toggle switch.*

The chart in Fig. 11 lists a number of toggle-switch positions. These basic designs can be used for momentary and maintained-action applications.

Pushbutton Switches. Pushbutton switches are available with momentary action and maintained action. They are also combined in groups to provide sequential action. A modification of the maintained-action form is the pull-to-operate switch, such as that used for automobile headlights. Sequential action is achieved by ganging switches together in an assembly so that pressure on a pushbutton actuates a switch

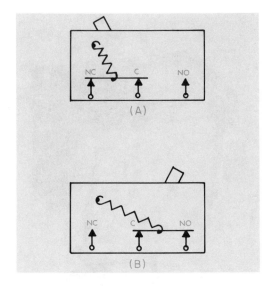

Fig. 10. *Momentary-contact SPDT toggle switch.*

ON		OFF
OFF		ON
ON		ON
ON	OFF	
	OFF	ON
ON	OFF	ON

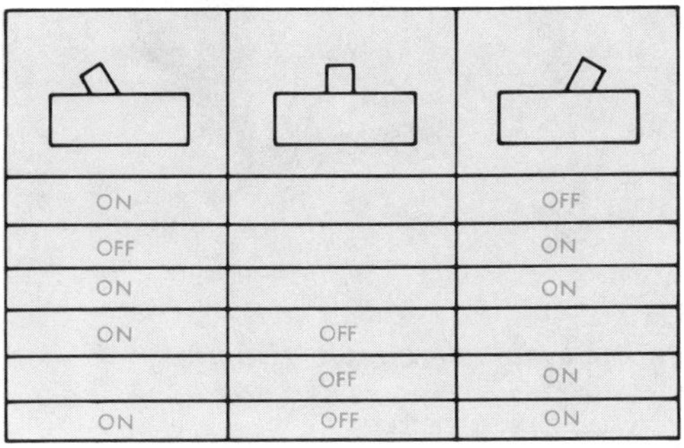

Fig. 11. *Typical toggle switch connections.*

and releases a previously actuated one. Two forms of pushbutton switches are shown in Fig. 12.

Rotary Switches. Rotary switches are actuated by a twisting motion, generally turning a knob. These switches can have many pairs of terminals or as few as two (a form of simple on-off switch). Terminals can be mounted on a number of decks which are fastened to a central shaft. Rotation of the shaft changes contact connections on each deck. In this way a few or many circuits can be switched at one time with one short turn of the switch shaft. Additional rotation multiplies the number of possible circuit changes. Fig. 13 shows a variety of rotary switches.

An important advantage of the rotary

Fig. 12. *Pushbutton switches: (A) single-circuit, and (B) multiple-circuit. (Courtesy of Micro Switch Div., Honeywell Corp.)*

switch is that it accomplishes what would be extremely difficult (in many cases impossible) with other types of switches: the simultaneous and sequential switching of many sets of contacts with the operation of a single actuator.

This switch performs such functions in television tuners, multimeters and other test equipment. Simpler forms of rotary switches are used as step controls for heaters, lights, motors and other industrial equipment.

Limit Switches

Limit switches are switch mechanisms usually operated by the motion of part of a machine such as a slide or cam, or other mechanical equipment such as a conveyor or elevator. These switches are generally used for two purposes: operation of equipment and shut-off for safety. Two commonly used forms are shown in Fig. 14.

As an operating device, a limit switch can

Fig. 13. *Rotary switches. (Courtesy of Centralab Electronics Div., Globe-Union, Inc.)*

be used to reverse the direction of a moving machine table. The switch is placed so that a cam or other tripping arrangement on the table actuates it when the table has completed its travel in one direction. The switch is wired into the drive-motor relay circuit so that its actuation causes reverse motor rotation, returning the table to its starting position. Another limit switch at the starting position can then reverse this sequence to produce forward motor rotation, moving the table forward again.

On the same machine another limit switch can act as a safety device to keep the table from going off the ways if the return switch

becomes inoperative or some other malfunction occurs. This safety switch is placed so that it is actuated if the table tends to go beyond its preset stopping point. Actuation of this switch deenergizes the drive motor and the table stops. Prevention of overtravel is an important application of limit switches. For this purpose they are used extensively in the control circuitry of conveyors, elevators, and other forms of moving equipment.

Forms of Limit Switches. A common form of limit switch, which has one set of NO contacts and one set of NC contacts, is illustrated in Fig. 15. This type can be oper-

(A)

(B)

Fig. 14. *Typical heavy-duty limit switches with actuator in two positions: (A) vertical, and (B) horizontal. (Courtesy of Micro Switch Div., Honeywell Corp.)*

ated in one direction only, from center, either clockwise or counterclockwise. This is illustrated in Fig. 16.

Fig. 17 illustrates a limit switch with two sets of NO contacts. Movement of the actuator in a counterclockwise direction closes one set of contacts as shown in view (A). Movement in a clockwise direction closes the other set as shown in view (C). A spring mechanism returns the actuator to the center-off position as shown in view (B) when the operating force is removed. The actuator travel in both directions is shown in view (D).

Limit Switch Actuators. There are a number of actuators (also called "operators" or "operating heads") available for the many different industrial applications of limit switches. Ones commonly used are: rotary operator, top push-roller, side push-roller, top pushbutton, and side pushbutton. The needs of some situations are met by specialized forms of actuators, such as the "wobble-stick" actuator and the "catwhisker" actuator. These are illustrated in Fig. 18. The wobble-stick type shown in view (A) can be operated in a number of directions, usually with a lower force than the regular rotary-lever type previously discussed. Where only a very small actuating force is

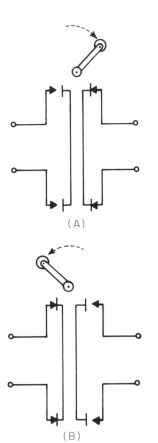

(A)

(B)

Fig. 15. *One form of limit switch operates as in view (A) or (B), but not in both directions.*

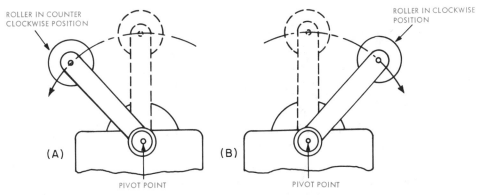

ROLLER IN COUNTER CLOCKWISE POSITION

ROLLER IN CLOCKWISE POSITION

(A)

(B)

PIVOT POINT

PIVOT POINT

Fig. 16. *Unidirectional limit-switch operation: (A) counterclockwise, (B) clockwise.*

11

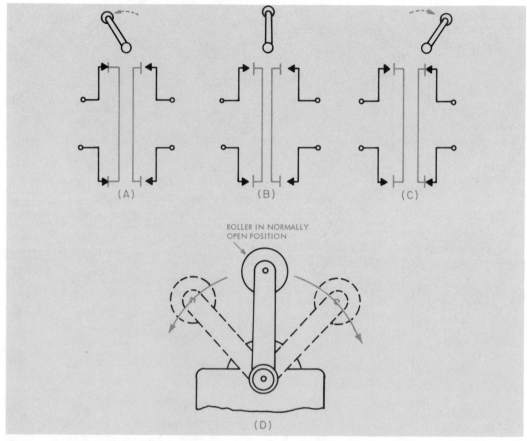

Fig. 17. *Contact actuation in bi-directional limit switch: (A) counterclockise, (B) off, and (C) clockwise; (D) enlarged view of roller lever.*

available, a limit switch with a catwhisker operator, as shown in view (B), can be used.

Precision Snap-Action Switches

A precision snap-action (PSA) switch is a small switch with closely spaced contacts (⅛ inch maximum separation). Spring action snaps the contacts together or apart very quickly and positively, with no lagging or stalling. To qualify as a precision switch, the device must operate with consistent precision (within a few thousandths of an inch or closer tolerance) upon repeated applications of the same actuating force, whether the force is applied gradually or rapidly.

The construction of a typical precision snap-action switch is shown in Fig. 19. Fig. 20 shows a number of PSA switches with a variety of actuators. Fig. 21 illustrates methods of applying force to the actuators.

(A)   (B)

Fig. 18. *Limit switches operated by two different types of actuators: (A) wobble-stick operator, and (B) cat-whisker operator. (Courtesy of Cutler-Hammer Inc.)*

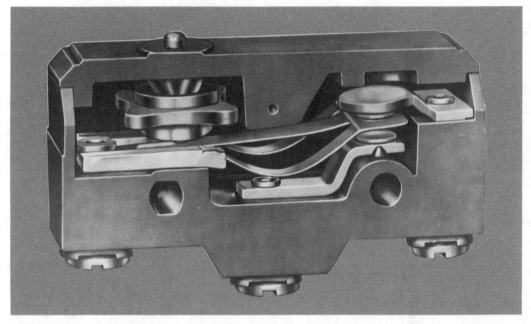

Fig. 19. *Cutaway showing construction of precision snap–action switch. (Courtesy of Micro Switch Div., Honeywell Corp.)*

Fig. 20. *PSA switches with various actuators. (Courtesy of Unimax Switch Corp.)*

Applications of PSA Switches. Precision snap-action switches are used in a great variety of applications, such as: safety interlocks on equipment doors, coin-operated machines, appliances, motor controls, as the basic switching element in limit switches, temperature controls, and in many military and space-exploration devices.

Certain applications are possible because of the low operating force required and the close and accurate spacing of the contacts. For example, temperature control can be accomplished by allowing the expansion of a bimetallic temperature-sensing element to exert a force on the pushbutton of a PSA switch, as shown in Fig. 22. In this manner a variety of loads can be controlled without relays. A snap-action switch with leaf-spring

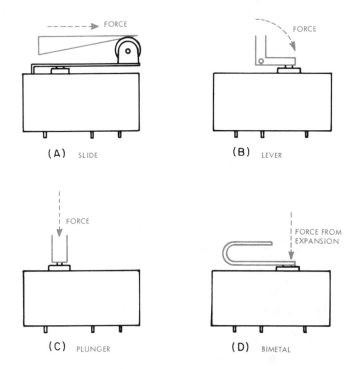

Fig. 21. *Typical operating mechanisms for precision snap–action switches: (A) slide, (B) lever, (C) plunger, and (D) bimetal.*

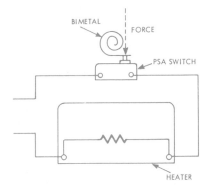

Fig. 22. *PSA switch operated by temperature-sensing element.*

or leaf-spring-roller actuator can be used to operate a counter as articles on a conveyor move past the switch, which is rigidly mounted in a fixed position. This application is illustrated in Fig. 23.

Thermal Switches

A thermal switch is one whose actuation depends on temperature change. This change can be sensed in three ways: (1)

15

electrically; (2) by the difference in expansion of dissimilar metals, causing distortion of the bimetallic element; and (3) by liquid or gas expansion. Temperature-sensing by electrical means utilizes thermistors, resistance thermometers, and thermocouples. These devices are beyond the scope of this unit, however, as they operate by thermo-electricity.

The differential–expansion method is based on the principle that dissimilar metals expand at different rates when exposed to the same temperature change. This difference in expansion can be utilized to produce movement in a definite direction, actuating a switch. The third method uses the principle that the volume of a gas or liquid changes with temperature. Such change is coupled mechanically to a switch mechanism.

Generally, temperature controllers are grouped according to how the components are assembled. If a temperature-sensing element and its switch are mounted in a single unit the assembly is called a *thermostat* or *local controller*. If the sensing element is remote from its switch the device is known as a *remote temperature controller*. This group includes gas, vapor, and liquid-filled units.

Bimetal Thermostats. Bimetal thermostats are available in two forms; strip and disc. A bimetal-strip thermostat is illustrated in Fig. 24. Here, two dissimilar metal strips are fused together where they interface. A temperature increase produces unequal expansion of the two metals, causing the strip to bend, and this action opens the switch contacts. A temperature decrease reverses the process, closing the contacts.

The bimetal-disc thermostat in Fig. 25 has a snap action which is achieved by forming the disc into a concave shape. A temperature increase causes uneven expan-

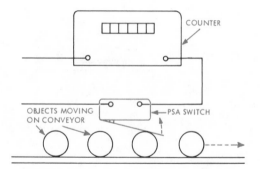

Fig. 23. *PSA switch operating counter.*

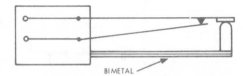

Fig. 24. *Bimetal-strip thermostat.*

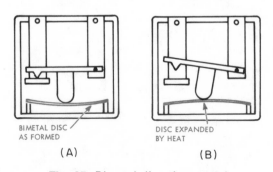

Fig. 25. *Bimetal-disc thermostat.*

sion of the two different metals. This heating overcomes the stress in the formed disc and inverts it with a snap action. This action opens the switch by raising the spring-loaded contact, as shown in view (B). A temperature decrease reverses the action, so the spring closes the contacts. These actions can be reversed, however. Closed contacts with temperature increase and open contacts with temperature decrease can be accomplished by turning the disc over. Then temperature increase will flex the disc downward and temperature decrease will flex it upward.

In some bimetal-disc thermostats one contact is fastened to the disc. This arrangement is often used in thermal cutouts and circuit breakers. Since the bimetal disc is part of the circuit, excess current caused by an overload heats the disc. The heat produces uneven expansion, which snaps open the contacts. Some of these devices have a manual reset which must be operated to re-close the circuit after warning of the overload. As with any circuit-breaking device, the cause of overload should be investigated and corrected before resetting.

A comparison of the strip-type and disc-type bimetal thermostats reveals that the strip-type has slow make-break action while the disc type has fast, positive action. The disc type has a fixed temperature setting; usually the strip type is adjustable. The disc type has a relatively large operating differential, while that of the strip type is smaller. The disc type has the advantage of small size, allowing it to be mounted in limited spaces and at the point where temperature sensing and control is desired.

Both types of thermostats are available with exposed or enclosed sensing elements and contacts. Enclosed units are used where dust, dirt or other contaminants could impair operation. However, the insulating effect of the enclosure slows the response to temperature changes. If the atmosphere is free of contaminants, thermostats with exposed sensing elements may be used to obtain faster response.

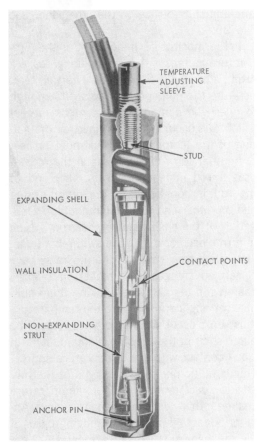

Fig. 26. *Strut-and-shell thermal switch. (Courtesy of Fenwall, Inc.)*

Single-Metal Thermostats. A thermostat in which a single metal is in contact with the changing temperature is illustrated in Fig. 26. This type is referred to as "mechanically-linked" because two low-expansion struts are mechanically connected to an outer casing of high-expansion metal. Insulation is placed between the casing and the strut-switch mechanism to minimize heating of the struts. A pair of normally closed contacts is mounted on facing sides of the struts. The struts are attached to the outer casing at one end and to a tempera-

17

ture-adjusting device on the other end. See Fig. 26.

In thermostats of this design, as the temperature increases the casing elongates, exerting a pull on the struts. At a certain temperature the pull spreads the struts enough to open the contacts. The temperature at which this occurs is determined by the setting of the temperature-adjustment device.

Another form of single-metal thermostat uses a rod instead of struts. One end of the rod is connected to the outer casing and the other end to a switch contact. Elongation of the casing moves the rod, which in turn closes or opens the switch contacts.

Mechanically-linked thermostats have certain advantages. They react well to small changes in temperature, making them suitable for applications where the temperature must be closely controlled. Also, since the outer shell is the sensing element, it is in close contact with the temperature source. This condition enables this type of thermostat to react more quickly to temperature changes than enclosed-sensor types. Another advantage is that the moving parts of the mechanically-linked thermostat are enclosed, protecting them from contamination.

Mechanically-linked thermostats have a greater temperature range than the bi-metal type, ranging from about 100°F to about 1500°F. They are found in a variety of industrial applications, including ovens, liquid heaters, dryers, and glueing equipment. They are also used as temperature-limit controls, both high and low. As such, they act as safety devices when other instruments malfunction and lose control.

Liquid-Filled Thermostats. A liquid-filled thermostat consists of a control switch, a bellows, and a tube containing an expandable liquid. A typical unit of this type is illustrated in Fig. 27. The tube is made of material which has high thermal conductivity. This provides good thermal transfer to the liquid. The kind of liquid used depends on the desired temperature range of the instrument.

In operation, the amount of heat transmitted to the liquid varies as the external temperature changes. This changes the volume of the liquid, and the changing volume acts on the bellows, which, in turn, actuates the switch.

The expandable sensing liquid may be outside the bellows (as in Fig. 27) or inside. When the liquid is inside, it reacts more slowly to temperature changes than the same fluid placed between the bellows and the tube. In either case the response time is longer than that of the differential-expansion thermostat. This is due to the greater time required by the sensing fluid for heating and expansion than is required by the metals in the differential-expansion type.

Generally, the switch in a fluid-filled thermostat is not an integral part of the sensing mechanism, as it is in some thermostats. This design allows for much freedom of choice among standard switches in terms of current rating, sensitivity, and contact configuration. This is an important advantage of liquid-filled thermostats, since in many applications they can be used to control high-current equipment directly, whereas bimetal thermostats would require the use of relays.

Remote Temperature Controls. A remote mechanical temperature control is a three-part system consisting of a sensing head (called a "bulb"), a switch, and a capillary tube which connects the bulb to the switch. The bulb and the capillary tube contain a fluid—either liquid, gas or vapor. A liquid-filled bulb and capillary-tube remote control is illustrated in Fig. 28. If the switch is replaced with a temperature-indicating

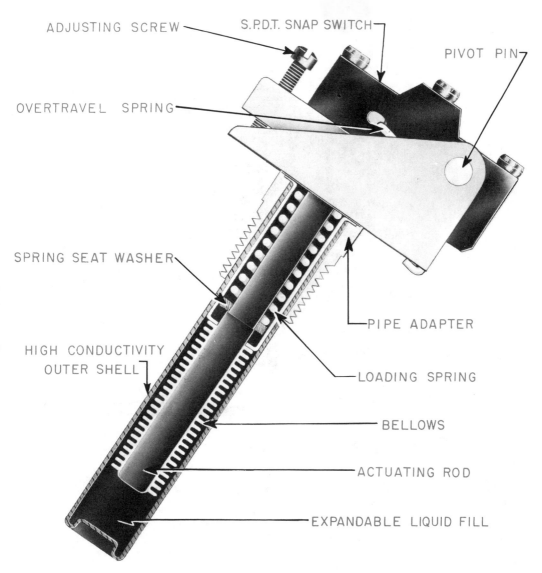

ADJUSTING SCREW

S.P.D.T. SNAP SWITCH

PIVOT PIN

OVERTRAVEL SPRING

SPRING SEAT WASHER

HIGH CONDUCTIVITY
OUTER SHELL

PIPE ADAPTER

LOADING SPRING

BELLOWS

ACTUATING ROD

EXPANDABLE LIQUID FILL

Fig. 27. *Liquid-filled thermal switch. (Courtesy of Fenwall, Inc.)*

meter the device becomes a thermometer (Fig. 29). If both switch and meter are included, the system is an indicating controller.

In a typical application of a remote control unit, an increase in temperature is transferred by the thermally conductive bulb from the media (atmosphere, liquid, surface, etc.) to the fluid. This rise in temperature expands the fluid, applying pressure through the capillary tube to a diaphragm, bellows, or other pressure-sen-

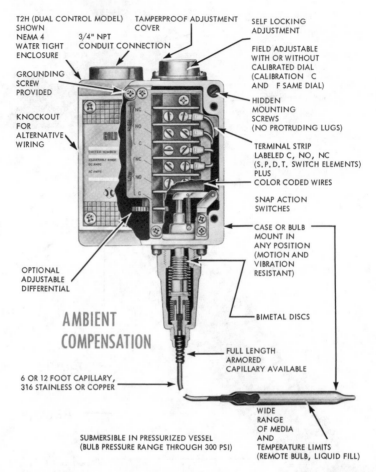

T2H (DUAL CONTROL MODEL) SHOWN NEMA 4 WATER TIGHT ENCLOSURE

3/4" NPT CONDUIT CONNECTION

TAMPERPROOF ADJUSTMENT COVER

SELF LOCKING ADJUSTMENT

FIELD ADJUSTABLE WITH OR WITHOUT CALIBRATED DIAL (CALIBRATION C AND F SAME DIAL)

GROUNDING SCREW PROVIDED

HIDDEN MOUNTING SCREWS (NO PROTRUDING LUGS)

KNOCKOUT FOR ALTERNATIVE WIRING

TERMINAL STRIP LABELED C, NO, NC (S.P.D.T. SWITCH ELEMENTS) PLUS COLOR CODED WIRES

SNAP ACTION SWITCHES

CASE OR BULB MOUNT IN ANY POSITION (MOTION AND VIBRATION RESISTANT)

OPTIONAL ADJUSTABLE DIFFERENTIAL

AMBIENT COMPENSATION

BIMETAL DISCS

FULL LENGTH ARMORED CAPILLARY AVAILABLE

6 OR 12 FOOT CAPILLARY, 316 STAINLESS OR COPPER

SUBMERSIBLE IN PRESSURIZED VESSEL (BULB PRESSURE RANGE THROUGH 300 PSI)

WIDE RANGE OF MEDIA AND TEMPERATURE LIMITS (REMOTE BULB, LIQUID FILL)

Fig. 28. *Bulb and capillary tube remote-action thermal control. (Courtesy of Barksdale Controls Div., De Laval Turbine)*

sitive element. This in turn actuates the switch. Single-pole, double-throw switches are common in these controls, and some units contain two or more.

In some applications the remote temperature control has an advantage over the local thermostat in that the bulb can be mounted in many places which cannot accommodate a local thermostat. Also, the bulb can be placed in remote or hazardous locations or in atmospheres where switches and electric wiring are undesirable or unsafe. The switch and its associated wiring can be installed at a convenient or safe location. A local thermostat incorporates the switch and sensor in the same unit and consequently the wiring must be brought to the sensor location.

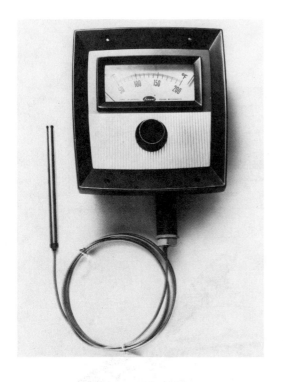

Fig. 29. *Liquid-filled temperature indicator. (Courtesy of Fenwall, Inc.)*

Mercury Switches

In its design, the mercury switch is a simple switch, much simpler than other types. Its unique construction and actuation by tilting make it useful in many situations where other switches would not be suitable. Because the mercury switch can be built in a variety of sizes, current capacities, and electrode arrangement, it is found in a large range of applications—from small, temperature-sensing devices to controllers for heavy industrial equipment.

The mercury switch has several characteristics which make it a valuable and versatile switching device: low actuating force, excellent repeatability, low contact resistance, good current-carrying capacity, and minimum sensitivity to ambient conditions. It can operate in temperatures from −35°F (near the freezing point of mercury) to over 400°F; in very dry atmospheres or high relative humidity; and even in a vacuum. Hermetically sealed, the mercury switch is not affected by oil, fumes, or dirt.

Mercury Switch Construction. The simplest form of mercury switch is shown in Fig. 30. Two electrodes and a small pool of mercury are sealed in a glass tube. Metal tubes are also used, but glass is much more common. Connections to the electrodes are made with flexible leads.

Mercury-switch electrodes are made of iron or iron alloy such as nickel-iron and chrome-iron. Molybdenum, tungsten, and platinum are also used. Molybdenum and tungsten are utilized in high-current switches. The use of platinum is limited due to its high cost. Usually a small piece of platinum is welded to a lead-in made of nickel-iron or chrome-iron. Although copper is a good conductor, it cannot be used as

21

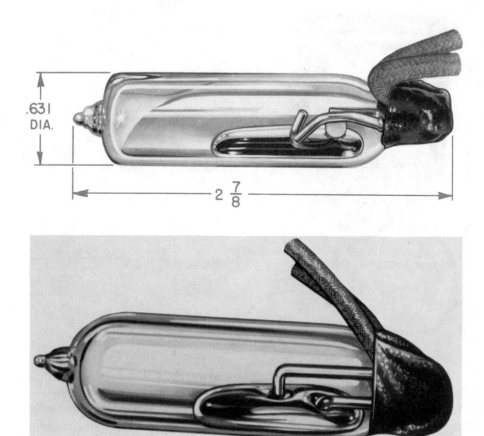

Fig. 30. *Basic SPST mercury switch in two standard styles. (Courtesy of Fenwall, Inc.)*

an electrode material because it dissolves in mercury. However, copper-cored electrodes can be used where lower electrical resistance is required.

The mercury used in switch construction is highly purified, with impurities of less than one part per million. Because mercury reacts with even very small amounts of oxygen, especially at the increased temperatures possible in a switch, any air in the tube is removed and replaced with hydro-

gen. This gas is used because it quickly quenches any arcing, thereby reducing electrode damage.

Although the basic design of mercury switches is very simple, as stated previously, the manufacturing processes are not, and the equipment used is sophisticated and elaborate. Stringent quality controls are necessary. Also, mercury is a highly toxic material, cannot be safely handled, and even its fumes must be continuously evacuated for the safety of personnel working in the manufacturing area.

Mercury Switch Operation; Types. The basic action of a mercury switch is shown in Fig. 31. The angle through which the switch is tilted in going from make to break or break to make is known as the differential angle or angle of displacement. General-purpose mercury switches (designed for 2 to 10 ampere loads) have differential angles from 1° to 15°. Miniature mercury switches (for maximum loads not exceeding 2 amperes) also have differential angles from 1° to 15°. Heavy-duty types (for loads above 10 amperes) have larger differential angles, usually from 3° to 25°. Precision-type, low-angle mercury switches have small differential angles, from about 0.1° to 1.5°.

Since a mercury switch has only one element (the pool of mercury) for connecting the electrodes together, these switches are "single-pole." They are available in a number of contact configurations, some of which are illustrated in Fig. 32. Whether a pair of electrodes is NC or NO depends on how the switch is mounted.

Figs. 32(A) and 32(B) are single-throw

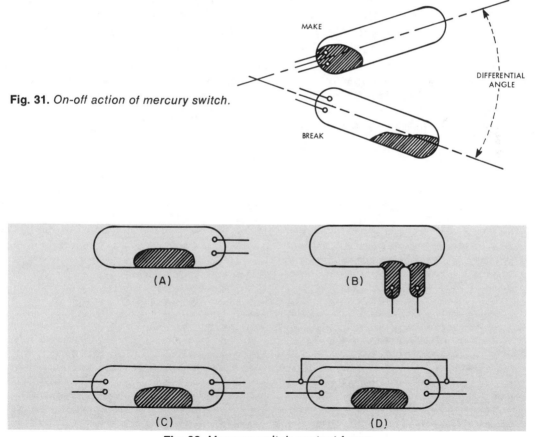

Fig. 31. *On-off action of mercury switch.*

Fig. 32. *Mercury-switch contact forms.*

designs. Fig. 32(B) shows mercury-to-mer-cury contact, which is used in heavy-duty switching. The switch in Fig. 32(C) is a two-circuit, break-before-make configuration. An SPDT configuration is illustrated in Fig. 33(D).

Some mercury-switch applications may require switches with rather large differential angles. Figs. 33(A) and 33(B) show two forms of switches which are available with differential angles up to almost 90°. In Fig. 33(A) snap action is provided by the sharp bend. The switch in Fig. 33(C) is a momentary-contact type. The length of closed-contact time depends on the speed of switching motion.

Time delay can be provided by a mercury switch, as shown in Fig. 33(D). Here, a baffle is attached to one of the electrodes. When the switch is tilted the mercury flows toward the second electrode at a rate determined by the size of the opening in the baffle. A rigid baffle provides delay on both make and break actions. Baffles hinged to move in one direction only can be used to produce delayed make and normal break,

or the opposite, normal make and delayed break. These actions are illustrated in Fig. 34.

Mercury Switch Applications. Several applications of mercury switches are illustrated in Fig. 35. In each, a normally-closed switch is shown. Reversal of the switch in the mounting clip will change the switch to normally open.

Fig. 35(A) shows a switch mounted on a spinning machine. If the machine becomes unbalanced the switch tilts. This opens the NC contacts, stopping the drive motor. In Fig. 35(B) a mercury switch is combined with a bimetallic strip to form a thermostat. Increase in temperature causes the strip to expand, tilting the mercury switch. This opens the switch contacts, de-energizing the circuit under control. In Fig. 35(C) the change in position of a shaft or machine part can be sensed by a mercury switch. Here, a cam attached to the moving machine part actuates the switch, which is mounted on a tilting lever acting as a cam follower.

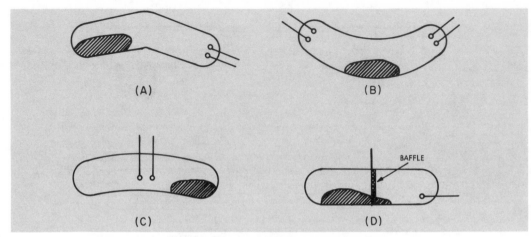

Fig. 33. *Forms of mercury switches.*

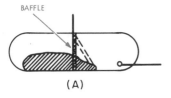

(A)

NORMAL MAKE, DELAYED BREAK

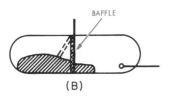

(B)

DELAYED MAKE, NORMAL BREAK

Fig. 34. *Time-delay mercury switches: (A) normal make, delayed break; (B) delayed make, normal break.*

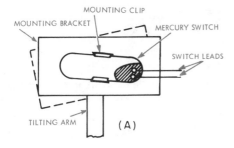

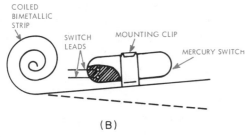

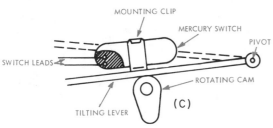

Fig. 35. *Mercury switch applications.*

Unit 1

section  Relays

R elays are among the most widely used control devices in industrial electronics. A great variety of types and forms are found in an almost unlimited number of applications. Relays perform important functions, such as: control of high-power load circuits, low-voltage control of remote equipment and the isolation of control circuits from load circuits.

Earlier definitions of the term "relay" considered it to mean an electrically operated device which closed and/or opened switch contacts in control of the operation of other electrical devices or equipment. This definition does not include relays which do not contain contacts, such as thyratrons and silicon controlled rectifiers. A broader definition is one which states that a relay is an electrically-controlled switch.

There is no clear-cut classification of relays. In some cases various manufacturers use different terms in naming the same device, such as "stepping switch" and "stepping relay." Also, certain devices not electrically–controlled are called relays. For example, photoelectric switches are also known as "photoelectric relays."

Relays are sometimes classified according to method of actuation, such as electromagnetic, thermal, etc., or by performance, such as sensitive, timing, latching, etc. They may also be classified according to type of mechanical action or type of enclosure. Discussed in the following paragraphs are relays classified as: *electromagnetic, dry-reed, mercury-wetted reed* and *mercury-wetted contact*. Relays which perform a time-delay function are more fully described in Unit 3, on timers.

Electromagnetic Relays

An electromagnetic relay is an electromechanical device consisting essentially of a switch mechanism and an electromagnet. A typical unit is shown in Fig. 36. Fig. 37 illustrates the basic components and operation of this type of relay. The armature is

Fig. 36. *Basic form of electromagnetic relay. (Courtesy of Potter & Brumfield Div. of AMF Inc.)*

hinged or otherwise fastened to allow it to move when attracted by the coil. The movable contact is mounted on the armature. In operation, current through the coil magnetizes the core, which attracts the movable armature. Movement of the armature opens the NC contact and closes the NO contact. (The NC contact is also called the "break" or "back" contact and the NO contact, the "make" or "front" contact.) Opening the coil circuit deenergizes the electromagnet and the spring returns the movable contact to the NC position.

When a relay operates it is said to "pick up" and the smallest amount of current needed to close (or open) a set of contacts is called the "pick-up current." If the current is decreased to a value at which the spring overcomes the magnetic pull, the relay "drops out." This current is called the "dropout" or "reset" value.

Relay Control Methods. There are various ways in which relays are connected to achieve control of load circuits. These control methods are identified by such terms as *direct, shunt, lockup, open-circuit, closed circuit*, etc.

Direct and Shunt Control. Direct control is the simplest arrangement, as illustrated in Fig. 38. Closing the switch applies line voltage directly to the relay coil, closing the relay contacts.

Shunt control is shown in Fig. 39. This form of control can be used if the relay is required to operate when another circuit is opened. Opening switch S deenergizes circuit A and removes the shunt from the relay coil allowing it to be energized, closing circuit B. Closing switch S reenergizes circuit A and shunts the relay coil deenergizing it. The deenergized coil releases the closed contacts, opening circuit B. A disadvantage of this circuit is that there is a continuous current drain whether the relay

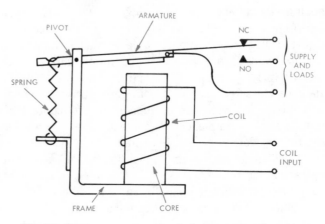

Fig. 37. *Basic components of electromagnetic relay.*

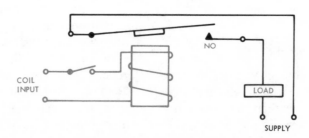

Fig. 38. *Direct relay control.*

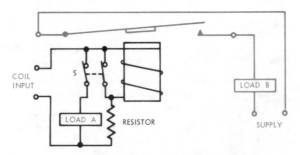

Fig. 39. *Shunt relay control.*

is operated or not. Also, a resistor is required, which increases cost.

Open and Closed Systems. The terms "open" and "closed" refer to conditions of the load circuit when the relay coil is de-energized. The circuit illustrated in Fig. 38 is called an open system because the load circuit is open when the control circuit is

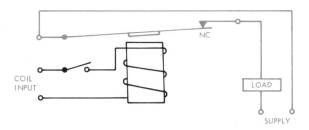

Fig. 40. *"Closed" relay system.*

open. Fig. 40 illustrates a closed system, in which the load circuit is closed when the control circuit is open.

When the switch in the control circuit is closed the energized relay holds the load contacts open. When the switch is opened the relay coil releases the armature and the load contacts close, completing the load circuit. In some applications the closed system is preferred. Defects in the control circuit, such as loss of voltage or a defective relay coil, become apparent because the relay becomes inoperative and the load is energized at all times. However, in the open-circuit system such defects are not detected until the switch in the control circuit is operated.

Locking Circuits. In direct and shunt circuits the control switches are independent of the relays. However, in a locking circuit the relay coil is connected through certain relay contacts so that the relay is involved in its own control.

The circuit in Fig. 41 illustrates "lock-up" operation. In view (A) both the relay circuit and load circuit are deenergized. In view (B) the start button is depressed, energizing the relay coil. The DPST NO contacts close, completing the load circuit and also a connection from the line to the relay coil. When the spring-loaded start switch is released, the relay coil remains energized through the closed contact *R* and the stop switch, as shown in view (C). To remove power from the load, the stop switch is de-

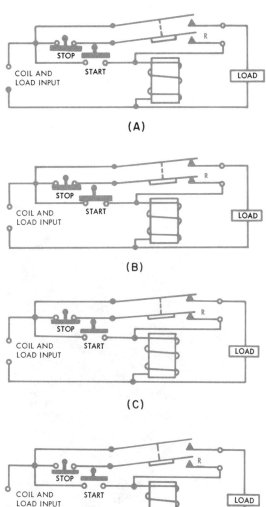

Fig. 41. *"Lock-up" relay operation.*

pressed, deenergizing the relay coil as is shown in view (D). This releases the closed contacts, opening the load circuit. This form of control often incorporates the familiar start-stop station shown in Fig. 42.

A make-before-break DPDT contact configuration shown in Fig. 43. When S-1 is closed the relay coil is energized through one of the NC contacts A. The NO contacts B and D close before the NC contacts open. Thus the coil is locked up through one NO contact and S-2. The load-circuit contacts C and D are actuated in conjunction with the relay-control contacts A and B. Opening switch S-1 will not deenergize the relay. To deenergize it and return the load contacts, S-2 is opened.

Fig. 44 illustrates a DPDT "lock-down" relay circuit. Here the NC relay contact C keeps the coil shorted out, preventing operation by S-1 until S-2 is opened. When the relay is energized through S-1 (while S-2 is open) and NC contacts are held open and further operation of S-2 does not affect the coil circuit. However, it can be used to control load circuit C. Load circuits A and B are controlled through contacts A and B.

The circuit shown in Fig. 45 also performs a lockdown function. Here, the relay coil cannot be energized through S-1 unless S-2 is open. The switching sequence for energizing this relay can be either S-2 open and S-1 closed, or S-1 closed and S-2 open.

Fig. 42. *Start-stop control. Form of switching device used in locking relay circuits. (Courtesy of General Electric Co.)*

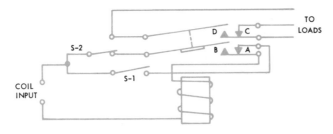

Fig. 43. *Make-before-break contacts perform locking function.*

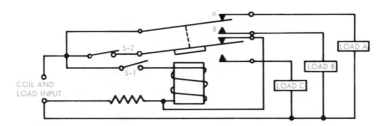

Fig. 44. *DPDT relay in "lock-down" circuit.*

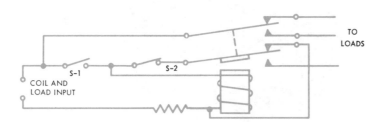

Fig. 45. *Variation of "lock-down" circuit shown in Fig. 44.*

Reed Relays

Basically, a reed relay consists of a magnetically-sensitive switch and a coil. The coil provides the magnetic field required to actuate the switch. Extensions of the basic design include additional coils and various contact arrangements. Fig. 46 illustrates the construction of a typical reed relay.

Figs. 47 and 48 show two available reed-relay assemblies. The octal-base plug-in unit is used in wired applications. The encapsulated unit is for printed-circuit work.

Reed relays have advantages over other type of relays. They are not subject to some of the failures associated with electromagnetic relays since they can be operated in a sealed, controlled environment

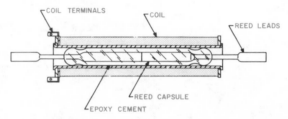

Fig. 46. *Construction of reed relay. (Courtesy of Magnecraft Electric Co.)*

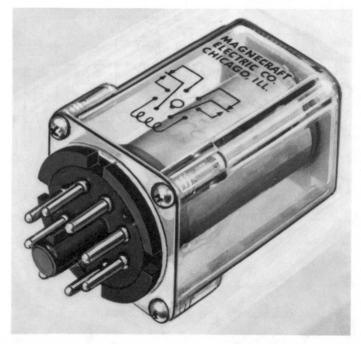

Fig. 47. *Octal-base reed relay. (Courtesy of Magnecraft Electric Co.)*

for millions of high-speed operations. An advantage of the reed relay over solid-state devices is that the reed relay provides isolation of control circuit from load circuit.

Reed Switches. The switches used in reed relays are of two types: *dry reed* and *mercury-wetted reed*. The basic dry-reed

switch consists of two flat metal reeds mounted in a glass tube, as shown in Fig. 49. The tube contains an inert atmosphere such as nitrogen. For high voltage applications the switch is usually mounted in a vacuum.

The blades of the reed switch are made

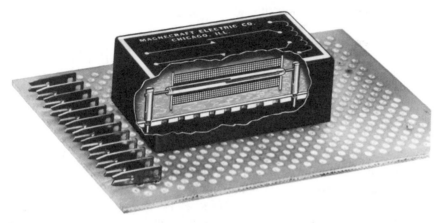

Fig. 48. *Encapsulated reed relay used in printed circuit applications. (Courtesy of Magne-craft Electric Co.)*

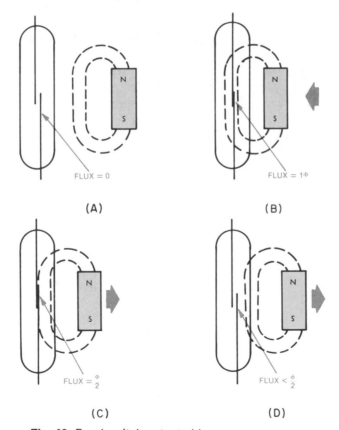

Fig. 49. *Reed switch actuated by permanent magnet.*

of magnetic material which responds quickly and uniformly to the application of a magnetic field. A nickel-iron alloy is commonly used for this purpose. The overlapping sections of the reed are usually plated with a precious metal, such as gold, silver, rhodium, etc., to provide good, long-lasting, electrical contact. The reeds must be so constructed and mounted that the correct gap is maintained between the contacts after thousands of operations.

Reed Switch Operation. Fig. 49 illustrates the operation of a reed switch actuated by a permanent magnet. In view (A) the switch is beyond the influence of the magnetic field. In view (B) the reeds are magnetized by the field. The free ends assume opposite polarities (N and S) and are attracted to each other, thus closing the switch contacts. The symbol 1ϕ indicates the flux strength required to close the switch (called "pick-up"); $\phi/2$ is the value needed to hold the contacts closed. This is shown in view (C), where the magnet is farther from the switch than in view (B). When the flux is less than $\phi/2$, "drop-out" occurs, as in view (D).

An "offset" reed switch is illustrated in Fig. 50. One member is stationary, the

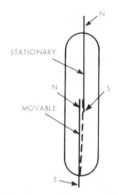

Fig. 50. *Offset reed switch.*

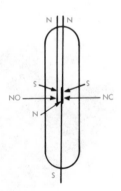

Fig. 51. *Mechanically-biased SPDT (Form C) reed switch.*

other is movable. Under the influence of a field both become magnetized, with the contact ends of opposite polarity. This causes the movable reed to be attracted to the fixed one, thus closing the switch.

Fig. 51 shows a "mechanically-biased" SPDT (Form C) reed switch. A movable center reed is mounted so that it exerts pressure on one fixed contact (NC). The other fixed contact (NO) is placed a short distance from the movable one. The NC contacts are of nonmagnetic material to minimize the magnetic attraction between the movable reed and the fixed reed carrying the NC contact.

When a magnetic field is applied the reeds become polarized as shown. If the field is strong enough, the attraction of the NO contact arm for the movable reed is greater than the mechanical bias and the reed moves from the NC contact to the NO contact. When the magnetic field is removed or reduced to a level below the "holding value" the movable reed returns to its normal position at the NC contact.

Reed Relay Operation. A magnetically-biased SPDT reed relay is illustrated in Fig. 52. The two fixed contact arms are similar to those in the mechanically-biased switch

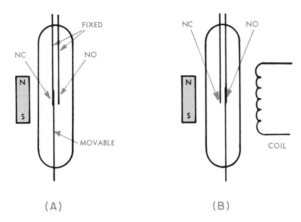

(A)   (B)

Fig. 52. *Operation of magnetically-biased reed relay.*

in Fig. 51. The movable reed is placed mid-way between the fixed contacts. Biasing is done with a permanent magnet which attracts the movable reed to one of the fixed contacts, making this the NC connection, as shown in Fig. 52(A).

An electromagnetic field can now be applied to the switch, as shown in Fig. 52(B), to overcome the permanent-magnet bias and cause the movable reed to transfer from the NC contact to the NO contact. This field should be strong enough to provide sufficient overdrive to attain good contact pressure. Removal of the electromagnetic field allows the biasing magnet to return the reed to the NC position. This relay is polarity-sensitive and requires voltage of proper polarity for operation.

Mercury-Wetted-Reed Relays. Magnetically, mercury-wetted-reed relays operate in the same manner as dry-reed relays. However, in the mercury-wetted type there is a pool of mercury at the base of the switch, as shown in Fig. 53. By capillary action the mercury is carried up the lower reed to the point of contact. Here both contacts become coated with mercury. For proper oper-

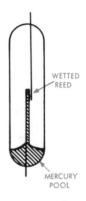

Fig. 53. *Mercury-wetted-reed relay.*

ation these units should be mounted within 30° of vertical. Fig. 54 shows a magnetically-biased mercury-wetted relay with one fixed and one movable reed.

The important difference between the dry-reed and the mercury-wetted-reed relay is that each time the mercury-coated switch operates, the contact surfaces are formed by liquid mercury. In this way "new contacts" are formed with each operation of the relay. This assures long life and allows for higher current rating than that of dry-reed relays of the same size and configura-

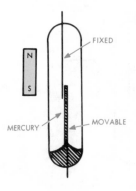

Fig. 54. *Magnetically biased, mercury-wetted-reed relay.*

cient flux ($\phi/2$) to hold the switch closed when the operate coil is deenergized.

In Fig. 56 a permanent magnet is used as the holding device. It is not strong enough to close the switch but is strong enough to hold it closed. The polarity of the magnet is opposite to that of the operate coil A. When this coil is energized the switch closes and is held closed by the permanent magnet after the coil is deenergized. Coil B can be used to open the switch.

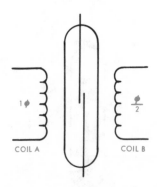

Fig. 55. *Electromagnetic latching reed relay.*

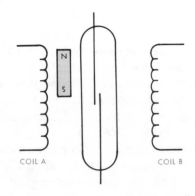

Fig. 56. *Magnetic latching reed relay.*

tion. Also, contact bounce is eliminated by the damping effect of the liquid mercury.

Latching Reed Relays. There are two basic types of latching reed relays: electromagnetic and magnetic. The electromagnetic type, illustrated in Fig. 55, uses two windings: one to operate the contacts, and the other to hold them in their actuated position. The holding coil may be energized through the reed contacts or other circuitry. Current through the operate coil A produces a flux (1ϕ) which magnetizes the reeds, closing the switch. Current through the holding coil B produces suffi-

Mercury-Wetted-Contact Relays

The mercury-wetted-contact (MWC) and the mercury-wetted-reed (MWR) relay are similar in construction, and both are fast and sensitive. However, they differ in capacity and application. Therefore they are not classified together. The MWR relay has limited capacity and is used in low-power applications, such as 150 milliwatts controlling a 15-volt-ampere load. The MWC relay has a greater power gain and controls much larger loads. With a 40 milliwatt input one can control a 250 volt-ampere load. Typical MWC relays are shown in Fig. 57.

Fig. 57. *Plug-in mercury-wetted-contact relays. (Courtesy of C. P. Clare & Co.)*

Construction of MWC Relays. Switching units for MWC relays are illustrated in Fig. 58. Each contains one or more sets of contacts, an armature and a pool of mercury. These components are hermetically sealed in a glass tube which is placed inside the actuating coil. The tube also contains hydrogen at a pressure of at least 150 psi. This eliminates formation of oxides on the metal parts, allowing them to be more easily wetted with mercury. Also, at this pressure the breakdown voltage of the small contact gap is increased, allowing higher-voltage operation. The gas pressure increases the temperature at which the mercury vaporizes, thereby reducing the amount which does vaporize with high-current switching. Fig. 59 shows MWC relays designed for printed-circuit application.

Standard MWC relays are available with such contact combinations as: SPDT with NO contact in parallel, NC contacts in parallel, DPDT with separate fixed contacts and a common armature. Also available are units containing up to four switches inside a single coil. Common contact configurations are shown in Fig. 60.

Permanent magnets can be attached to the NO contacts to make the relay more or less sensitive. This bias can either aid or oppose the coil flux. Such magnets can also be used as holding devices for latching operation.

Operation of MWC Relays. As in MWR relays, capillary action carries mercury from a pool at the bottom of the MWC relay to the armature contacts. In turn, the armature contacts furnish mercury to the fixed contacts. Contacts thus coated have large contact areas compared with the decreasing contact areas which develop in other forms of switches as a result of wear, pitting, and corrosion.

The action of an SPDT break-before-make (Form C) MWC relay is illustrated in Fig. 61(A). At A the relay is deenergized and the armature contact is held against the NC contact. At B and C actuation of the relay coil moves the armature toward the NO contact. Because of surface tension, the mercury forms into a filament which breaks in two places before the armature reaches the contact, producing in this way the break-before-make action. At D the switching action is completed. When the relay coil is deenergized reverse operation occurs.

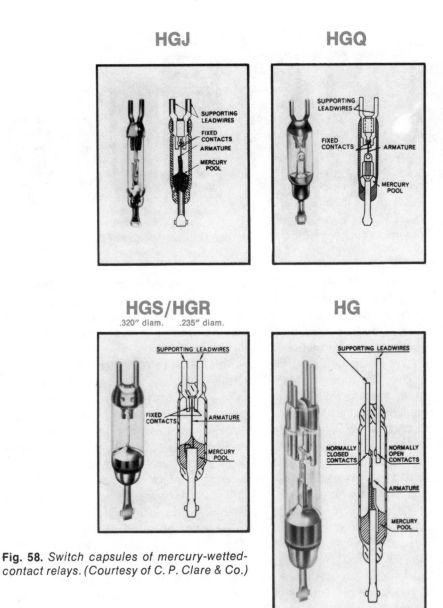

Fig. 58. *Switch capsules of mercury-wetted-contact relays. (Courtesy of C. P. Clare & Co.)*

Fig. 61(B) shows operation of an SPDT make-before-break (Form D) MWC relay. Before the relay is actuated the armature is connected to the NC contact, as at A. When the coil is energized the armature moves to the NO contact and a mercury filament is formed. For an instant the armature and both contacts are connected together. At D the filament breaks, opening the connection. At E the operation is completed. Re-

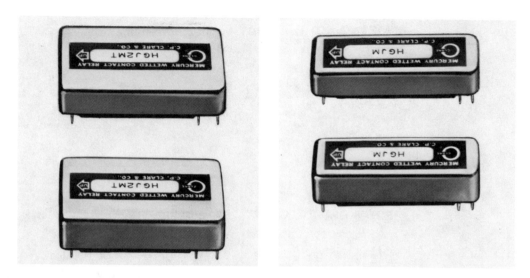

Fig. 59. *Mercury-wetted-contact relays for printed circuit applications. (Courtesy of C. P. Clare & Co.)*

Fig. 60. *Typical contact forms of MWC relays. (Courtesy of C. P. Clare & Co.)*

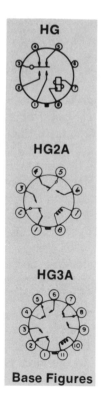

39

FORM C ACTION (SPDT break-before-make)

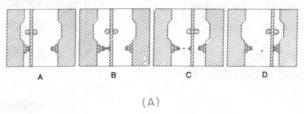

(A)

FORM D ACTION (SPDT make-before-break)

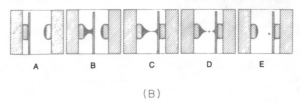

(B)

Fig. 61. *Switching action in MWC relays. (Courtesy of C. P. Clare & Co.)*

verse action occurs when the coil is de-energized.

If sufficient heat is produced by current flow through the contacts some of the mercury coating is vaporized. Capillary action replaces this loss, plus that which drops to the pool when the filament breaks. This replacement of mercury loss and the fluid nature of the mercury on the contacts combine to assure new contact surfaces for each operation of the relay. This action is so effective that MWC relays are capable of billions of troublefree operations when used as recommended by the manufacturers.

Applications of MWC Relays. Because their low contact resistance produces negligible voltage drop, MWC relays are very suitable for low-voltage circuits. They are valuable also where any change in a switched voltage due to contact-drop would cause an error, as could happen in thermocouple circuits. Because the low contact resistance of these relays remains constant over a long service life, they can be used to advantage in transducer circuits where even small changes in resistance produce errors. These relays are useful where exact voltages must be switched accurately, as in computers and various control devices.

The high reliability and long life of MWC relays permit their use in equipment which must be left unattended for extensive periods of time, and in applications requiring billions of operations. Their high repetition rate and lack of contact bounce make them suitable for high-speed switching applications such as in logic and counting circuits.

Unit 1

section 4 — Circuit Breakers

Circuit breakers are control devices used extensively in industrial, commercial, and household applications. Fig. 62 shows some available models.

The function of a circuit breaker is to carry rated current until an overload occurs, at which time the breaker opens the circuit automatically. Some breakers are designed to respond quickly to an overload of 25 percent. Others have a time-delay mechanism which requires overload current flow for a longer period of time before the breaker trips and opens the circuit.

Short time delays (a few seconds) are used to protect electronic equipment. Circuit breakers with longer delays (up to 30 seconds) are used with small motors and some heating equipment. As the current through a circuit breaker increases beyond the 125% point (trip level) the time delay decreases.

Most of the available general-purpose circuit breakers are variations of three basic types: *thermal, thermal-magnetic,* and *hydraulic-magnetic.*

Thermal Breakers

A thermal circuit breaker contains a bimetal element as the actuating member. Fig. 63 illustrates the operation of this breaker. In operation, circuit current flows through the switch contacts and the bimetal element. If the current does not exceed the rated value of the breaker, the thermal element does not react sufficiently to trip the switch, as shown in Fig. 63(A). However, if the current increases to a value 25 percent greater than the rated value, the increased temperature due to the excess current expands the bimetal element. The uneven expansion of the two metals causes the element to bend and unlatch the switch contacts, allowing the spring to pull them apart

41

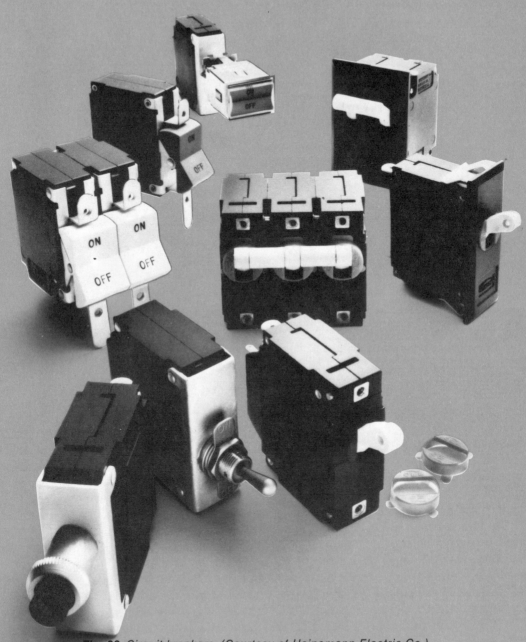

Fig. 62. *Circuit breakers. (Courtesy of Heinemann Electric Co.)*

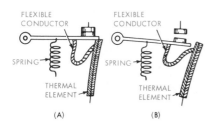

Fig. 63. *Basic components and operation of thermal circuit breaker. (Reprinted from* Machine Design, *Penton Publishing Co., Cleveland, Ohio)*

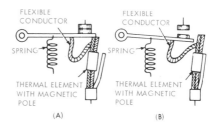

Fig. 64. *Thermal circuit breaker with auxiliary magnetic plate. (Reprinted from* Machine Design, *Penton Publishing Co., Cleveland, Ohio)*

quickly, as shown in Fig. 63(B). Higher overload currents create more heat and the element bends more quickly, reducing the time delay.

Thermal-Magnetic Breakers

Some thermal-type circuit breakers have an additional magnetic feature, and are known as thermal-magnetic breakers. Their operation is illustrated in Fig. 64.

In view (A) the breaker is operating under rated load. In view (B) the breaker has been tripped by an overload. As in the regular thermal breaker, the bimetal element bends due to the high temperature caused by excessive current. In this type of breaker tripping of the switch by the thermal element is aided by the magnetic plate as it is attracted to the stationary member. In some models a coil wired in series with the thermal element provides the magnetic action.

Temperature Compensation

Some thermal and thermal-magnetic breakers contain an additional bimetal element which compensates for the effects of ambient temperature changes on the over-

load element. The added element operates in opposition to the overload element.

When an increase in ambient temperature bends the overload element toward unlatching, the compensating element bends in the opposite direction, maintaining the correct amount of latching surface. As the ambient temperature decreases, the action is reversed, with additional latching surface provided by the compensating element.

Hydraulic-Magnetic Breaker

The essential components of the hydraulic-magnetic circuit breaker are illustrated in Fig. 65. The actuation of this breaker is accomplished by a solenoid and a hydraulic dashpot. The purpose of the dashpot is to set the time delay.

In operation, circuit current flows through the switch contacts and the solenoid coil. At rated current the solenoid field is too weak to attract the core, as shown in view (A). When the circuit current exceeds the rated value of the circuit breaker the field of the solenoid is sufficient to draw the core up into the coil against the return spring, as shown in view (B). The time this action takes depends on the thickness of the hydraulic fluid (usually silicone). Thicker

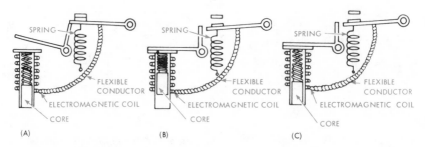

Fig. 65. *Basic construction and operation of hydraulic-magnetic circuit breaker. (Reprinted from* Machine Design, *Penton Publishing Co., Cleveland, Ohio)*

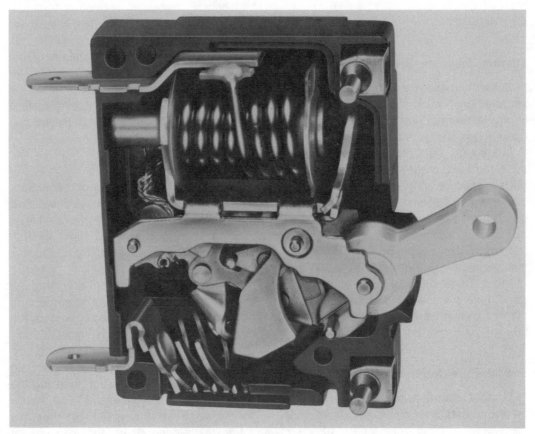

Fig. 66. *Cutaway of a typical hydraulic-magnetic circuit breaker. (Courtesy of Heinemann Electric Co.)*

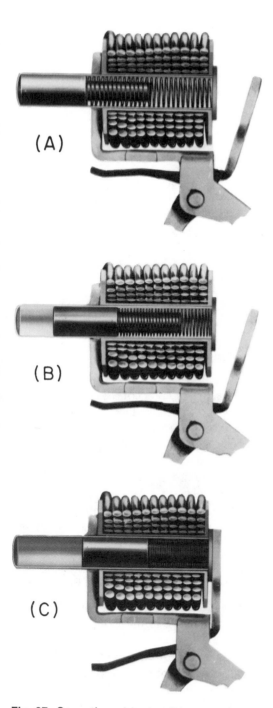

(A)

(B)

(C)

fluids are used for longer time delays and thinner fluids for shorter. As the core is drawn into the coil it becomes magnetized. When it contacts the pole piece, the piece becomes part of the magnet. The pole piece now attracts the trip arm, unlatching the switch mechanism and allowing the spring to separate the contacts quickly, breaking the circuit.

On large overloads the core moves faster, a larger field flux is created, and the pole piece becomes magnetized before the core reaches it. Thus the switch is opened more quickly. When the overload is excessive (at least ten times rated current) the field built up around the coil is sufficient to magnetize the pole piece and trip the switch before the core is drawn into the coil, as shown in view (C). In this case time delay is minimum.

Fig. 66 shows the internal construction and Fig. 67 the electromagnetic action of a commercial hydraulic-magnetic circuit breaker.

Fig. 67. *Operation of hydraulic-magnetic circuit breaker. (Courtesy of Heinemann Electric Co.)*

Unit 1

section 5

Laboratory Procedures

The laboratory procedures outlined in this Section assume that the student has access to the devices and equipment listed for each experiment, is familiar with basic circuits and circuit diagrams, and performs the work under the supervision of an instructor.

Some of the devices and circuits require 120 Vac. Adequate precautions should be observed.

Electromagnetic Relay: Basic Form

Purpose: To study construction and operation of a basic form of electromagnetic relay.

Devices and Equipment: Relay, electromagnetic, dc (Potter and Brumfield type LB, 6 V—2,500Ω, 9 V—5,000Ω, 12 V—10,000Ω, or equivalent); power supply, 0—24 V dc; vacuum-tube voltmeter (VTVM); milliammeter; ohmmeter; switch, SPST.

Procedure:

1. Study construction of relay. Operate manually.
2. Study ratings of selected relay. Determine required coil voltage and milliammeter range.
3. Read and record resistance of relay coil.
4. Wire circuit as shown in Fig. 68. Have wiring approved.
5. Increase applied voltage until relay operates. Record pull-in voltage and current.
6. Decrease applied voltage and record drop-out (reset) voltage and current.
7. Test operation at rated voltage.
8. Write a statement explaining any difference between pull-in and drop-out values.

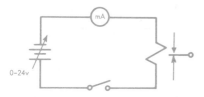

Fig. 68. *Electromagnetic-relay test circuit.*

Relay Application: SPDT (Form C) Action

Purpose: To design, wire, and test an SPDT relay application.

Devices and Equipment: Relay, SPDT; relay-coil supply; 2 loads and load supply; switch, SPST. If relay has 120 V contacts, loads may be 120 V lamps with 120 V line supply.

Procedure:

1. Design circuit so that when the SPST switch is closed the relay is energized, closing one load circuit and opening the other. Have diagram approved.
2. Wire circuit. Have wiring approved.
3. Test operation of circuit.
4. Write a statement describing two practical applications of this form of relay circuit.

Relay Application: Locking Circuit

Purpose: To design, wire and test a locking circuit using an SPDT (Form C) relay.

Devices and Equipment: Relay, SPDT, 120 V coil, 120 V contacts; switch, SPST (S_1); switch, SPST, momentary-contact (S_2); lamp, 120 V.

Procedure:

1. Design circuit so that:
   closing switch S_1 completes load circuit through NC contacts;
   closing switch S_2 (momentary-contact) energizes relay, opening load circuit;
   closed NO contacts shunt S_2 (S_1 closed), maintaining coil circuit when S_2 is released;
   opening S_1 opens coil circuit, deenergizing relay (S_2 open).
2. Have circuit diagram approved.
3. Wire circuit. Have wiring approved.
4. Test operation of circuit.
5. Write a statement describing a practical application of this form of relay circuit.

Latching Relay, Mechanical

Purpose: To study construction, operation and application of a mechanical latching relay.

Devices and Equipment: Relay, latching, open-type, 120 V ac (Potter and Brumfield

KUB series, Guardian IR—1200/1200—4C, or equivalent); 2 switches, SPST, momentary-contact; lamp, 120 V.

Procedure:

1. Study constructional details of relay. Operate latching mechanism manually.
2. Design latching-relay circuit. Include a lamp load. Place one switch in the operate-coil circuit and one in the latching-coil circuit. Have circuit diagram approved.
3. Wire circuit. Have wiring approved.
4. Test operation of circuit.
5. Write a statement explaining the advantages of a latching relay.

Latching Relay, Magnetic

Purpose: To study construction, operation and application of a magnetic latching relay.

Devices and Equipment: Relay, latching, magnetic, single-coil, dc (Potter and Brumfield KUL Series—6, 12, 24, 48, 110 V dc, or equivalent); power supply, dc; lamp, 120 V; switch, reversing—may be DPDT center-off switch with jumpers.

Procedure:

1. Study specifications and constructional details of selected relay.
2. Diagram relay circuit. Include coil supply, reversing switch, load and load supply. Have diagram approved.
3. Wire circuit. Have wiring approved.
4. Test operation of circuit.
5. Write a statement explaining operation of the magnetic latching relay.

Dry-Reed Relay (Form A)

Purpose: To study operation of an SPST (Form A) dry-reed relay.

Devices and Equipment: Relay, dry-reed (Magnecraft Class 101 MPC—6, 12, 24 V dc Potter and Brumfield JRA 100 series —6, 12, 24 V dc, or equivalent) ; power supply, dc; vacuum-tube voltmeter (VMTV); load and load supply.

Procedure:

1. Study specifications and ratings of selected relay.
2. Design circuit to test operation of relay. Select load values (resistance and voltage) which result in operation below contact maximums. Have design approved.
3. Wire circuit. Connect VTVM across coil. Have wiring approved.
4. Apply load voltage.
5. Increase coil voltage gradually from zero. Record pull-in voltage.
6. Decrease coil voltage gradually and record drop-out voltage.
7. Reverse polarity of coil voltage and test relay operation.
8. Write a statement describing a practical application of the dry-reed relay.

Dry-Reed Relay (Form C)

Purpose: To study operation of an SPDT (Form C) dry-reed relay.

Devices and Equipment: Relay, dry-reed (Magnecraft Class 103 M—6, 12, 24 V dc, Potter and Brumfield JR series—6, 12, 24, 48 V dc, or equivalent); power supply, dc; 2 loads and load supply.

Procedure:

1. Study specifications and ratings of selected relay.
2. Design circuit to test operation of relay. Select load values (resistance and voltage) which result in operation below contact maximums. Have design approved.
3. Wire circuit. Have wiring approved.
4. Apply load voltage.
5. Apply coil voltage and check operation of relay circuit.
6. Reverse polarity of coil voltage and test relay operation.
7. Write a statement describing advantages of reed relays in certain applications.

Mercury-Wetted-Contact Relays

Purpose: To study operation of mercury-wetted-contact relays (Forms C and D).

Devices and Equipment: Relay, mercury-wetted-contact, SPDT (Form C), non-bridging, (Potter and Brumfield JMA 1000 series, Clare HGS 5000 series, or equivalent); relay, mercury-wetted contact, SPDT (Form D), bridging, (Potter and Brumfield JMA 3000 series, Clare HGS 1000 series, or equivalent); power supply, dc; vacuum-tube voltmeter (VTVM); 2 loads and load supply.

Procedure:

Part A

1. Study specifications and ratings of selected Form C relay.
2. Design circuit to test operation of relay. Select load values (resistance and voltage) which result in operation below contact maximums. Have design approved.
3. Wire circuit. Connect VTVM across coil. Have wiring approved.
4. Apply load voltage.
5. Increase coil voltage gradually from zero. Record pull-in voltage.
6. Decrease coil voltage and record drop-out voltage.
7. Reverse polarity of coil voltage and test operation of relay.

Part B

1. Repeat procedure using a Form D (bridging) relay.
2. Write a statement explaining how applications of mercury-wetted-contact relays might differ from those of dry-reed relays.

Try writing out the answer
to each question before look-
ing up the answer.

Review Questions

1. How may switches be classified?
2. Describe the capability of a rotary switch.
3. List some forms of limit-switch operators.
4. What is unique about precision snap-action switches?
5. Why are dissimilar metals used in some thermal switches?
6. Compare the features of strip and disc thermostats.
7. Describe construction of the strut-type single-metal thermostat.
8. What are the main components of a liquid-filled thermostat?
9. What components form a remote indicating controller?
10. What features of the mercury switch make it appropriate for a variety of applications?
11. Why is hydrogen used in mercury switches?
12. How can time delay be achieved in a mercury switch?
13. List the component parts of an electromagnetic relay.
14. In relay terminology what is "pickup current"?
15. Describe the construction of a typical reed switch.
16. What is an offset reed switch?
17. Why is the reed switch in Fig. 51 mechanically-biased?
18. What are some advantages of mercury-wetted-reed relays over the dry-reed type?
19. Describe the construction of an MWC-relay switching unit.
20. Differentiate between MWC-relay form-C and form-D operation.
21. How does capillary action contribute to the long life of MWC relays?
22. Where can the low resistance of MWC relays be used to advantage?
23. What are the three basic types of circuit breakers?
24. Why is a magnet added to the basic thermal circuit breaker?
25. Explain operation of a hydraulic-magnetic circuit breaker with(a) overload and(b) excessive overload.

Cover this page with a piece
of paper until you are sure
of the answer.

Answers to
Review Questions

1. Switches may be classified according to their construction, function or form of operation.
2. Depending on its design, a rotary switch can close or open a few or many circuits at one time or sequentially.
3. Common forms of limit-switch operators include rotary actuators, top and side push-rollers, and top and side pushbuttons.
4. Precision snap-action switches have closely spaced contacts which close and open very quickly and positively. They operate consistently within close tolerance limits upon repeated actuations.
5. Dissimilar metals are used in some thermal switches to utilize their different rates of expansion in producing movement of a member which actuates the switch contacts.
6. Disc-type bimetal thermostats have fast make-break action; action of the strip type is slower. Generally the strip-type has adjustable temperature setting and the disc-type operates at fixed temperatures.

7. In a single-metal thermostat two low-expansion struts are connected at one end to an outer casing of high-expansion metal and at the other end to an adjusting mechanism. A pair of switch contacts is mounted on facing sides of the struts.
8. A liquid-filled thermostat consists mainly of a tube containing an expandable liquid, a bellows, and a switch.
9. A remote indicating controller is made up of a fluid-filled sensing head and capillary tube, a temperature-indicating meter, and a switch.
10. The mercury switch requires low actuating force, has low contact resistance and good repeatability, can be hermetically sealed, and operates well over a wide temperature range.
11. Hydrogen serves two purposes in mercury-switch capsules: (1) it is used to replace air, since the oxygen in air reacts chemically with mercury; and (2) it quenches arcing at the electrodes.
12. A baffle can be included in a mercury switch to slow the movement of the mercury, thereby creating a time delay.

13. In general, a typical electromagnetic relay consists of a frame, an electro-magnetic coil and core, an armature and spring, and a switch mechanism containing NC, NO or a combination of NC and NO contacts.

14. "Pickup current" is the current required to actuate a relay.

15. A typical reed switch consists of two closely-spaced, flat, metal reeds mounted in a glass tube containing an inert gas such as nitrogen.

16. An offset reed switch is a unit in which one reed is stationary and the other is movable. In operation, the movable reed is attracted to the stationary one.

17. The reed switch in Fig. 51 is mechanically-biased to allow for SPDT action. Mechanical bias assures the armature-NC contact.

18. Unlike the dry-reed relay, the mercury-wetter-reed relay forms new mercury-coated surfaces each time the relay operates. This provides longer life and higher contact rating. In addition, the damping effect of the mercury eliminates contact bounce.

19. The switching unit of an MWC relay consists of a hydrogen-filled glass tube containing a pool of mercury, an armature and one or more sets of contacts.

20. In an MWC relay with form C action, the armature-NC connection is opened (mercury filament broken) before the armature reaches the NO contact (break-before-make). With form D action the armature-NO connection is made before the armature NC connection is broken (make-before-break).

21. Capillary action provides a continuous supply of mercury to the switch contacts of MWC relays, forming "new contacts" with each actuation of the switch —assuring a life of billions of operations.

22. The low resistance of MWC relays can be used to advantage in low-voltage circuits and in applications where changes in voltage due to contact drop can produce errors, as in thermocouple circuits.

23. The three basic types of circuit breakers are thermal, thermal-magnetic and hydraulic-magnetic.

24. A magnet is added to the basic thermal circuit breaker to assist the bi-metal element in operating the contacts.

25. (a) When current through a hydraulic-magnetic circuit breaker exceeds the rated value by about 25%, the solenoid field becomes strong enough to attract the core. The core contacts the pole piece, magnetizing it. The pole piece attracts the trip arm which unlatches the switch, and the contacts open.

    (b) When the overload is excessive the solenoid field is strong enough to magnetize the pole piece and complete the breaking action before the core is pulled into the coil.

UNIT 2

Timers

Unit 2

Contents

List of Illustrations

Unit 2

List of Tables

Unit 2

section 1

Introduction

Timing is indispensable to the proper operation of many types of industrial equipment, from the simplest to the most complex. For this reason timing devices, or *timers*, are important components in industrial electronics.

Devices used to perform timing operations as well as on-off switching operations may be classified according to function or according to how the timing is accomplished. However, the classification of these devices is not hard and fast. For example, relays which perform a time-delay function may be found listed as relays or as time-delay devices, and include the pneumatic, dashpot, and mercury-displacement types.

Classifications

When grouped according to function, there are three main divisions: (1) *delay timers*, which provide delay before switch actuation; (2) *interval timers*, which set the

57

length of time a load is energized; and (3) *cycle timers*, which operate switches according to preset sequences.

Based on how timing is accomplished, timers may be classified into such groups as: *thermal, dashpot, motor-driven, mechanical, electrical, electronic,* and *electrochemical.* These will be described and illustrated in sections which follow.

One of the basic applications of timing is causing an operation to occur (heat on, motor off, etc.) at a certain time after another operation has occurred. The delay required between the operations might range from a fraction of a second to many days.

Some timing applications require a slow-operate, quick-return (SO-QR) device, one in which there is a time delay between timer energization and switch-contact operation. In other cases the timer may be required to operate quickly and release slowly (QO-SR) with a time delay between deenergization and operation of the switch contacts. Still other time-delay devices are designed to provide both slow-operate and slow-release actions (SO-SR) with a delay between timer energization and switch-contact operation and also between timer deenergization and return action of the contacts.

Unit 2

section 2   Thermal Timers

The effects of heating certain metals are utilized in a group of timers called *thermal time-delay relays*. These thermal relays provide time delays from a few seconds to three or four minutes. They are generally small, lightweight, inexpensive and relatively trouble-free. They do not chatter and they operate on alternating or direct current.

Most thermal timers are temperature-compensated and many have time-setting adjustments. Hermetically-sealed units are not affected by altitude, moisture or other atmospheric conditions. These timers are commercially available in two types: *bimetal* and *expansion*.

Bimetal Timers

There are a number of forms of bimetal timers. One is shown in Fig. 1. Most of these devices contain two bimetal struts which have the same thermal-expansion properties. This provides compensation for ambient temperature changes. Any effect pro-

Fig. 1. *Thermal delay timer (Courtesy of Industrial Timer Corp.).*

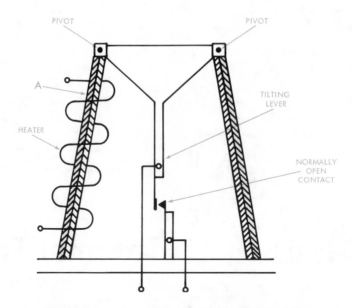

Fig. 2. *General construction of bimetal-strut timer.*

duced in one strut by an ambient temperature change is also produced in the other strut. The struts are so mounted that these changes cancel, maintaining the movable switch arm in correct unactuated position. Fig. 2 illustrates a method of mounting the struts.

In operation, when current flows through the heater (timer energization) the two metals in strut A expand at different rates, causing the strut to bend. After a certain time the strut bends sufficiently to deflect the contact arm until the contacts close. Thus a time delay is produced between the energization of the timer and the closing (or opening) of a set of contacts.

Fig. 3 shows a single-pole, double-throw (SPDT), spring-loaded, thermal timer. This design provides quick closing and opening of contacts, minimizing contact deterioration and other effects associated with slow operation. The actuating member and the armature mount are both bimetal. Conse-

quently, any changes in ambient temperature affect both equally, cancelling the effects of ambient temperature variations on the operation of the timer.

Expansion Timers

An expansion-type thermal timer is illustrated in Fig. 4. Current through the heater expands the actuating member upward. This tilts the armature on its pivot, closing the contacts. Timing is determined by the expansion rate of the actuator and the setting of the adjustment screw.

Another form of thermal-expansion timer is shown in Fig. 5. In this device one end of the actuator is compressed against one end of the movable armature. The adjustment mechanism controls the compression between the actuator and armature and also the tension on the armature. When current flows through the heater, expansion of the actuator applies pressure to the upper end

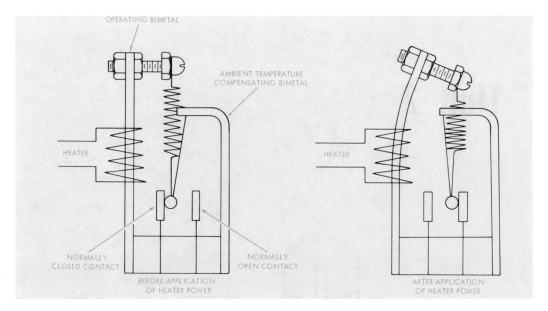

Fig. 3. *Operation of spring-loaded bimetal timer (Courtesy of Relay Specialties Inc.).*

of the armature, tilting the contact end toward the stationary normally-open (NO) contact. The time elapsed between initial energization of the timer and contact closure depends on the setting of the adjustment mechanism. In the model illustrated the delay is variable from one second to three minutes.

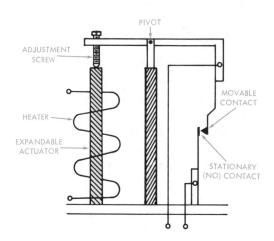

Fig. 4. *Form of thermal expansion timer.*

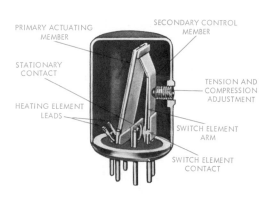

Fig. 5. *Thermal expansion timer, commercial model (Courtesy of Relay Specialties, Inc.).*

Unit 2

section 3 Dashpot Timers

Dashpot timers are those in which the timing period is determined by how long it takes a certain amount of liquid or air to pass through an opening or orifice. The size of the orifice can be fixed or adjustable, thereby making the timing period fixed or adjustable. Three forms of dashpot timers are quite common in industry: *hydraulic-magnetic*, *pneumatic*, and *mercury*.

Hydraulic-Magnetic Timers

A form of hydraulic-magnetic timer is illustrated in Fig. 6. When current flows through the coil the field magnetizes the core, pulling it into the coil. As the core moves it displaces a fluid, usually a silicone. (Silicones are used in these devices because their viscosities are quite constant from −30°F to 120°F [−34.4°C to 49°C].) When the magnetized core reaches the end of its travel it attracts the armature, resulting in operation of the switch. The amount

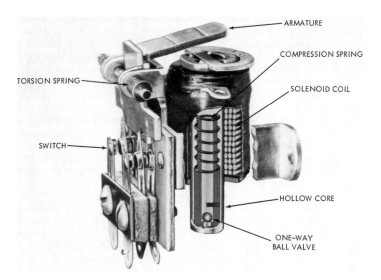

Fig. 6. *Hydraulic-magnetic timer (Courtesy of Heinemann Electric Co.).*

of delay between energization of the coil and switch operation depends on the time taken to displace the silicone with the core. When the coil is deenergized the spring returns the core to its starting position.

The return time is much shorter than the delay time, due to the action of a one-way ball valve in the hollow core. When the core is being pulled into the coil the valve is held closed by pressure of the silicone. However, when the spring is returning the core the pressure of the silicone on the ball is in the opposite direction, causing the valve to open. This allows much of the silicone to be displaced through the hollow core. Due to this valve action, release time is generally 10% to 20% of delay time.

Pneumatic Timers

The delay of a pneumatic timer (air dashpot) depends on the rate at which air is forced from a chamber by pressure on a diaphragm. Fig. 7 shows the construction

and operation of available "on-delay" and "off-delay" models.

A deenergized on-delay unit is shown at (A) of Fig. 7. In this mode the armature contacts are held against the NC contacts (lower). At (B) the coil is energized, the core moves upward and compresses the operating spring which applies pressure to the diaphragm. Pressure on the diaphragm forces air out through the needle valve at a rate determined by its setting. The time required is the time delay. At (C) core travel is complete (end of delay) and the lower collar on the core spindle actuates the snap-action switch—causing the armature contacts to transfer from the NC to the NO contacts. When the coil is deenergized the one-way air valve allows the operating spring to return the core and reset the switch almost instantly.

The illustration at (D) shows a deenergized off-delay timer. Here the upward position of the core flexes the diaphragm into the chamber reducing its capacity. Also, in this mode, the armature contacts are held

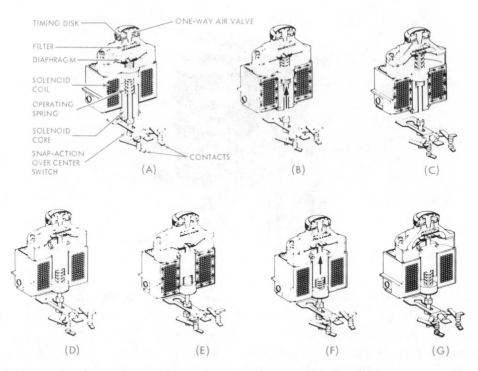

Labels (A):
TIMING DISK
ONE-WAY AIR VALVE
FILTER
DIAPHRAGM
SOLENOID COIL
OPERATING SPRING
SOLENOID CORE
SNAP-ACTION OVER CENTER SWITCH
CONTACTS

(A)   (B)   (C)

(D)   (E)   (F)   (G)

Fig. 7. *Construction and operation of "on delay" and "off delay" pneumatic timers (Courtesy of Amerace Corp.).*

against the NC contacts (upper). At (E) the energized coil pulls the core downward, compressing the spring. Immediately switch action transfers the armature contacts from the NC to the NO contacts (lower). At the same time the core pulls the diaphragm downward. This action expands the chamber and air rushes in.

When the coil is deenergized the time delay begins. This is shown at (F). With the field removed the compressed spring starts moving the core and diaphragm upward, forcing air from the chamber. The time required to complete this action depends on the air-valve setting. When the core reaches its upper position (end of delay) the switch

is tripped by the spindle and the armature contacts return to the NC contacts (shown at (G).

Pneumatic timers are available with delays (both on and off) ranging from a fraction of a second to many minutes. Some models have calibrated dials; less expensive units are set by trial. Both alternating- and direct-current models are available. Some pneumatic timers have auxiliary momentary contacts which are operated directly by the electromagnet. These are multipurpose devices, which, in many applications, eliminate additional relays. Fig. 8 shows a unit which incorporates such contacts.

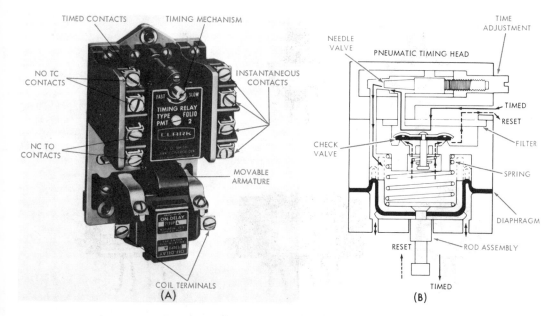

Fig. 8. *Pneumatic timer with auxiliary contacts (A), and cutaway drawing (B) showing pneumatic mechanism (Courtesy of A. O. Smith Co., Clark Control Div.).*

Mercury Timers

A mercury timer consists essentially of two sections: (1) a sealed housing containing a plunger (movable core), cushion springs, mercury and a gas (most models); and (2) a solenoid coil surrounding a section of the housing. Several models are shown in Fig. 9. Since operation of this timer depends on the displacement of mercury by a plunger it is commonly called a "mercury plunger relay" or "mercury-displacement relay." The cutaway in Fig. 10 shows the component parts of a typical unit.

Mercury relays can be used to advantage where changes in voltage or temperature would impair the operation of other types of relays. Because of the mercury-to-mercury contact they have high current-carrying capacity, low contact resistance and no contact corrosion or deterioration. As time-delay relays they are available in various combinations of operate-release times, such as quick-operate, slow-release (QO-SR); slow-operate, quick-release (SO-QR); or slow-operate, slow-release (SO-SR).

65

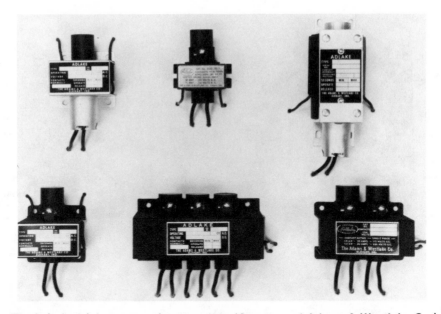

Fig. 9. *Industrial mercury plunger relays (Courtesy of Adams & Westlake Co.).*

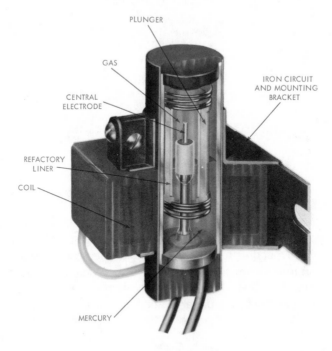

Fig. 10. *Cutaway showing construction of typical mercury plunger relay (Courtesy of Adams & Westlake Co.).*

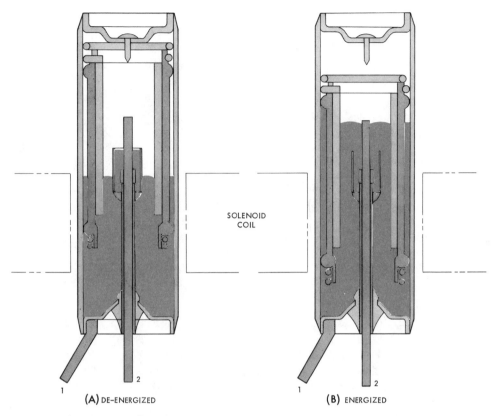

SOLENOID
COIL

2   2
1   1
(A) DE-ENERGIZED   (B) ENERGIZED

Fig. 11. *Construction and operation of normally-open, quick-operate, quick-release mercury plunger relay (Courtesy of* **Machine Design,** *the Penton Publishing Co.).*

Operation of Mercury Timers (Mercury Plunger Relays). The operation of a mercury-plunger relay depends on the displacement of a pool of mercury which makes the connection between two electrodes. This is illustrated in Fig. 11, which shows the construction and operation of the simplest form of this relay. This is not a time-delay model. It is a normally-open, quick-operate, quick-release (QO-QR) relay.

In operation, when current flows through the solenoid coil the plunger is attracted downward into the coil. The downward move-ment of the plunger displaces some of the mercury, raising its level until the pool of mercury makes contact with the mercury in the cup. Since one relay terminal is connected to the pool and the other to the mercury in the cup, the two "switch" terminals are now connected through the continuous mercury, as shown at (B). When the coil is deenergized the plunger returns upward. The mercury returns to the original level, breaking the connection between terminals 1 and 2.

Fig. 12 illustrates a normally-closed,

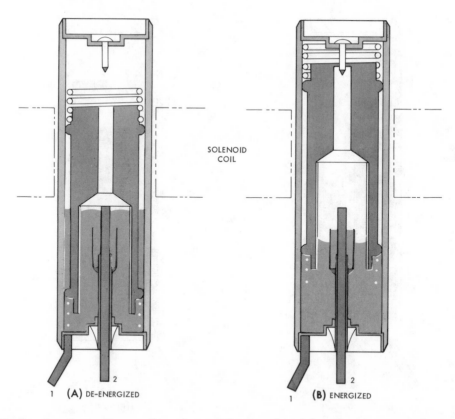

SOLENOID
COIL

1 (**A**) DE-ENERGIZED

1 (**B**) ENERGIZED

Fig. 12. *Construction and operation of normally-closed, quick-acting mercury plunger relay (Courtesy of **Machine Design,** the Penton Publishing Co.).*

quick-acting, mercury-plunger relay (not a time-delay form). When the coil is deenergized there is a connection through the mercury from terminal 1 to terminal 2. Energization of the coil moves the plunger upward, causing the level of the mercury pool to drop below the edge of the cup. This breaks the mercury-to-mercury contact, opening the normally-closed connection between terminals 1 and 2.

Delay is added to the basic relay by controlling the time taken by the plunger to displace the mercury. Fig. 13 shows a nor-

mally-open, slow-operate, quick-release (SO-QR) relay. The time taken to displace the mercury depends on the time required to force a gas through a section of porous ceramic. Various degrees of porosity provide various time delays. The thimble T contains the gas involved in the timing.

At (A) the relay is in a deenergized state with no connection between terminals 1 and 2. When the coil is energized the plunger moves downward, forcing the mercury upward into the thimble through orifice O. This forces the gas through the ceramic section

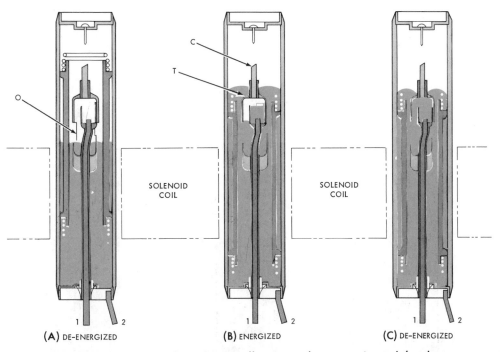

SOLENOID
COIL

SOLENOID
COIL

1   2
(A) DE-ENERGIZED

1   2
(B) ENERGIZED

1   2
(C) DE-ENERGIZED

Fig. 13. *Construction and operation of normally-open, slow-operate, quick-release mercury plunger relay (Courtesy of* **Machine Design,** *the Penton Publishing Co.).*

C. The mercury rises in the thimble until it spills over the edge of the cup, completing the circuit from terminal 1 to terminal 2, as shown at (B). The length of time required for the plunger to force the mercury high enough to make contact depends on how fast the gas passes through the ceramic. When the coil is deenergized the plunger moves upward, allowing the mercury level to drop quickly below the edge of the cup, breaking the connection between terminals 1 and 2. "On" delays ranging from tenths of a second to many minutes are possible with this form of relay.

A quick-operate, slow-release (QO-SR) normally-open relay is illustrated in Fig. 14. Timing of this relay depends on the rate of flow of mercury through a small hole. At (A) the coil is deenergized and the mercury contact is broken. At (B) the coil has been energized and the plunger pulled down. This displaces the mercury upward in the thimble where it contacts the mercury in the cup, closing the circuit between terminals 1 and 2. The plunger moves upward when the coil is deenergized and the mercury in the outer chamber drops quickly. However, the mercury in the thimble drops slowly as it bleeds through hole *H*. The time it takes the level of the mercury in the thimble to reach the edge of the cup, where contact is broken, is the time delay. This is determined by the size of the hole.

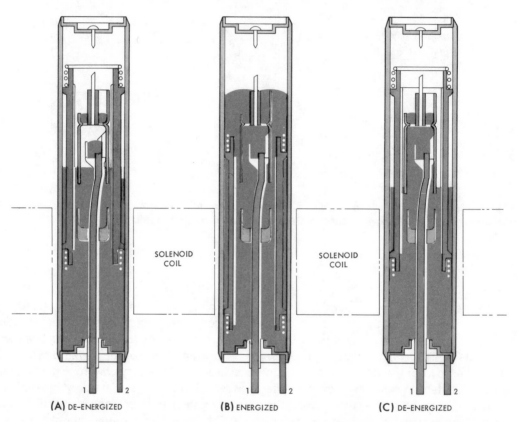

Fig. 14. *Construction and operation of normally open, quick-operate, slow-release mercury plunger relay (Courtesy of* **Machine Design,** *the Penton Publishing Co.).*

Unit 2

Motor-Driven Timers

A motor-driven timer consists essentially of a motor and a clutch, driving a mechanism which actuates a switch or switches at the end of a preset time period or at intervals during the period. Motor-driven timers have a number of advantages over other timers, which make them more suitable for some applications. They can provide multiple switching and are superior in applications which require rather long time delays. They usually contain synchronous motors which run at constant speeds, making them more accurate than most other timers. Many have well-calibrated dials which provide accurate adjustment of desired timing periods.

Some of the many functions which motor-driven timers perform are: providing on and off delays, interval timing, recycling, running-time recording and sequential operation of multiple switches. Some timers reset automatically when the timing period ends. Some are simple on-off devices; others offer many combinations of functions and circuitry. Motor-driven timers are loosely classified into groups according to function, construction or some unique feature; such as: interval, cycle, reset, cam, etc.

Clutches: Internal and External

A clutch is used in a motor-driven timer to engage and disengage the motor and switch-actuator. This is necessary to permit the timer to return to its starting position after completion of the timing period. A clutch which is an integral part of the motor is illustrated in Fig. 15. This clutch is called an *internal clutch* and the motor is called a *clutch motor*.

When there is no current through the motor a spring (not shown in the simplified illustration) holds the rotor and rotor pinion disengaged from the gear train, as shown at (A). Current through the motor magnetizes the stator which then attracts the rotor. This moves the rotor and pinion to the engaged position (B). Now rotation of the rotor is transferred to the gear train. At the end of the timing period deenergization of the motor allows the spring to disengage the clutch from the gear train. This permits resetting of the gear train.

The clutch-motor timer is commonly used for time delays up to one minute. For longer delays an "external clutch" mechanism is

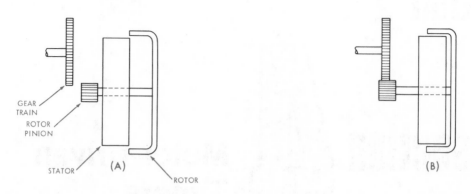

GEAR
TRAIN
ROTOR
PINION
STATOR
(A)
ROTOR
(B)

Fig. 15. *General construction and operation of internal-clutch motor (Courtesy of **Machine Design,** the Penton Publishing Co.).*

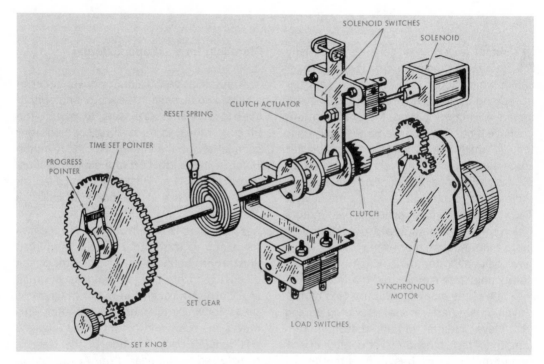

SOLENOID SWITCHES
SOLENOID
CLUTCH ACTUATOR
RESET SPRING
TIME SET POINTER
PROGRESS
POINTER
CLUTCH
SYNCHRONOUS
MOTOR
SET GEAR
LOAD SWITCHES
SET KNOB

Fig. 16. *General construction of external-clutch timer (Courtesy of **Machine Design,** the Penton Publishing Co.).*

preferred. A sketch of such a mechanism is given in Fig. 16. This is essentially a solenoid-operated jaw-clutch. In operation, when current flows through the solenoid it attracts the core and clutch actuator. This causes the two sections of the clutch to engage, thereby connecting the motor to the timing gears. When the solenoid is deenergized it releases the core and actuator, which are returned to the disengaged position by a spring. Shown in the illustration is a reset spring which becomes loaded by the rotation of the shaft during the timing period. When the clutch is disengaged at the end of timing this spring resets the timer. Load switches and actuator are also shown.

Interval Timers

Interval timers are those which automatically switch circuits on or off after, or during, a preset time interval. They are available in both manual and automatic reset types. Most models have a time dial, with a knob and pointer for setting the time period manually. Many have adjustable stops which can be positioned to ensure accurate resetting for successive periods of operation. Fig. 17 shows a typical manual-set timer.

In one form of this timer, when the knob is set to a time on the dial the motor starts

and the NC contact of a single-pole, double-throw (SPDT) switch is set closed and the NO contact is set open. At the end of timing the NO contact closes and the NC contact opens. Without automatic reset the switch remains in this state.

In automatic-reset models the contacts are returned immediately to NC closed and NO open. The wiring diagrams of two units are shown in Fig. 18. The unit at (A) incorporates an internal clutch; the one at (B) has an external clutch.

Cycle Timers

There are many industrial operations which are repeated at set time intervals. There are also situations in which a number of circuits must be energized for various periods of time in certain sequences. These and similar requirements are met by a group of devices called *cycle timers*. This group may be further classified into *cam timers*, *percentage timers, and time switches.*

Cam Timers. A motor-driven cam timer

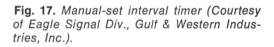

Fig. 17. *Manual-set interval timer (Courtesy of Eagle Signal Div., Gulf & Western Industries, Inc.).*

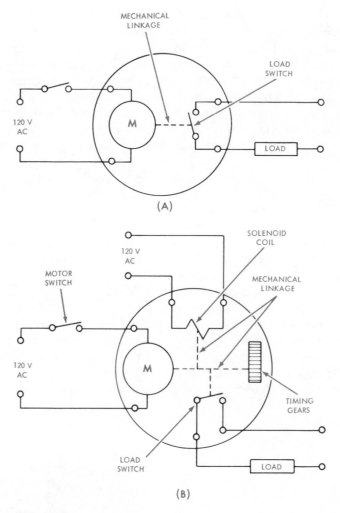

Fig. 18. *Wiring of timer circuits: (A) internal-clutch, and (B) external-clutch.*

consists of a drive motor and gear assembly, one or more shaft-mounted cams and one or more cam-operated switches. Fig. 19 shows an adjustable single-cam timer. Two forms of multiple-cam timers are shown in Fig. 20.

Cams are either adjustable or non-adjustable. Non-adjustable cams are discs into which "on-off" programs are cut. Adjustable cams usually consist of two discs which are reduced in diameter along a section of their circumference, as illustrated in Fig. 21.

Fig. 22 shows cam settings for a number of timing periods. Cams are available which can be adjusted for switch operation from 2% to 98% of one shaft revolution.

A desired switching time is set by adjust-

Fig. 19. *Single-cam, motor-driven timer(Courtesy of Industrial Timer Corp.).*

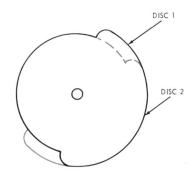

Fig. 21. *Two-disc adjustable cam.*

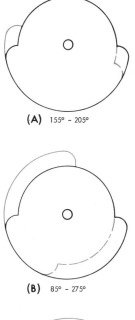

(A) 155° – 205°

(B) 85° – 275°

(C) 20° – 340°

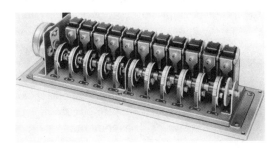

Fig. 20. *Two forms of multiple-cam timers (Courtesy of Industrial Timer Corp.).*

Fig. 22. *Timer-cam settings.*

75

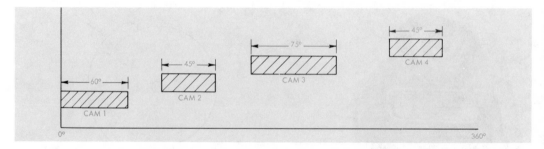

Fig. 23. *Timing chart for 4-cam timer; no overlap.*

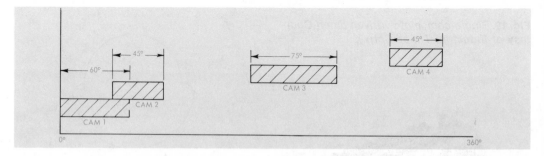

Fig. 24. *Timing chart for 4-cam timer, with overlap.*

ing the relative positions of the two discs. This is usually facilitated by markings on the discs. The discs are locked together and fastened in position on the drive shaft. In a multiple-cam timer each cam must be positioned in proper relation to the other cams. This is best accomplished if a timing chart is prepared. The timing chart in Fig. 23 shows a planned sequence of operation of four cams during one revolution of the camshaft. This plan calls for time intervals between the operating times of the cams. In another application of this timer it might be necessary for cam No. 2 to operate its switch before cam No. 1 completes its operate time. The layout for this application is given in Fig. 24. The actual length of each timing period (seconds, minutes, etc.) depends on the setting

of each cam and the rotational speed of the camshaft, which could be a few seconds or several hours per revolution.

When an application requires that the cam timer run continuously, repeating its cycle of operation over and over, the circuit in Fig. 25 is used. When voltage is removed from the motor the timer stops where it is. When voltage is again applied to the motor the cycle resumes at the point where the timer stopped.

Some cam timers include a stop contact for stopping the timer at the end of one cycle. Fig. 26 shows the drive-motor circuit of such a timer. In operation, the momentary-contact start switch is held closed for a few degrees of rotation (A). During this time the stop switch closes (B). The start switch is re-

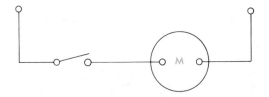

Fig. 25. *Circuit for continuous timer operation.*

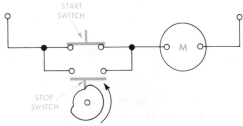

(**A**) START SWITCH COMPLETES MOTOR CIRCUIT

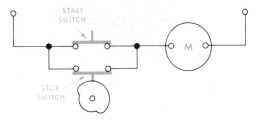

(**B**) CAM CLOSES STOP SWITCH

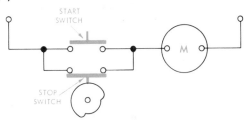

(**C**) STOP SWITCH MAINTAINS MOTOR CIRCUIT

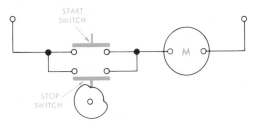

(**D**) CAM RELEASES STOP SWITCH; TIMER STOPS

Fig. 26. *Timer motor circuit with cam-operated stop switch.*

leased and the stop switch maintains the motor circuit (C) until the end of one revolution, at which time it is tripped open, stopping the motor (D).

Sometimes an industrial application requires that switching be coordinated with the operation of a machine which runs at non-uniform speeds. To accomplish this the timer motor is replaced as the camshaft driver by a rotating shaft on the machine. The two shafts are connected by direct coupling or by a set of gears. Thus the sequential operation of the cam switches is controlled by the operation of the machine. If the machine stops at any point in its operation the switching also stops. When the machine is restarted the switching continues from where it stopped.

Percentage Timers. A percentage timer is a simple cycle timer with a dial marked in percentage (0 to 100%). A typical unit is shown in Fig. 27. Most percentage timers operate a single switch. Many have the total running time indicated on the dial face. In operation, when the dial is set at a certain percentage the switch is closed during that part of the total cycle time and open for the remainder of the cycle. For example, if the dial on a five-minute cycle timer is set at 20% the load is switched on for one minute and off for four minutes continuously, as long as the timer motor is energized.

Some percentage timers have fully-on and fully-off settings. When the indicator is set

Fig. 27. *Typical percentage timer (Courtesy of Automatic Timing and Controls, Inc.).*

Fig. 28. *Seven-day time control carrying several sets of trippers (Courtesy of Tork Time Controls, Inc.).*

at zero the load switch is held open, when it is set at 100% the load switch is held closed. Some models have a switch which can be used to deenergize the timer motor at the end of the timing period.

Percentage timers are used in applications which require repetitious switching of heat, light, air, lubrication, etc. For example: one can be used to replace a wattage-dissipating rheostat in a heating device wherein the temperature may be maintained at an average rather than a constant value. Percentage timers can also be used to control the intermittent replenishing of lubricants to industrial machinery.

Time Switches. A time switch is essentially a motor-driven clock which operates a switch at selected times. It consists of a synchronous motor, a switch, and a time dial to which ON and OFF trippers are fastened. It also has a means (usually a fixed pointer)

for setting the clock to the correct time of day. Both 24-hour and 7-day models are available. Typical units are shown in Figs. 28 and 29.

If it is desired to close a circuit for two hours four times a day, four sets of on-off trippers are used on a 24-hour dial. They are mounted on the edge of the dial, two hours apart at the desired switching times. The clock motor is energized and the dial adjusted to the correct time of day. As the dial revolves it carries the trippers past the switch. As they pass the switch they trip it

Fig. 29. *Multi-switch seven-day time control (Courtesy of Tork Time Controls, Inc.).*

on and off at the selected times. The complete cycle repeats day after day until the motor is deenergized.

If different programs are desired on certain days of the week a seven-day time switch can be used. When a seven-day unit is used, selected days can pass without switching. The load switch can be either open or closed during these times.

Some time switches incorporate an automatically-wound spring which takes over from the motor in case of a temporary power failure. This spring continues operation of the time switch for many hours. When the motor is reenergized it rewinds the spring.

Time switches are utilized in many commercial and industrial applications. One widespread commercial use is the switching on and off of store-window lights during the evening hours. These switches are also used in homes in similar light-switching applications and in switching on electric incinerators for an hour or two at certain times each day.

Unit 2

section 5

Electronic Timers

Developments in solid-state electronics have made possible increased production and utilization of electronic timers. Some units are combinations of timing circuits and electromagnetic relays; others are completely electronic. In the latter, load switching is done by a solid-state switching device such as a silicon controlled rectifier. Some timers incorporate a thyratron tube as the load switch. Most available units are directly interchangeable with mechanical, pneumatic and thermal timers. Fig. 30 shows two available commercial models.

Electronic timers are capable of quite accurate timing, from about ten milliseconds to several minutes. Units can be provided with time periods up to several hours, but they are not as common as shorter-time units. Table 1 gives a number of typical ranges available in stock timers.

The electronic timer has an advantage in that it can be zener-regulated to free it from the effects of supply-voltage variations. It can also be temperature-compensated to cancel the effects of ambient temperature changes. Another advantage is the ease with which the timing period can be accurately adjusted.

Operation of Electronic Timers

Basically, the timing function of most electronic timers depends on the charging time of a capacitor in a resistive-capacitive (RC) circuit. When the charge on the capacitor reaches a certain value it triggers a switching circuit. If a transistor is used as

Fig. 30. *Two models of solid-state electronic timers: (A) plug-in, and (B) rear-mount (Courtesy of General Time).*

TABLE 1. TYPICAL ADJUSTABLE TIMING PERIODS OF ELECTRONIC TIMERS (SECONDS)

0.1 – 1	2.4 – 240
0.5 – 50	3.0 – 300
0.9 – 90	3.6 – 360
1.2 – 120	4.2 – 420
1.8 – 180	4.8 – 480

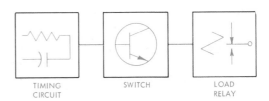

TIMING CIRCUIT — SWITCH — LOAD RELAY

Fig.31. *Simplified diagram of electronic-timer function.*

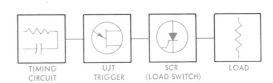

TIMING CIRCUIT — UJT TRIGGER — SCR (LOAD SWITCH) — LOAD

Fig. 32. *Electronic timer incorporating unijunction transistor (UJT) and silicon controlled rectifier (SCR).*

the switch it could have a power relay as its load, as in Fig. 31.

Fig. 32 shows a block diagram of an RC timing circuit triggering a unijunction transistor (UJT) which, in turn, fires a silicon controlled rectifier (SCR) into conduction. In some applications the SCR switches the load directly; in others, the SCR controls a relay through which the load current flows, as in Fig. 33. The length of the timing period can be adjusted over the timer range by a potentiometer in the RC circuit.

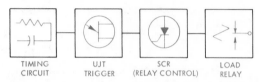

TIMING CIRCUIT   UJT TRIGGER   SCR (RELAY CONTROL)   LOAD RELAY

Fig. 33. *Electronic timer with SCR-controlled relay.*

Electronic timers are available in a number of different timing modes. These include: *delay on energization, delay on deenergization, single-shot,* and *automatic repeat cycle.*

Delay on Energization. In this mode delay starts when the timer is energized. At the end of the timing period the output con-

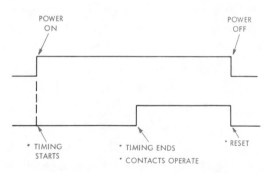

Fig. 34. *Timing diagram showing delay-on-energization.*

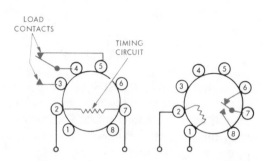

Fig. 35. *Base diagrams of two delay-on-energization timers.*

tacts operate. The timer resets when deenergized. Fig. 34 shows a plot of the timing. Fig. 35 illustrates the connections to two plug-in octal units.

Delay on Deenergization. Fig. 36 shows a timing diagram and Fig. 37 the wiring of a unit which provides delay on deenergization. Voltage is applied to this timer at all times. When the remote single-pole, double-throw (SPDT) switch is operated, the output contacts transfer and remain in this position. When the switch is returned to its original

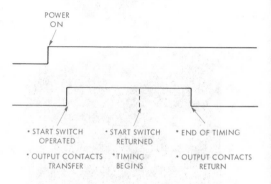

Fig. 36. *Timing diagrams for delay-on-deenergization timer.*

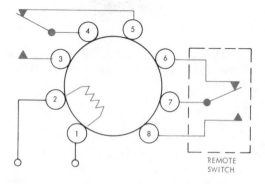

Fig. 37. *Wiring of delay-on-deenergization timer.*

state, timing begins. At the end of a preset time delay the output contacts revert to their original positions.

Single-Shot Timer. Figs. 38 and 39 show the timing diagram and wiring of a single-shot timer. Voltage is applied to this circuit at all times. When a remote momentary-contact switch is closed, the output contacts transfer and timing begins. When the time delay is completed, the output contacts return to their original state and the timer is ready for another cycle. Removal of supply voltage during the timing cycle resets this timer.

Automatic Repeat-Cycle Timer. As shown in Fig. 40, this timer runs continuously through off and on periods. When the unit is energized, timing of the off-period begins. At the end of the off period the output contacts transfer and the on-period begins. When the on-time is completed, the contacts return to their original state and the off-time starts again. Removal of the supply voltage at any time resets the unit to the start of the off-period. This timer is also available with the on-period initiated first. A typical wiring diagram showing remote timing adjustment is given in Fig. 41.

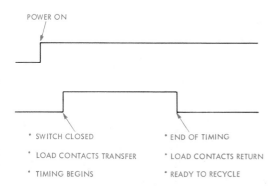

Fig. 38. *Timing diagram for single-shot timer.*

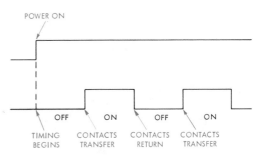

Fig. 40. *Timing diagram for repeat-cycle timer.*

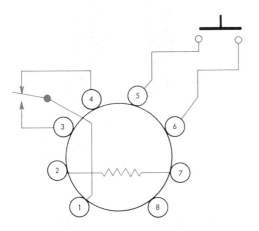

Fig. 39. *Wiring of single-shot timer.*

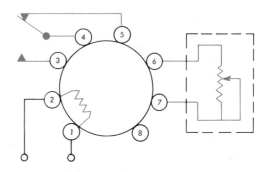

Fig. 41. *Wiring of repeat-cycle timer with remote timing adjustment.*

Unit 2

section 6

Electrochemical Timers

The electrical transfer of metal from one electrode to another through an electrolyte is the basis of a versatile group of timing devices. These devices are small and rugged and use little power. One form, which has silver and gold electrodes, is generally known as an *electrolytic cell*. Another, which has two mercury electrodes, is called a *coulometer*.

Electrolytic Cells

Commercially-available electrolytic cells are shown in Fig. 42. The cross-section and circuit symbol of this cell are illustrated in Fig. 43. The "working" electrode is made of gold. The container is made of silver and serves as the "reservoir" electrode. The electrolyte is the vehicle for ion conduction between the electrodes.

Operation of Electrolytic Cell. Fig. 44 shows an electrolytic cell connected through a resistor to a low-voltage dc supply. As elec-

Fig. 42. *Leaded and plug-in electrolytic timing cells (Courtesy of Plessey Electro-Products).*

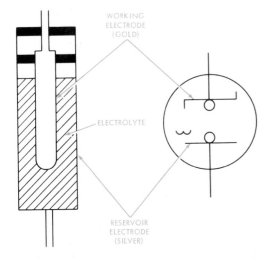

Fig. 43. *Cross-section and circuit symbol of electrolytic cell.*

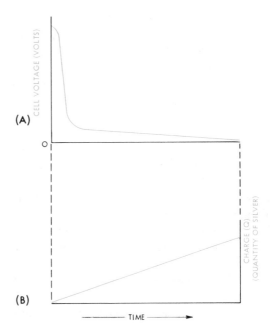

(A)

(B)

Fig. 45. *Decrease in cell voltage (A) and increase in charge (B) as cell is set.*

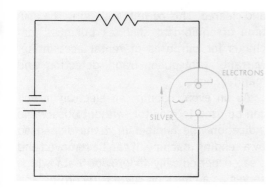

Fig. 44. *Setting (charging) an electrolytic cell.*

than 100 ohms. This plating process is also known as "setting" or "charging" the cell. Figs. 45(A) and 45(B) show the cell voltage and charge during the setting time.

If the polarity of the applied voltage is reversed, the movement of electrons and silver ions reverses (Fig. 46), removing the sil-

trons flow from the gold to the silver electrode, silver is transferred by electrolytic action from the silver to the gold electrode. For every electron leaving the gold electrode an ion of silver is deposited on it. Since there is an ample supply of silver available to go into solution and the electrolyte is a good conductor, the impedance of the cell is low during this "plating" period, generally less

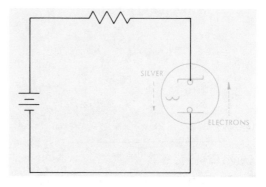

Fig. 46. *Clearing (deplating) circuit.*

85

ver from the gold electrode. When all the silver is returned to the silver electrode there is no further supply to the electrolyte. Consequently, the impedance of the cell goes up rapidly to the megohm range and the voltage across the cell increases at the same rate to the range of 0.7 to 1.0 volt.

The process of deplating the gold electrode is called "clearing." Fig. 47(A) shows the rapid increase in voltage which takes place at the end of clearing. Fig. 47(B) shows the decrease in charge during clearing. "Stop condition" is the term used to denote the cleared state: high impedance and maximum voltage (also called "stop voltage"). The electrolytic cell can be used as a timing device because the amount of silver deposited on the gold electrode is directly proportional to the current and length of charge time. Since current and time are the factors which determine the charge, Q, the unit of charge is the microampere-hour (μA h), the product of current and time. For example: in 100 hours a current of three microamperes will deposit a charge of 300 μA h.

Applications of Electrolytic Cells. Electrolytic cells are used industrially and commercially in such applications as: data accumulation, use-time measurement and accounting, guarantee-time monitoring, single-cycle and repeat-cycle timing, monitoring of temperature, pressure, radiation, stock, traffic, and battery charging.

One important advantage of the electrolytic cell is that it can collect data which remains confidential until the cell is removed and cleared. This permits recording the use-time of equipment such as business machines for purposes of rental accounting, warranty protection, fraud detection and maintenance.

As an event counter an electrolytic cell can be used to monitor, without observable indication, the number of items dispensed by a vending machine. It can be removed and cleared periodically to provide data which serves as a check on regular recording and accounting methods. In most applications electrolytic cells are used either as timers or accumulators (integrators).

In a typical timing application the electrolytic cell is preset to a selected current-time value (charge) by passing a certain amount of current through the cell in the plating direction for a certain time, as in Fig. 44. The charged cell is then ready to start timing.

During timing a clearing current is passed through the cell, deplating the gold electrode (Fig. 46). When deplating is com-

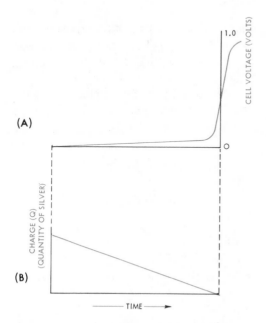

Fig. 47. *Increase in cell voltage (A) and decrease in charge (B) as cell is cleared.*

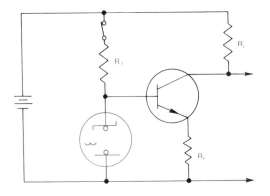

Fig. 48. *Voltage rise across timed-out cell triggers transistor amplifier.*

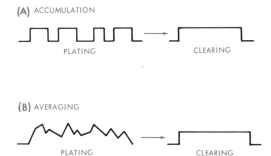

(A) ACCUMULATION

PLATING   CLEARING

(B) AVERAGING

PLATING   CLEARING

Fig. 49. *Timing diagrams of electrolytic cell applications: (A) accumulation, and (B) averaging.*

pleted the voltage across the cell rises, providing an output which can be used to activate an electrical circuit.

If an application requires a time delay of 10 hours, an electrolytic cell can be set at 50 μAh and cleared (during timing) at a constant five μA. At this rate it "times out" in 10 hours. Time ranges from seconds to months are possible with electrolytic timers.

Fig. 48 shows a simple electrolytic-cell circuit during timing (deplating). At stop condition (timed out) the voltage across the cell will rise and provide an input to the transistor. The transistor, in turn, will provide an amplified output to an indicator, control or other device.

Electrolytic Accumulator (Integrator). Since the amount of silver deposited on the gold electrode is directly proportional to the product of current and time ($I \times T$), the electrolytic cell can be used as an accumulator of data. It can accumulate the total running time of equipment or it can accumulate signals from a sensor (thermocouple, photocell, strain gage, etc.) which vary continuously over a period of time. In the first application clearing provides the total running time; in the second, it provides the average of temperature, light, strain, etc. Fig. 49(A) illustrates accumulation, and Fig. 49(B) illustrates averaging.

For use as an accumulator (or integrator), the cell is first cleared. Then, as the equipment or sensor is operated, silver is plated onto the gold electrode. For the accumulation of running time it is done at a constant rate. However, when the cell is receiving signals from a sensor, the rate at which silver is deposited varies with the signal strength.

After a time interval (minutes, hours, etc.) the cell is cleared by a constant current. The product of this current and the time required to clear the cell ($I \times T$) is equal to the charge, Q. From this figure the running time of equipment can be determined. In the case of varying signals from a sensor the average of many values is readily determined from Q.

Mercury Coulometers

The mercury coulometer is an electrochemical timer which has the electrolytic transfer of mercury as its basis of operation. Fig. 50 illustrates the construction of a typical unit and Fig. 51 shows an available commercial model.

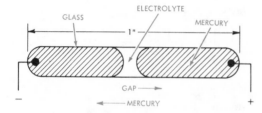

Fig. 50. *Construction of mercury coulometer.*

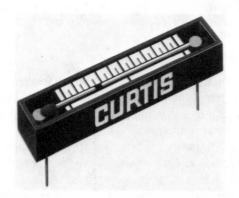

Fig. 51. *Mercury coulometer (electrochemical timer) (Courtesy of Curtis Instruments, Inc.).*

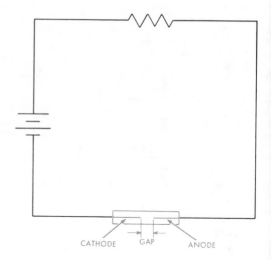

Fig. 52. *Mercury-coulometer circuit.*

As shown in Fig. 50, a mercury coulometer consists of a glass tube containing two columns of mercury and a small amount of electrolyte (generally mercuric iodide (HgI_2) and potassium iodide (KI) in water. Terminals are connected to the columns. Some models also have a metal sheath over the glass tube. With the glass as the dielectric, this sheath forms a capacitor with each column of mercury.

Operation of Mercury Coulometer. A mercury-coulometer circuit is shown in Fig. 52. The mercury column to which the negative supply lead is connected becomes a cathode. The other column is the anode.

When electrons flow from cathode to anode, mercury is transferred by the action of the electrolyte from anode to cathode. As mercury is removed from one column and added to the other, the electrolytic gap moves in the opposite direction, toward the anode. Thus the anode shortens and the cathode lengthens. The amount of gap displacement in any given time depends on the length of that time and the rate of current flow. A constant current flow produces an exact rate of movement. The direction of gap movement can be reversed by interchanging the power-supply leads.

Full-scale travel of the gap in a desired time is accomplished by proper selection of the current-limiting resistor. Table 2 gives the currents required by a typical mercury cell for various full-scale operating times. They are based on a gap movement of 0.156 inch per milliampere-hour across a 0.650 inch scale. The data show that the operating times are inversely proportional to the current: 4.16 microamperes causes full-scale

TABLE 2. CURRENTS REQUIRED FOR SELECTED OPERATING TIMES OF A TYPICAL MERCURY COULOMETER (CURTIS INSTRUMENTS, INC. MODEL 120–PC)

FULL SCALE HOURS	CURRENT (μA)
100	41.6
500	8.34
1000	4.16
2000	2.08
3000	1.38

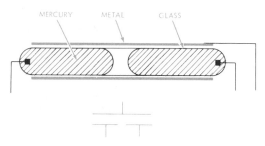

Fig. 53. *Metal-sheathed coulometer contains two capacitors.*

displacement in 1000 hours while ten times that current, 41.6 microamperes, causes full-scale displacement in 100 hours.

In addition to direct measurement of gap movement, a capacitive readout is possible with some mercury cells. As illustrated in Fig. 53, a metal sheath placed over the glass tube forms a capacitor with each column of mercury. The glass is the dielectric. As mercury is plated across from anode to cathode, the anode shortens, thereby reducing the sheath-to-anode capacitance. At the same time the cathode lengthens, increasing the sheath-to-cathode capacitance. These capacitance changes can be incorporated into an output circuit to perform a timing function.

Applications of Mercury Coulometers. Mercury electrochemical timers are used in the same kinds of applications as are silver-plating timers. In some applications the direct-reading feature of the mercury cell makes it more useful than the silver cell, since the silver cell requires deplating to determine running time. Mercury cells can be installed in electrical equipment during the manufacturing process. Thus, timing can be recorded on the meter scale from initial operation of the equipment. This provides guarantee data and time-to-failure (T.T.F.) data.

In conjunction with a photocell, a mercury electrochemical timer can be used to provide a signal after some preselected time (hours, days, months). Fig. 54 illustrates the operation of this arrangement. Current is first passed through the cell to shift the gap to a desired position (A). To perform the timing operation, current is passed through the cell in the opposite direction at a rate calculated to move the gap to a position between the lamp and the photocell in the required time. When the gap reaches this position it acts as an optical shutter, allowing light from the lamp to reach the photocell, activating it (B). If a photoresistor is used its resistance decreases and current in the relay circuit increases, operating the relay after the desired time delay. Commercial unit are available which include the meter element, lamp and photocell in one compact package.

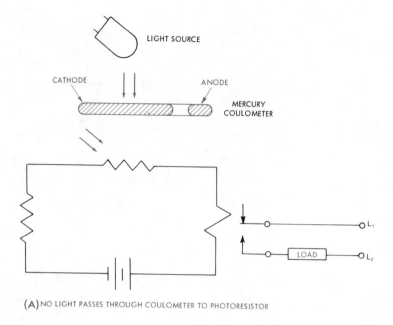

(A) NO LIGHT PASSES THROUGH COULOMETER TO PHOTORESISTOR

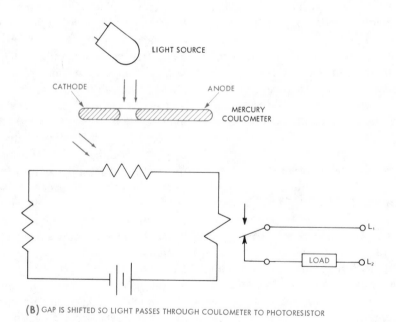

(B) GAP IS SHIFTED SO LIGHT PASSES THROUGH COULOMETER TO PHOTORESISTOR

Fig. 54. *Coulometer provides time delay for photoresistor-relay circuit.*

Unit 2

section 7 Laboratory Procedures

The laboratory procedures outlined in this Section assume that the student has access to the devices and equipment listed for each experiment, is familiar with basic circuits and circuit diagrams, and performs the work under the supervision of an instructor.

Some of the devices and circuits require 120 V ac. Adequate precautions should be observed.

Thermal Time-Delay Relay

Purpose: To study operation and application of a thermal time-delay relay.

Devices and Equipment: Relay, time-delay, thermal, 115 V ac, glass-enclosed (Edison 501 series, Amperite 2N (NO) or 2C (NC), or equivalent); ac supply, fixed, 120 V ac supply, variable, 0-120 V; VTVM; switch, SPST; load - 120 V lamp, etc.

Procedure:
1. Study construction of selected relay.
2. Study specifications and ratings of relay. Determine heater voltage, contact ratings, and time delay.

3. Sketch wiring diagram showing load circuit connected to fixed supply and heater circuit connected to variable supply. Include SPST switch in heater circuit. Have diagram approved.
4. Wire circuit. Have wiring approved.
5. Apply voltage to load circuit.
6. Adjust heater supply voltage to heater rating.
7. Close heater-circuit switch and record time elapsed between switch closure and relay operation.
8. Reduce heater voltage in steps. Record corresponding time delays.
9. Plot time delay as a function of heater voltage.
10. Write a statement listing some advantages and applications of this form of time-delay relay.

Thermal Time-Delay Relay Modifications

Purpose: To modify operation of thermal time-delay relay to obtain additional delay times.

Devices and Equipment: Two relays, time-delay, thermal, 115 V ac, glass-enclosed (Edison 501 series, Amperite 2N (NO) or 2C (NC), or equivalent); ac supply, fixed, 120 V; switch, SPST; load - 120 V lamp, etc.

Procedure:

Part A

1. Sketch wiring diagram showing heaters of two relays in series, load through set of contacts and switch in heater circuit. Have diagram approved.
2. Wire circuit. Have wiring approved.
3. Apply load voltage.
4. Apply rated heater voltage of one relay to the series-connected heaters. Record time delay.
5. Compare time delay with device rating.

Part B

1. Sketch wiring diagram showing: heater of one relay connected to rated voltage through SPST switch; heater of second relay connected to rated voltage through contacts of first relay; load connected to supply voltage through contacts of second relay. Have diagram approved.
2. Wire circuit. Have wiring approved.
3. Connect circuit to supply voltage (heater switch open).
4. Close heater switch. Record time delay.
5. Compare delay with that in Part A.
6. Write a statement detailing a modification which permits a range of variation of the time delay of one of the above thermal relays.

Electropneumatic Time-Delay Relay

Purpose: To learn to utilize and adjust an electropneumatic time-delay relay.

Devices and Equipment: Relay, time-delay, electropneumatic, air-dashpot type, 24 V dc or 120 V ac, on-delay or off-delay (Magnecraft Class 112C, Agastat 7000 series, or equivalent); coil supply; load and load supply; switch, SPST. *Note:* Some electropneumatic time-delay relays have auxiliary switch contacts which provide additional capability.

Procedure:

1. Study specifications and ratings of selected relay. Determine actuating voltage, contact ratings and time-delay range.
2. Sketch wiring diagram showing actuating and load circuits. Include switch in actuating circuit. Have diagram approved.
3. Wire circuit. Have wiring approved.
4. Energize load circuit.
5. Test operation of relay. *For on-delay models:* close control switch and record time elapsed between switch closure and relay operation. *For off-delay models:* Close control switch, actuating relay. Begin by opening control switch. Record time elapsed between switch opening and relay reset.
6. Operate relay through full timing range. Determine accuracy of unit.
7. Write a statement detailing one on-delay and one off-delay application of electropneumatic time-delay relays.

Interval Timer

Purpose: To study construction, operation and application of an interval timer.

Devices and Equipment: Interval timer, 120 V ac, such as Industrial Timer series RS, LVR, PBM, Automatic Timing and Controls, Inc. series 305C, 309D; switch, SPST; motor and load supply; loads - 120 V lamps, etc.

Procedure:

1. Study construction of timer, noting operation of clutching and reset mechanisms.
2. Study timer specifications. Determine motor voltage and switch ratings.
3. Circuit-trace unit.
4. Draw wiring diagram showing timer and load circuits. Include SPST line switch. Have diagram approved.
5. Wire circuit. Have wiring approved.
6. Test operation of timer.
7. Write a statement describing the operational sequence of the timer.

Motor-Driven Cam Timer

Purpose: To study construction, operation and application of motor-driven cam timer.
Devices and Equipment: Cam timer, 120 V ac. Selection of device may be made from: single-cycle and recycling, single-cam and multiple-cam timers, such as Industrial Timer series CM, MC, B, RA and RC, Bristol Motors series 31, Automatic Timing and Controls, Inc. series 324; switch, SPST; motor and load supply; loads - 120 V lamps, etc.

Procedure:

1. Study construction of timer. Note camshaft drive and cam adjustment arrangement.
2. Study timer specifications. Determine motor voltage and switch ratings.
3. Sketch wiring diagram showing motor and load circuits. Include SPST switch in motor circuit. Have diagram approved.
4. Set cams at 50% on—50% off. If multiple-cam model, set switch sequence.
5. Wire circuit. Have wiring approved.
6. Test operation of system.
7. Change cam settings and switch sequence, if multiple model. Check operation.

8. Write a statement describing operation of a selected timer in a particular application.

Time Switch

Purpose: To study construction, operation and application of a time switch.
Devices and Equipment: Time switch, 24-hour model, such as Paragon 4000 series, Tork model 1191, or seven-day unit such as Paragon 7000 series, Tork "W" series; load or loads - lamps, etc.

Procedure:

1. Study specifications of selected time switch. Determine switching features and maximum load.
2. Study construction of unit and action of switch-tripping mechanism.
3. Circuit-trace unit. Draw diagram showing motor and switch circuitry. Add line and load circuits. Have diagram approved.
4. Wire time switch and load (or loads). Have wiring approved.
5. Test operation of system.
6. Write a statement describing two or three different applications of a time switch.

Electronic Time-Delay Relay

Purpose: To learn to utilize and adjust a solid-state time-delay relay.
Devices and Equipment: Relay, solid-state, external-resistor type (Potter and Brumfield CU series—input voltages: 24 V and 120 V ac, 24 V and 48 V dc) or equivalent; input voltage supply; switch, SPST; potentiometer, 2 W; resistors, $\frac{1}{4}$-$\frac{1}{2}$ W; 2 loads and load supply.

Procedure:

1. Study specifications and ratings of selected relay. Determine input voltage, contact ratings and external timing-resistor values.
2. Sketch wiring diagram. Include control input, loads to be switched, external timing resistor and SPST switch in control circuit. Have diagram approved.
3. Wire circuit. Use maximum specified timing resistor. Have wiring approved.
4. Apply voltage to load circuits. Note load conditions.
5. Apply rated control voltage. Record time elapsed between switch closure and relay operation.
6. Reduce timing resistance to zero (short circuit) in several steps. Record delay time for each resistance value.
7. Repeat testing procedure with potentiometer as timing resistance.
8. Write a statement explaining operation of the solid-state time-delay relay.

Electrochemical Timer: Mercury Coulometer

Purpose: To study operation and application of an electrochemical timer.

Devices and Equipment: Mercury coulometer (Curtis Instruments Inc. model 150-SP2 or equivalent): power supply, low voltage dc; milliammeter or microammeter; ballast resistors.

Procedure:

1. Study specifications and ratings of selected timer. Note amount of gap movement per milliampere-hour (mA h) and maximum allowable current.
2. Select a rate of gap movement suitable for observation.
3. Assuming a low value of supply voltage (5 to 10V dc) and no resistance in the coulometer, calculate a ballast resistance which will allow a current that will move the gap at the desired rate. Observe maximum current rating.

   Example: The current through a 10,000 ohm resistance and a Curtis series 150 coulometer connected in series to a 10 volt source is about 1.0 mA—resulting in a gap movement of about 0.1″ per hour.
4. Wire circuit as shown in Fig. 55. Have wiring approved.
5. Energize circuit and adjust supply voltage for desired current.
6. Record current, running time and distance of gap movement over a number of scale divisions. Determine time for full-scale travel.
7. Change rate of movement (resistance substitution or voltage adjustment) and repeat step 6.
8. Check data from steps 6 and 7 against published device data. Note any difference.
9. Write a statement describing various applications of a mercury coulometer.

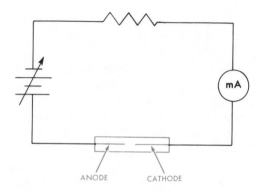

Fig. 55. *Mercury-coulometer test circuit.*

Try writing out the answer
to each question before look-
ing up the answer.

Review Questions

1. How is ambient-temperature compensation achieved in the timer of Fig. 2?
2. What is a dashpot timer? What are the common forms?
3. Describe a typical mercury timer (mercury plunger relay).
4. What good features of mercury-relay operation are due to the mercury-to-mercury contact?
5. In a non-delay mercury plunger relay how is switching accomplished?
6. What are the components of a typical motor-driven timer?
7. List some advantages of motor-driven timers.
8. Differentiate between internal and external clutches.
9. For what purposes are cycle timers used?
10. Describe (A) a non-adjustable cam and (B) an adjustable cam.
11. For what service is the percentage timer suitable?
12. What are the basic components of a time switch?
13. What is an advantage of seven-day time switches over 24-hour units?
14. What feature allows some time switches to continue operation during a power failure?
15. What determines the time delay of most electronic timers?
16. List some timing functions performed by electronic timers?
17. How does a single-shot timer function?
18. What is the basic action in an electrochemical timer?
19. Describe the construction of an electrolytic cell.
20. What occurs during the charging of an electrolytic cell?
21. Describe "clearing" of an electrolytic cell.
22. What advantage does the electrolytic cell have over clocks and counters in certain applications?
23. Describe the construction of a typical mercury coulometer.
24. Briefly explain the operation of a mercury coulometer.
25. What effect does the value of the resistor in Fig. 54 have on the rate of gap movement?

Answers to
Review Questions

1. In Fig. 2 both struts are bimetallic. Therefore, any ambient-temperature effect in one strut is compensated for by the same change in the other strut.

2. Dashpot timers are units in which the delay depends on the time required for a fluid or air to pass through an opening. Common forms are: mercury, pneumatic, and hydraulic-magnetic.

3. The main components of a mercury plunger relay are a solenoid coil and a sealed unit within the coil. The sealed unit contains a movable core (plunger), springs, mercury, and usually a gas.

4. Mercury-to-mercury contact results in low contact resistance, no contact deterioration, and high current density.

5. Energization of the solenoid coil moves the plunger, displacing some of the mercury—thereby making or breaking a mercury-to-mercury contact.

6. A typical motor-driven timer consists essentially of a motor, clutch, switch or switches, and a switch-actuating mechanism.

7. Motor-driven timers can provide multiple switching and long time delays. Driven by synchronous motors, they have a high degree of accuracy.

8. An internal clutch is an integral part of the timer motor. An external clutch is a separate mechanism which couples the motor to the timing gears.

9. Cycle timers are used in applications requiring repetitious actuation of circuits for preset time periods. They can also be used to energize circuits for set periods of time in desired sequences.

10. (A) A non-adjustable cam is a single disc into which an on-off sequence is permanently cut. (B) An adjustable cam generally consists of two discs, each having a reduced diameter over part of the circumference.

11. The percentage timer is suitable for applications requiring repetitious switching of circuits for selected time intervals.

12. The basic components of a time switch are a synchronous motor, a switch (or

switches), and a time dial with on-off switch trippers.

13. Unlike 24-hour time switches, seven-day units can be used in applications requiring a variety of daily programs.

14. To assure operation during a power failure some time switches contain an automatically-wound spring which drives the clock mechanism for a number of hours when the motor is deenergized.

15. The time delay of most electronic timers is determined by the time-constant of a resistor-capacitor combination.

16. Among the timing functions performed by electronic timers are: delay on energization or deenergization, single-shot and repeat-cycling.

17. When the switch controlling a single-shot timer is closed, the output contacts transfer and the time delay starts. When the delay is completed the contacts return and the timer is ready to repeat the cycle.

18. The basic action in an electrochemical timer is the electrolytic transfer of metal from one electrode to another.

19. One form of electrolytic cell consists of a gold (working) electrode, an electrolyte and a silver container which serves as the reservoir electrode.

20. Silver is transferred by electrolytic action from the silver electrode to the gold as electrons move through the electrolyte from the gold electrode to the silver electrode.

21. "Clearing" of an electrolytic cell occurs when the silver is removed from the gold electrode and returned through the electrolyte to the silver electrode.

22. The electrolytic cell has an advantage over clocks and counters in certain applications in that its stored data can remain confidential until the cell is removed and cleared.

23. A typical mercury coulometer consists of a glass tube containing two thin columns of mercury separated by a small amount of electrolyte. Connections are made to the mercury columns.

24. As current flows through a mercury coulometer from one mercury column (cathode) to the other (anode) mercury is transferred by electrolytic action from anode to cathode. This transfer lengthens the cathode and shortens the anode, resulting in gap movement in the direction of the anode.

25. The rate of gap movement varies directly with the value of the resistor.

UNIT 3

Power Tubes
and
Solid-State Controls

Unit 3

Contents

Unit 3

Unit 3

Unit 3

List of Illustrations

Unit 3

Unit 3

Unit 3

Unit 3

Unit 3

section 1

Introduction

3

In many industrial electronic applications electron tubes, especially vacuum types, have been replaced by solid-state devices—transistors, SCR's, integrated circuits, etc.

Functions of low-power electron tubes, such as rectification, amplification and switching, can now generally be performed more efficiently and economically by solid-state devices. However, industrial power tubes are still used in handling large amounts of current. These include two-element, gas-filled and mercury-vapor tubes (diodes) and similar three-element tubes, known as thyratrons.

Another industrially-important, high-current tube, which differs considerably from low- and medium-power gaseous and vapor rectifiers, is the ignitron. Ignitrons have mercury-pool cathodes and other features which allow some models to carry very high (thousands of amperes) short-duration currents.

These industrial tubes—diodes, thyratrons and ignitrons—are used in the rectification and control of a large range of currents in the circuitry of welders, heaters, motors and other industrial equipment.

Solid-state devices, such as the silicon controlled rectifier (SCR), unijunction transistor (UJT), triac and others, are used extensively in control of such equipment as motors, heaters, lighting installations, air conditioners, battery chargers, etc. In conjunction with various transducers, these devices can provide automatic adjustment of high-power circuits to changes in light, temperature, speed and other variables.

Although the use of solid-state devices has become extremely widespread, much industrial equipment utilizing electron tubes is in use today and will continue to be used and maintained until its replacement with solid-state forms is technically and economically feasible. Therefore, it is necessary and reasonable for the electronic technician to understand the construction, operation and applications of both electron tubes and solid-state devices.

Unit 3

section 2

Gas and Vapor Diodes

G as-filled and vapor diodes have been used extensively as high-current rectifiers for several reasons. They can be constructed at reasonable cost to cover a large range of current requirements. They are efficient, have low internal voltage drop and good regulation.

Construction of Gas and Vapor Diodes

The diode shown in Fig. 1 represents the construction of most gas-filled and vapor rectifiers. The essential components are anode, cathode, gas or vapor, and an en-

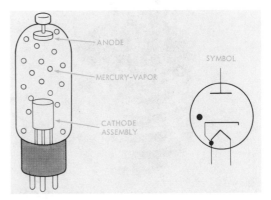

Fig. 1. *Components of mercury-vapor diode. (Courtesy of National Electronics, Inc.).*

velope. The cathode in most models is a heated filament coated with electron-emitting material. Each tube contains a small amount of argon, xenon or mercury. Some contain both mercury and a gas. In tubes containing mercury, heat from the filament vaporizes the mercury and the tubes operate in a manner similar to gas-rectifier operation.

Shown in Fig. 2 is a 619 mercury recti-

Fig. 2. *Industrial mercury-vapor rectifier rated at 6 amperes, 90 volts, dc. (Courtesy of National Electronics, Inc.).*

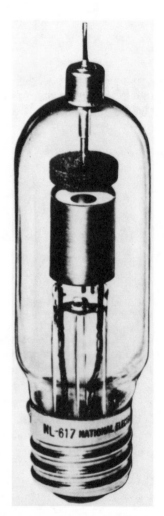

Fig. 3. *Mercury-vapor rectifier rated at 5 amperes, 600 volts, dc. (Courtesy of National Electronics, Inc.).*

fier with dc ratings of six amperes and 90 volts. The tube in Fig. 3 is a 617 mercury vapor rectifier designed for industrial applications at potentials of 250 volts to 600 volts dc.

Operation of Gas and Vapor Diodes

The operation of gas- and vapor-filled rectifiers differs from that of vacuum rectifiers. Ionization and deionization, which are important aspects of gas and vapor tube operation, are not utilized in vacuum tube operation. Also, space charge, a factor in vacuum tube operation, is neutralized in gas and vapor tubes.

Ionization and Deionization. When the cathode in a gas or vapor diode is heated, electrons emitted from the cathode and accelerated toward the anode "collide" with gas or vapor molecules. The repulsion between the emitted electrons and the loosely-held valence electrons of the gaseous atoms cause some of the valence electrons to separate from their atoms. Thus, negative ions (electrons) and positive ions (atoms minus electrons) are created in the tube. The electrons become part of the tube current and the positive ions move toward the negative cathode. In the cathode area they acquire free electrons to complete their atomic structures. (This recombination of atoms and electrons is known as deionization). The deionization which occurs in the area of the cathode prevents the formation of a space charge—a cloud of electrons in the cathode area which has a limiting effect on tube current. Ionization and deionization are factors which make it possible for a gas or vapor tube to carry current many times greater than a vacuum diode of similar size.

Ionization Potential. To cause ionization of the gas or vapor, the emitted electrons must reach a certain acceleration or energy level. This is achieved by applying a positive potential to the anode. If this potential is increased slowly from zero at a certain value the tube fires (ionization begins). This is illustrated by the general gas-tube volt-

Fig. 4. *General gas-tube volt-ampere characteristic.*

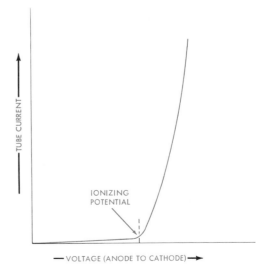

IONIZING
POTENTIAL

TUBE CURRENT

— VOLTAGE (ANODE TO CATHODE) —

ampere characteristic in Fig. 4, which shows the sudden flow of current when the tube fires. The anode voltage at which it fires is known as the "ionizing potential" or "anode starting voltage." It is comparatively low for gas and vapor tubes. The anode starting voltage of the 617 mercury vapor rectifier (Fig. 3) is 12 volts, and that of the 619 rectifier (Fig. 2) is 9 volts.

Arc Drop. The voltage from plate to cathode in a vacuum tube varies with changes in plate current: as the plate current increases, the plate voltage decreases; as plate current decreases, plate voltage increases. This is due to the changing resistance of the tube. However, in the gas or vapor tube the cathode-to-anode voltage, known as the "arc drop" does not vary with the current. It remains relatively constant as the tube current changes with changes in load requirements. The circuit parameters affected are shown in Fig. 5.

If the load resistance in Fig. 5 decreases, the circuit current increases (assuming the supply voltage remains constant). At the same time, the voltage across the load tends to decrease and that across the rectifier tube to increase.

Counteracting this effect, however, increased voltage across the tube causes increased ionization, reducing the effective resistance of the tube. The decrease in tube resistance serves to retain the previous voltage distribution across the tube and load. In terms of resistance and current, the decrease in tube resistance matches the increase in current, maintaining the pre-change IR drop (arc drop) across the tube.

When the load resistance increases an opposite effect occurs, maintaining a constant arc drop. An increase in load resistance tends to decrease the tube anode voltage. Reduced anode voltage produces less ionization. Decreased ionization results in a higher value of tube resistance which

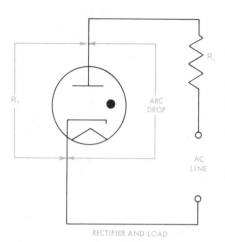
RECTIFIER AND LOAD

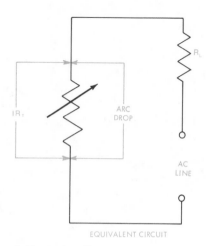
EQUIVALENT CIRCUIT

Fig. 5. *Gas-tube rectifier and equivalent circuit.*

maintains the pre-change tube-load voltage distribution. In terms of tube current and resistance: the IR drop (arc drop) across the tube remains constant because the decrease in current is offset by the increase in the tube resistance. The arc drops of most gas and vapor rectifiers range from 10 to 15 volts. The peak-current arc drop of the 617 and 619 mercury-vapor rectifiers is 10 volts.

Maximum Peak Inverse Voltage (PIV). This is the highest value of reverse voltage which can safely appear across a rectifier tube. When it is exceeded the resulting current flow can reach short-circuit values. If this current is not interrupted immediately, the tube and associated equipment can be severely damaged. The maximum peak-inverse-voltage rating of the 617 mercury rectifier is 1,000 volts and that of the 619 mercury rectifier is 300 volts.

Maximum Current Ratings. Gas and vapor rectifiers have three current ratings: (1) maximum ac short-circuit current, (2) maximum instantaneous amperes output, and (3) maximum dc amperes output. These three ratings are explained in numbered paragraphs that follow.

(1) The maximum ac short-circuit current rating indicates the maximum current a tube can carry without damaging effects. It is also indicative of the capability of the tube to function in a circuit with a power-supply capacity equal to the tube's maximum ac short-circuit current rating. This rating of the 617 and 619 rectifier tubes is 250 amperes.

(2) The maximum instantaneous amperes output is the peak value of the sine wave of current a gas or vapor tube can carry safely. Exceeding this maximum can result in cathode damage due to sputtering and increased temperature. The 617 and 619 tubes are rated at 20 amperes.

(3) The maximum dc amperes output rating signifies the maximum average current a gas or vapor tube can safely carry—as measured on a dc ammeter. For the 617 tube this rating is 5 amperes and for the 619 it is 6 amperes.

To check an intermittent tube current against this rating, the average tube current must be calculated. For this purpose tubes have a "maximum-averaging-time" rating which is the maximum time over which currents may be averaged. For the 617 and 619 tubes it is 15 seconds.

Thermal Effects. Although temperature is a consideration in the operation of gas-filled tubes, it is a more important factor in the proper operation of mercury-vapor tubes. In both types sufficient time should be allowed for the cathode to reach proper operating temperature before current is drawn (anode voltage applied).

In a mercury-vapor tube, application of the anode voltage should be delayed long enough for the temperature of the mercury to reach the rated minimum temperature limit. This is the lowest temperature at which sufficient mercury vapor is produced. If anode voltage is applied before this temperature is achieved there will be excessive arc drop due to decreased vapor pressure. This effect is known as "surging." Surging produces high rates of change of current and excessive circuit voltages, which can sometimes damage associated devices such as supply transformers. In addition to surging, low-temperature operation of a mercury-vapor tube also increases ionization time. Premature operation can also cause cathode damage through insufficient emission and positive-ion bombardment. Recommended heating time of the 617 and 619 mercury-vapor rectifiers is 60 seconds.

Mercury-vapor tubes also have high-temperature limits. If one is operated above its maximum it can be fired by an inverse anode potential which is less than its peak-inverse-voltage rating. The resulting current is known as "arc back." The tube reverse-fires at this reduced voltage because of the increased vapor pressure which accompanies increased temperature. If the vapor pressure remains above a critical value the tube does not operate as a rectifier but conducts in both directions.

Operation of gas-filled tubes is related to gas density—a parameter not affected by temperature. Consequently, temperature variations do not affect the operation of such tubes. Temperature ratings of gas-filled tubes are based on other considerations, such as materials and structure.

Applications of Gas and Vapor Diodes

Gas and vapor diodes are used to provide a large range of direct current to welders, motors and other industrial equipment. This is accomplished with circuitry ranging from simple half-wave rectifiers to multi-phase full-wave rectifiers involving many tubes.

Single-Phase Half-Wave Rectifier. The application of a power diode as a half-wave rectifier with a resistive load is illustrated in Fig. 6. This circuit can be used where power requirements are not high and half-wave direct current is adequate for operation of the load.

The filament transformer has a high-current, low-voltage secondary—usually 2.5 volts. The center tap provides a load circuit connection to the cathode. (Manufacturers' tube data are usually based on load returns to this center tap.) Operation of the circuit is shown by the waveforms in Fig. 7.

When the line connected to the anode is positive and the applied voltage, shown at (A), is increasing from zero it appears across the tube as the anode-to-cathode potential—shown at (B). During this time the

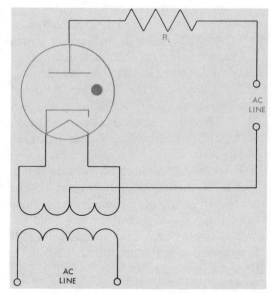

Fig. 6. *Gaseous rectifier with center-tapped filament transformer.*

load voltage is zero (waveform (C). When the voltage across the tube reaches the ionization potential, the tube fires, current flows and the voltage across the tube changes quickly to the arc-drop level. This can be more or less than the ionization potential. (The 617 mercury rectifier has an anode starting voltage of 12 volts and a peak-current arc drop of 10 volts, while the 617 mercury rectifier has an anode starting voltage of 9 volts and a peak-current arc drop of 10 volts.)

As the tube fires and conduction begins, the load voltage, shown at (C), increases from zero. It follows the waveform of the line voltage and is equal to the difference between the line voltage and the arc drop. As the line voltage decreases toward zero the voltage across the tube drops below the ionization potential, current flow ceases and

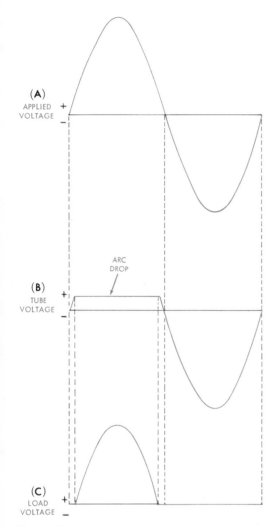

(A)
APPLIED +
VOLTAGE −

ARC
DROP

(B)
TUBE +
VOLTAGE −

(C)
LOAD +
VOLTAGE −

Fig. 7. *Voltage waveforms of gas-tube half-wave rectifier circuit with resistive load.*

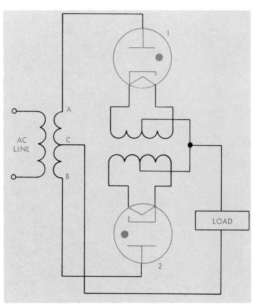

AC
LINE

A

C

B

LOAD

Fig. 8. *Full-wave gaseous-rectifier circuit.*

for conversion of single-phase alternating current to full-wave direct current is shown in Fig. 8. Half-cycle operation of this circuit is similar to operation of the circuit previously shown in Fig. 6. Half of the transformer secondary voltage (A to C) is across tube 1 and the load. The other half (B to C) is across tube 2 and the load.

When A is positive with respect to C and the voltage, A-C, increases to the ionization potential of tube 1, the tube conducts and current flows through the load, tube 1 and upper half of the transformer secondary. A potential is developed across the load, negative at the C connection and positive at the filament transformer connection. During this half-cycle point B and the anode of tube 2 are negative with respect to C; therefore, tube 2 is non-conducting.

During the next half-cycle when the secondary polarities are reversed, point B becomes positive with respect to C and point

the load voltage reduces to zero. During the alternate half-cycle the anode is negative, consequently the tube does not conduct and the load voltage and current remain at zero until the next conducting half-cycle.

Single-Phase Full-Wave Rectifier. A circuit utilizing a pair of gas or vapor diodes

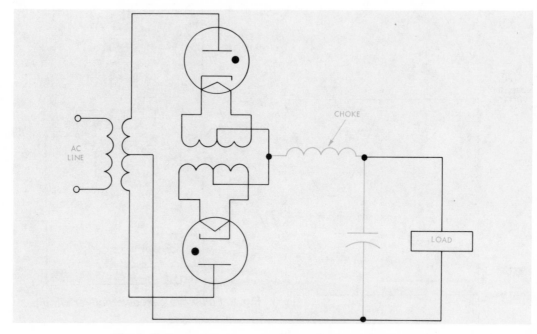

Fig. 9. *Full-wave gaseous rectifier with choke-input filter.*

A becomes negative. Tube 1 has a negative anode potential and does not conduct. When the potential at the anode of tube 2 reaches the ionization level the tube conducts and current flows through the load in the same direction as during the previous half-cycle. The polarity of the voltage developed across the load during this half-cycle is again negative at the C connection and positive at the filament transformer connection.

Although the output of the full-wave rectifier is smoother than that of the half-wave rectifier, it may still fluctuate too much for some applications. To reduce the fluctuations, filtering may be added. However, a capacitor-input filter is not recommended for use with gas or mercury-vapor tubes. With this form of filter an uncharged capacitor connected directly to the cathode

would cause excessive current through the low-resistance rectifier tube when the tube fired. However, as illustrated in Fig. 9, a choke-input filter may be used. This is permissable because the choke is a current-limiting device. If more filtering is desired, an additional choke and capacitor may be added.

Three-Phase Half-Wave Rectifier. Three-phase rectifier systems have several advantages over single-phase systems: more power can be provided with devices of a given rating, less wire is required for a given amount of power, line imbalance can be avoided, and reduced ripple is present in the output.

The use of gas or vapor tubes with a three-phase supply is illustrated in the three-phase half-wave rectifier shown in

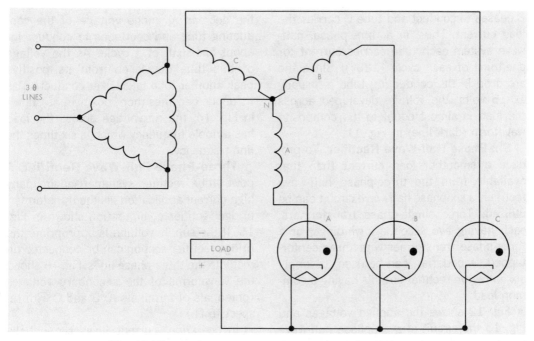

Fig. 10. *Three-phase half-wave gaseous-rectifier system.*

Fig. 10. The output of this circuit has a ripple frequency which is three times the line frequency. (The output frequency of a single-phase half-wave rectifier is equal to the line frequency.)

The waveforms of the voltages developed in the secondary coils in Fig. 10 are shown in Fig. 11. Because these voltages are at phase differences of 120° they cause the rectifier tubes to conduct in succession. As the voltage in phase A decreases from a peak positive value the voltage in phase B increases toward a positive peak. When the increasing voltage across the phase-B tube exceeds the decreasing voltage across the phase-A tube, tube B starts conducting and tube A becomes non-conducting. When the voltage across tube B decreases below the increasing positive potential of tube C tube

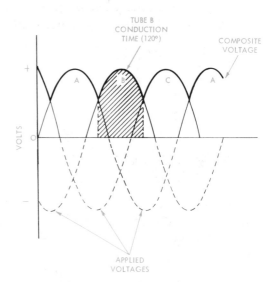

Fig. 11. *Waveforms of applied voltages and composite rectified-voltage waveform in three-phase half-wave rectifier.*

B ceases to conduct and tube C carries the load current. Thus, in a three-phase, half-wave system each tube carries current for one-third of each cycle (120°). Since the arc drop in the conducting tube is usually 10-15 volts, the voltage developed across the load is almost equal to the composite waveform (dark line) in Fig. 11.

Six-Phase Half-Wave Rectifier. To produce a smoother load current than that available from the three-phase half-wave rectifier, a six-phase half-wave circuit can be utilized. Three single-phase transformers, each having two secondary windings, or a three-phase transformer with three center-tapped secondaries, can be used to supply six half-wave rectifier circuits having a common load.

Fig. 12 shows the applied voltages and Fig. 13 the circuit of a six-phase half-wave rectifier. This circuit operates in the same manner as the three-phase half-wave circuit. Each tube conducts in sequence during a portion of the half-cycle when its anode is positive. It begins conduction when its increasing anode voltage is about equal to the decreasing anode voltage of the conducting tube and continues to conduct for about one-sixth of a cycle. As the voltage of this tube decreases from its positive peak another tube takes over conduction as its anode becomes more positive. As shown in Fig. 14, the dc voltage across the load has a ripple frequency which is six times the line frequency.

Three-Phase Full-Wave Rectifier. A power-tube rectifier system used in many high-current applications is the transformer-bridge rectifier configuration shown in Fig. 15. If the supply voltage is appropriate the bridge rectifier section can be connected directly to the three-phase lines. Fig. 16 shows the waveforms of the secondary voltages (potentials of terminals A, B and C with respect to N.)

In operation, current flows sequentially through pairs of series-connected diodes and the load. When terminal A is highly positive and terminal B is more negative than C (time 1 in Fig. 16) current flow is from B through diode 2, the load and diode 4 to terminal A. Shortly thereafter, when

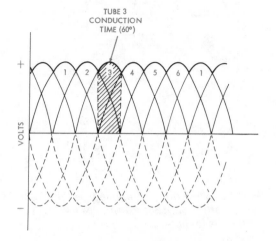

Fig. 12. *Waveforms of voltages applied to rectifier circuits in six-phase half-wave system.*

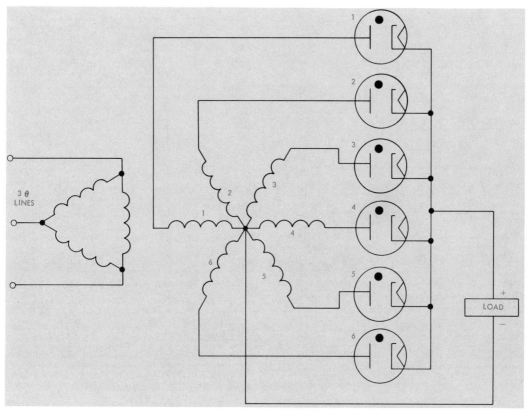

Fig. 13. Circuit diagram of six-phase half-wave rectifier system.

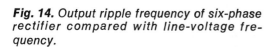
Fig. 14. Output ripple frequency of six-phase rectifier compared with line-voltage frequency.

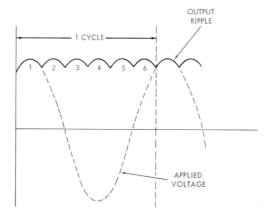

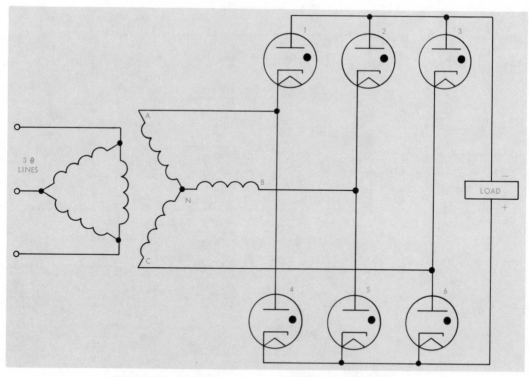

Fig. 15. *Three-phase full-wave gaseous-rectifier circuit.*

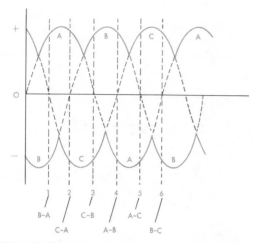

Fig. 16. *Waveforms of secondary voltages in three-phase full-wave rectifier, and conduction sequence.*

terminal C becomes more negative than B and A is still highly positive, (time 2) conduction shifts from diode 2 to diode 3 and current flow is from terminal C through diode 3, the load and diode 4 to terminal A. At time 3 terminal B has become more positive than A but C is still highly negative—so current flow is now from C through diode 3, the load and diode 5 to terminal B. Terminal B is still highly positive at time 4 but A is more negative than C—consequently, conduction has transferred from diode 3 to diode 1 and current is from terminal A through diode 1, the load and diode 5 to terminal B. At time 5 terminal C has become more positive than B. Terminal A is highly negative so conduction is from A through diode 1, the load and diode 6 to terminal C. Terminal C is still highly positive at time 6 but terminal B has become more negative than A and conduction is from B through diode 2, the load and diode 6 to terminal C.

The foregoing sequence of operation occurs during one cycle of line-voltage frequency. It repeats continuously as long as the line potentials are applied.

The output voltage of the three-phase, full-wave system is twice that of the three-phase, half-wave system. This is shown by

a comparison of the waveforms in Figs. 16 and 11. Fig. 16 shows that the potential producing the output of the full-wave system is the sum of two voltages—the voltage of the terminal most positive with respect to N plus that of the terminal most negative with respect to N. Fig. 11 shows that, in the half-wave system, the voltage across the load is developed only during the positive half-cycles of the applied voltage. In the full-wave system shown in Fig. 16 the dc voltage across the load has a ripple frequency of six times the line frequency.

Unit 3

section 3   Thyratrons

Thyratrons are grid-controlled rectifiers used extensively in industrial switching and control applications. Unlike contactors, they have no moving parts and operate silently. They are available in a large range of sizes and ratings. Some are xenon-filled to meet quick-starting requirements, as in timing applications. The 5632/C3J shown in Fig. 17 is an example of this type of thyratron. It has a maximum commutation factor rating of 0.66 (V/μsec. $\times$ A/μsec.) and a deionization time of less than 1000 microseconds. Because it contains xenon it can operate over a wide ambient temperature range ($-55°$C to $+75°$C).

Thyratrons for high-voltage operation contain mercury. The KY-21A is a mercury-vapor thyratron having a peak-forward-voltage rating of 5,500 volts and a peak-inverse-voltage rating of 11,000 volts. The 5563A is a mercury-vapor thyratron with both PFV and PIV ratings of 20,000 volts.

Fig. 17. *Thyratron, xenon-filled for quick starting. (Courtesy of National Electronics, Inc.).*

Fig. 18. *Thyratron used in ignitor-firing and controlled-rectifier applications. (Courtesy of National Electronics, Inc.).*

The 710A/6011 thyratron shown in Fig. 18 contains gas and mercury. It is used over a wide temperature range in controlled-rectifier and ignitron-firing applications. The gas-mercury combination ensures quick-starting and stable operation. It is rated at 2.5 amperes dc and has PFV and PIV ratings of 1500 volts.

The 760P thyratron shown in Fig. 19 is a mercury and gas-filled tube which is used in welding and motor-control applications. Its PFV and PIV are both 1500 volts. Its maximum dc ampere output rating is 6.4 amperes.

123

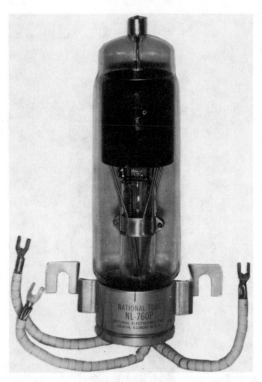

Fig. 19. *Thyratron designed for welding and motor-control applications. (Courtesy of National Electronics, Inc.).*

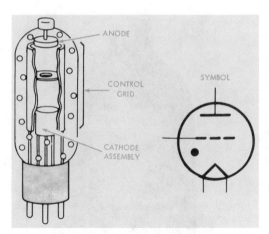

Fig. 20. *Construction of negative-grid thyratron. (Courtesy of National Electronics, Inc.).*

Thyratron Construction

Most thyratrons found in industrial applications are triode structures containing anode, cathode, control grid, a gas and/or mercury. Some are tetrodes containing a second grid. Practically all thyratrons have negative grid structures. A few models have positive structures. The cathodes of most thyratrons are coated filaments. A few have heater-cathode structures, such as tetrodes 632B, 5559/FG-57, and 5560/FG-95.

The construction of a triode thyratron differs from that of a vacuum triode. In the vacuum triode a wire-mesh grid is so placed that it has variable control over tube cur-

rent. Its potential can be adjusted to allow current flow, increase it, decrease it, or turn it off. In the thyratron the grid is structured so that its potential allows the tube to conduct suddenly and has no further control of the current until it decreases to zero.

To achieve triggering over practical ranges of anode and grid potentials, the negative-grid thyratron is generally constructed as illustrated in Fig. 20. As the illustration shows, the thyratron grid is much different from that in a vacuum tube. It is a large electrode consisting of a cylinder and a disc. The cylinder surrounds the cathode and extends toward the anode. The disc, mounted inside the cylinder, forms a baffle between cathode and anode. Because electrons from the cathode area must pass through the hole in the baffle to reach the anode, the grid, with sufficient negative bias, can effectively prevent current flow until the desired turn-on time.

The positive-grid thyratron is similar in construction to the negative-grid thyratron except that it has two grid baffles contain-

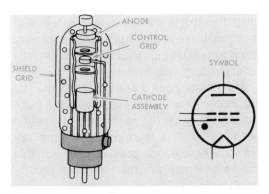

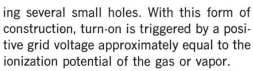

Fig. 21. *Construction of shield-grid thyratron. (Courtesy of National Electronics, Inc.).*

Fig. 22. *Tetrode thyratron used in relay and motor-control applications. (Courtesy of RCA Corp.).*

ing several small holes. With this form of construction, turn-on is triggered by a positive grid voltage approximately equal to the ionization potential of the gas or vapor.

When a triode thyratron is operating, a small grid current flows. In some applications, especially where the grid-circuit impedance is high, problems are created by this current. To minimize this problem the shield-grid (tetrode) thyratron was developed. The construction of this tube is illustrated in Fig. 21. The shield grid, consisting of a cylinder and two baffles, is in the same position in the tetrode as the control grid in the triode. The control grid in the tetrode is an electrode placed between the two baffles. This arrangement reduces grid current to a minimum.

The shield grid of the tetrode thyratron can be operated at either a negative or positive potential. Generally, when the control grid is negative the shield grid is set at a positive potential and vice-versa. The average control characteristics of the 2D21 gas tetrode show a shield-grid potential ranging from +8 volts to −3 volts for a control-grid range of −7 volts to +17 volts. The

tetrode thyratron may also be operated with the shield grid at cathode potential (connected externally to the cathode). In this mode it operates essentially as a triode thyratron.

The 3D22A thyratron in Fig. 22 is a negative-control tetrode type used extensively in relay and motor-control service. Two 3D22A's in a full-wave rectifier circuit can handle up to 600 watts at 400 volts dc maximum. When used to control alternating current, two 3D22A's can control up to 800 watts.

Thyratron Ratings

Most of the ratings which apply to gas and vapor rectifiers also apply to thyratrons, such as: arc drop, maximum peak-inverse-voltage, heating time, temperature limitations and anode operating and short-circuit currents. Additional ratings concern parameters which relate to the tube as a grid-controlled rectifier. These include: maximum grid-voltage and grid-current limits, ionization and deionization times and maximum peak forward voltage.

Maximum Grid Voltage and Current. The "maximum negative grid voltage before conduction" is the highest voltage which can be applied safely to the grid of a non-conducting thyratron. A number of thyratrons, such as the 5632/C3J and 5665/C16J, have ratings of 100 volts. Some tubes have higher ratings. The KY21A, 710/6011, and the 760 series are rated at 500 volts.

The "maximum negative grid voltage during conduction" indicates the highest value of control voltage allowable on the control grid of a particular thyratron during operation. Although the tubes listed above show two different non-conducting grid-voltage maximums they all have the same conducting maximum: 10 volts.

The maximum-grid-current rating is related to the heat-dissipation capacity of the thyratron grid structure. To ensure that grid current does not exceed this rating a grid-circuit resistor is usually required. Ten microamperes is the rated maximum of a number of thyratrons.

Ionization and Deionization Times. Many thyratrons conduct within 10 microseconds of the application of a trigger voltage to the grid. This short lapse of time is known as the ionization time. Of greater significance for proper operation of a thyratron is the rated deionization time (approximately 1000 microseconds for many tubes). This rating is also known as the "recovery time"—the time between the cessation of the tube current and the instant when the grid regains control. This rating is important in applications involving three-phase circuitry, induction loads and frequencies above 60 hertz. For some applications above power-line frequencies hydrogen-filled thyratrons can be used. Because of their small mass, hydrogen ions move very quickly to recombine with electrons, thereby reducing deionization time.

Maximum Peak Forward Voltage. The maximum peak forward voltage is the highest positive potential which may be applied to the anode of a thyratron for normal operation. If the anode potential exceeds this maximum it can fire the tube prematurely, resulting in the loss of grid control.

In some thyratrons the peak-forward-voltage and peak-inverse-voltage ratings are equal. The PFV and PIV ratings of the 710/6011 and 760 tubes are both 1500 volts. For many tubes the PFV is less than the PIV. The PFV of the 5665/C16J is 1000 volts and the PIV is 1250 volts. The PFV of the high-voltage KY21A thyratron is 5500 volts and the PIV is 11,000 volts.

Operation of Negative-Grid Thyratron

The thyratron is essentially a power rectifier with a control grid. Although the most common thyratron is a triode it does not operate like a vacuum triode. It operates as a controlled rectifier. In both vacuum triode and thyratron a highly negative grid can prevent current flow. However, unlike the vacuum-triode grid, the grid of the thyratron loses control when tube current starts to flow. This occurs because, as the tube conducts, positive ions move to the grid, neutralizing its charge.

DC Operation of Thyratron. DC operation of a thyratron is illustrated by the circuit diagram in Fig. 23 and the general control characteristic in Fig. 24. If the grid voltage is set at −2 volts and the positive anode voltage increased from zero, the tube will fire at 100 volts. If the grid voltage is increased to −4 volts the anode voltage must be increased to 300 volts to fire the tube. The grid-control characteristic shows

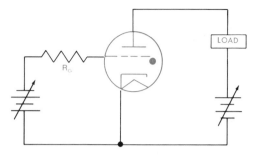

Fig. 23. *Thyratron connected for dc operation.*

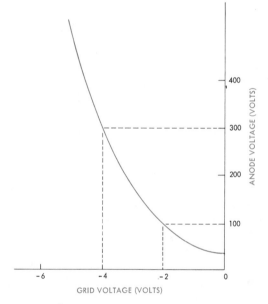

Fig. 24. *General thyratron control characteristic.*

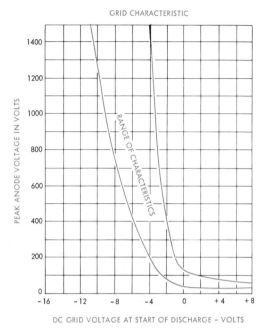

GRID CHARACTERISTIC

PEAK ANODE VOLTAGE IN VOLTS

RANGE OF CHARACTERISTICS

DC GRID VOLTAGE AT START OF DISCHARGE – VOLTS

Fig. 25. *Control characteristic of general-purpose 760 thyratron. (Courtesy of National Electronics, Inc.).*

that as the grid voltage is increased over a range of several volts, increasingly greater anode voltages are required to fire the tube. The grid control characteristic of the 760 gas and mercury-vapor thyratron is given in Fig. 25. The operating range of critical grid control is indicated by the two curves.

AC Operation of Thyratron. Operation of a thyratron as a controlled rectifier is illustrated in Fig. 26, where the control characteristic is shown with the conduction half-cycle of anode voltage. When the grid bias is set at −2 volts and the anode voltage increases from zero the tube is nonconducting until the anode voltage reaches 100 volts. At that point the tube fires, the anode voltage drops to the conduction value (arc drop) and the tube passes current for the remainder of the half-cycle or until the extinction voltage is reached—shortly before zero. The extinction voltage is the minimum voltage required to maintain the conduction arc.

If the bias is increased the thyratron fires

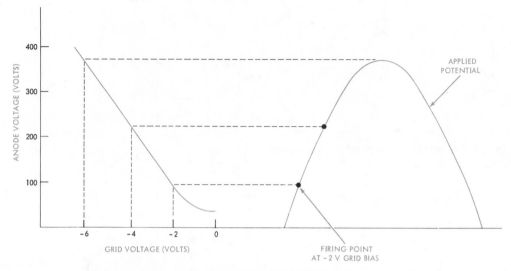

Fig. 26. *Thyratron operation with ac voltage applied to anode.*

at a later point in the first quarter cycle. According to the characteristic, with a bias of −6 volts the tube starts conducting when the anode voltage reaches its peak. This is the latest point in the conducting half-cycle at which a thyratron can be fired with this form of grid control. In actual practice the highest value of bias at which this tube will trigger could be somewhat less than −6 volts. This is because the anode voltage changes very little during the maximum portion of its cycle and a fine variation in control over this small amplitude variation cannot be achieved to retard firing to exactly 90°.

Control Locus. Bias values on the control characteristic and corresponding firing potentials on the anode-voltage waveform can be projected to form a "control locus." Fig. 27 shows the construction of such a curve. Bias voltages are transferred to the vertical scale below the horizontal axis, then projected horizontally to intersect with

corresponding anode voltages projected downward. The curve thus formed is the control locus. According to this locus any grid bias greater than −6 volts will prevent this tube from firing at any time with an anode voltage which peaks at 375 volts.

Phase-Shift Control of Thyratron. A variable dc potential on the grid of a thyratron can provide triggering at various times during the first quarter-cycle of positive anode voltage. The minimum current possible is that which flows when the tube is triggered at about 90°. To lower the current further the tube must be triggered during the second quarter-cycle of positive anode voltage. Such delayed firing cannot be achieved with dc grid bias. However, the "phase-shift" method of firing control can trigger a thyratron over most of the full positive half-cycle of anode voltage. This method of control provides almost a full half-cycle range of currents.

Limited phase-control of a thyratron by

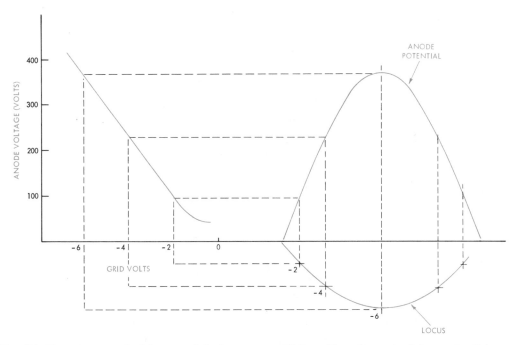

Fig. 27. *Thyratron control locus: plot of corresponding grid and anode firing potentials.*

a low-value ac grid voltage is illustrated in Fig. 28. The tube in this circuit fires when the anode is positive and the grid is zero or positive. As shown in Fig. 29, if the grid and anode voltages are in phase, conduction begins shortly after the two voltages cross the zero axis and become positive. It continues through the half-cycle (shaded area) until the extinction voltage is reached. During the half-cycle when both voltages are negative the tube is non-conducting.

If the terminals of one ac supply are interchanged the grid and anode voltages will be out of phase by 180° and the grid will be negative at all times when the anode is positive (shown at (B)). Consequently, at no time will there be current flow.

Fig. 29 shows the extremes of half-wave

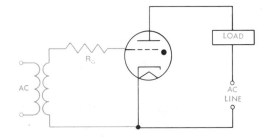

Fig. 28. *Thyratron with ac control.*

conduction—full-on or zero. To achieve variable control of the tube in Fig. 28, provision must be made for the grid to become positive at any time during the conduction half-cycle.

129

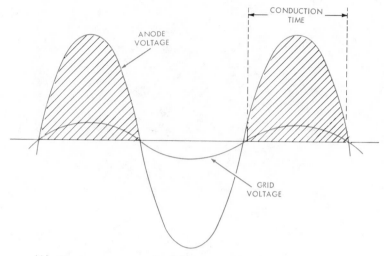

(**A**) GRID AND ANODE VOLTAGES IN PHASE. MAXIMUM CONDUCTION.

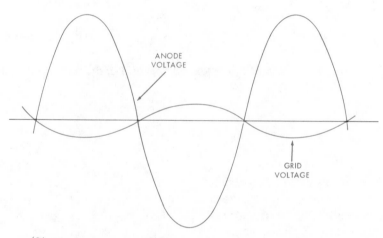

(**B**) GRID AND ANODE VOLTAGES 180° OUT OF PHASE. NO CONDUCTION.

Fig. 29. Grid-anode phase relations for conduction and non-conduction in circuit of Fig. 28.

In Fig. 30 a phase-shifting circuit is added to the grid circuit to cause the grid voltage to lag the anode voltage. By adjustment, the angle of lag can be varied from 0° to almost 180°, changing the instant during the positive anode half-cycle when the grid becomes positive, triggering the tube into conduction. Maximum current flows when the anode and grid become positive together (in phase, 0° phase angle). As the phase angle between the anode and grid voltages is increased, the grid becomes positive later during the conduction half-cycle. Current flows for shorter periods of

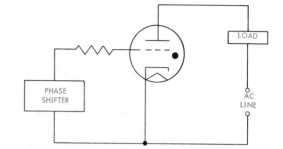

Fig. 30. *Phase-shift control of thyratron.*

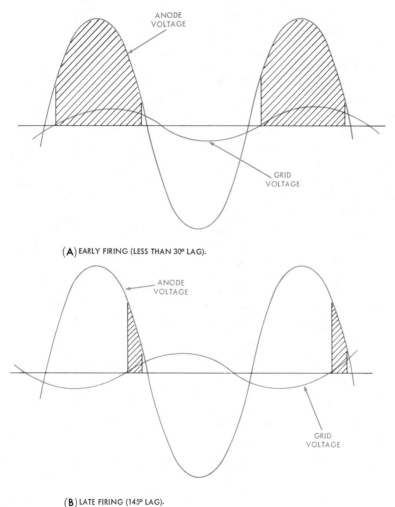

(**A**) EARLY FIRING (LESS THAN 30° LAG).

(**B**) LATE FIRING (145° LAG).

Fig. 31. *Early and late firing of thyratron by phase-shifting method.*

time, resulting in lower average load currents. This is illustrated in Fig. 31, which shows conduction at two phase angles—early firing and late firing. When the angle of lag approaches 180° no load current flows (as in Fig. 29(B)). Thus, the phase-shifter has virtually complete half-cycle control of the thyratron tube.

Phase-Shift and Control Locus. Relationships between phase-shifted control voltages and the control locus of a thyratron are illustrated in Fig. 32. In Fig. 32(A) the control voltage is 180° out of phase with the anode voltage and is at all times greater than the locus values, thereby keeping the tube in the off state. If the control voltage lags the anode voltage by a smaller angle (Fig. 32(B) shows a 30° lag) it will drop to a value on the locus as it decreases from its negative maximum. At this grid voltage the tube is triggered on because, at this instant, the anode and grid potentials are correct for firing. The time of current flow is indicated by the shading.

Operation with a larger phase angle is illustrated in Fig. 32(C). Here the control-grid voltage lags the anode voltage by about 135°. In this case the control voltage does not decrease to a locus value until late in the conduction half-cycle. At this time the tube fires and conduction continues until the anode voltage decreases to the extinction level. According to Fig. 32, conduction is maximum when the phase angle is minimum and minimum when the angle is maximum.

Phase-Shift Circuit. A basic circuit for varying the phase angle between two voltages is given in Fig. 33. The combination of center-tapped transformer and resistive-capacitive (RC) circuit provides a phase-shift range of almost 180°. Although a transformer is used in most industrial applications, it can be replaced by two re-

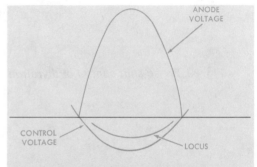

(**A**) CONTROL VOLTAGE (LAGGING 180°) EXCEEDING LOCUS VALUE: NO CONDUCTION.

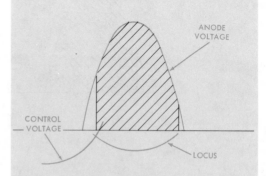

(**B**) CONTROL VOLTAGE (LAGGING 30°) DECREASES TO LOCUS VALUE, TRIGGERING CONDUCTION.

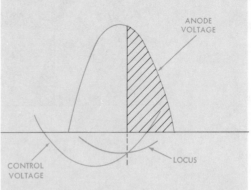

(**C**) CONTROL VOLTAGE (LAGGING 135°) TRIGGERS TUBE LATER IN HALF–CYCLE.

Fig. 32. *Relationships between control voltage and control locus of thyratron at various grid-anode phase angles.*

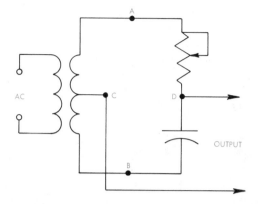

Fig. 33. *Circuit for producing phase-shifted voltages.*

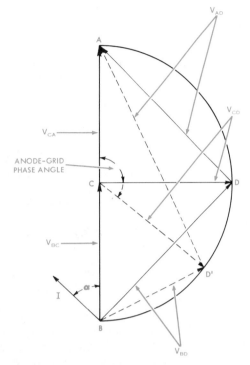

Fig. 34. *Vector diagram showing phase relations in phase-shift circuit of Fig. 33.*

sistors in series. Also, the RC circuit can be replaced by a resistive-inductive (RL) circuit.

The purpose of the circuit in Fig. 33 is to vary the phase angle between voltages V_{CA} and V_{CD}. When it is used to change the phase angle between the anode and grid voltages of a thyratron, V_{CD} becomes the grid voltage and the anode is connected to a line potential of the same polarity as point A. Operation of the circuit in Fig. 33 is shown by the vector diagram in Fig. 34. Vectors BC and CA represent V_{BC} and V_{CA}, the two halves of the secondary voltage, V_{BA}. V_{BA} creates a leading current through the RC circuit. This is shown by the vector, I, which leads BA by angle α.

Because the voltage across a capacitor lags the current by 90°, vector BD, representing V_{BD}, lags I by 90°. Vector CD represents the terminal voltage, V_{CD}. The semicircle is the locus of point D as the resistance of R is varied.

In this diagram the vectors, DA and BD are equal, indicating that the resistance and capacitive reactance are equal. Under these

conditions angle θ is 90° and the voltages, V_{CA} and V_{CD} are out of phase by 90°.

As the resistance of R is varied the voltages across the resistor and capacitor vary, changing the lengths of vectors, DA and BD. This, in turn, changes the angle between the vectors of V_{CA} and V_{CD} but does not alter the magnitude of V_{CD}, whose vector (CD) has a constant length (radius of semicircle).

If the resistance of R is varied from zero to maximum, the phase angle varies from 0° to almost 180°. The maximum angle depends on the ratio of resistance to reactance. When it is 20/1 the phase angle be-

133

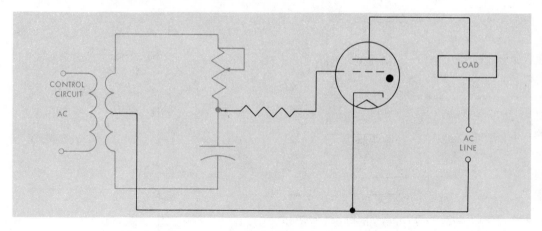

Fig. 35. *Thyratron controlled by RC phase-shift circuit.*

tween V_{CA} and V_{CD} is 174°. The dashed lines on the diagram show the vector relationships when the R/X_C ratio is some value less than 20/1 but greater than 1/1.

Utilization of the phase-shift circuit of Fig. 33 in control of a thyratron is illustrated in Fig. 35. Here the anode of the thyratron is connected to a potential of the same polarity as that at the top of the transformer secondary. This is the correct polarity, relative to the grid-control signal, necessary for turn-on control over the conducting half-cycle. As the resistance is varied the phase angle between the grid voltage and the anode voltage is varied, thereby controlling the flow of current through the tube and load.

Phase-Shift and Amplitude Control. Control of a thyratron by means of a dc potential at the grid is known as "amplitude control." A very effective form of thyratron control is a combination of the phase-shift and amplitude methods. A simplified diagram incorporating this type of control is given in Fig. 36. Operation is illustrated in Fig. 37.

In operation, if the dc bias is set at zero the operating level is the zero line. The control potential at the grid is the ac voltage developed by the phase-shift circuit. This signal triggers the thyratron at point A on the control locus.

If the dc bias is increased from zero to a certain negative value, the operating level changes to bias line B. The control voltage is now the algebraic sum of the dc bias and the ac output of the phase-shifter. It increases above, and decreases below, the dc bias level as the ac voltage adds to, and subtracts from, the dc bias voltage. When the composite potential decreases to a value at which it intersects the control locus (point B) the thyratron fires.

When the dc bias is reduced, the operating level is at a reduced potential and the composite signal fires the tube earlier in the conducting half-cycle. If the dc bias is increased sufficiently, the grid voltage will not intersect the control locus and the tube will not conduct at any time. In many applications the output of the phase shifter is at a fixed 90° angle with the anode voltage.

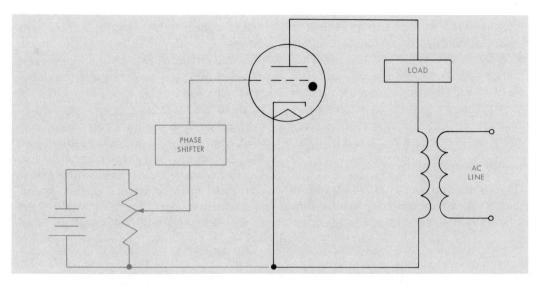

Fig. 36. *Thyratron control: amplitude plus phase-shift.*

Fig. 37. *Thyratron operation with phase-shift control and combination of phase-shift and amplitude control.*

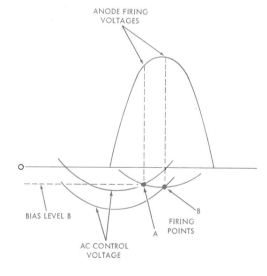

This is known as "quadrature-ac" and is used in conjunction amplitude control. With this arrangement thyratron firing time is varied by adjustments in the dc bias. This system is often referred to as "dc-plus-quadrature-ac" control.

135

DC-plus-quadrature-ac control is used in many industrial thyratron circuits. It is used frequently in the automatic compensation of motor speeds for changes in load. This form of control is also utilized as a means of incorporating signals from various transducers (photoelectric, thermoelectric, etc.) to effect automatic control of load currents.

Thyratron Applications

Thyratrons are used in a variety of applications: motor controls, welding timers, ignitron-firing circuits, adjustable-speed drives, photo-relay circuits, and many others.

In the circuit of Fig. 38 the thyratron is an amplifying device between a low-power phototube and a relay. When the phototube is unilluminated it acts as an open switch. During this time the thyratron cannot conduct, even though its anode is positive when the top of the transformer secondary is positive. This is because the control grid is connected to the other end of the secondary, which is highly negative with respect to the cathode. Thus, the thyratron is off

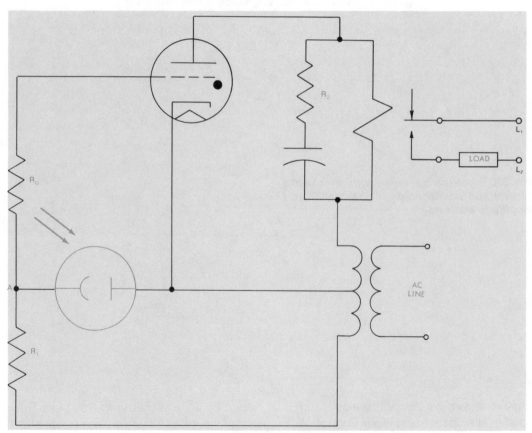

Fig. 38. *Thyratron-relay circuit triggered by phototube.*

when the phototube is dark. When the phototube is illuminated it conducts, completing a circuit through resistor, R_1 and part of the transformer secondary. The voltage across the resistor makes point A less negative, reducing the grid bias enough to trigger the thyratron. The resulting current flow operates the relay. When the anode goes negative, capacitor discharge provides current to the relay coil. Resistor R_2 limits the capacitor charging current, preventing damage to the thyratron. Interruption of the illumination turns the thyratron off, deenergizing the relay.

A general-purpose thyratron timer is shown in Fig. 39. This circuit can be used in various applications, such as welding, heat-sealing, etc. To start the timing operation switch S is actuated. Contacts 1 and 2 connect the coil of relay RY2 across the supply, energizing the relay. The RY2 load contacts close, completing a load circuit (welder, heater, etc.). Although the anode of the thyratron is connected to the posi-

tive line terminal through contacts 1 and 2, the tube does not conduct because the negative potential at the grid is too high.

When the switch is closed, capacitor C starts charging through the resistor network. After a time the charge voltage reduces the bias and the thyratron conducts. Anode-circuit current through the coil of relay RY1 opens contacts 5 and 6, deenergizing the load-relay circuit. The load contacts open, breaking the load circuit.

The thyratron continues to conduct until the switch is returned to the off position. With the switch in the off position the capacitor discharges through contacts 3 and 4 and the circuit is ready for another timing cycle.

The time-delay is determined by the charging time of the capacitor. Step changes in the delay are achieved by switching in other capacitors and fine adjustments are made with the potentiometer.

Two thyratrons are utilized as grid-control rectifiers in the full-wave circuit of Fig.

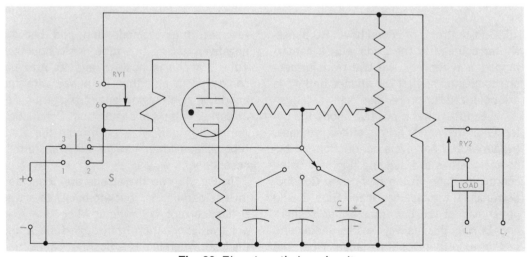

Fig. 39. *Thyratron timing circuit.*

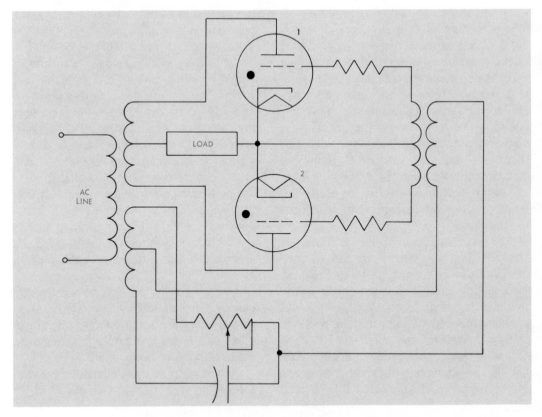

Fig. 40. *Phase-controlled thyratrons in full-wave circuit.*

40. Grid control is provided by an RC phase-shifter coupled to the grids with a center-tapped transformer. The two transformers are connected so that the anodes and grids are polarized for proper control.

When tube 1 has a positive anode the potential at its control grid is either in phase, triggering full half-cycle conduction, or becomes positive at a lagging angle, causing conduction later in the half-cycle. Conduction occurs through the load, tube 1 and upper half of the line-transformer secondary. During this half-cycle the anode and gate of tube 2 are both negative. When the polarity of the line-transformer secondary reverses, tube-1 anode and grid become negative, making this tube non-conductive. Tube-2 anode is positive and its grid becomes positive, either in phase with the anode or at a lagging angle, triggering full or partial half-cycle conduction. Conduction during this half-cycle is through the load, tube 2, and lower half of the transformer secondary.

In Fig. 41 two thyratrons are connected inverse-parallel or "back-to-back" to act as a high-current ac switch. When line A is positive, conduction is through tube 2 and the load. When line B is positive, conduction is through tube 1 and the load. When each

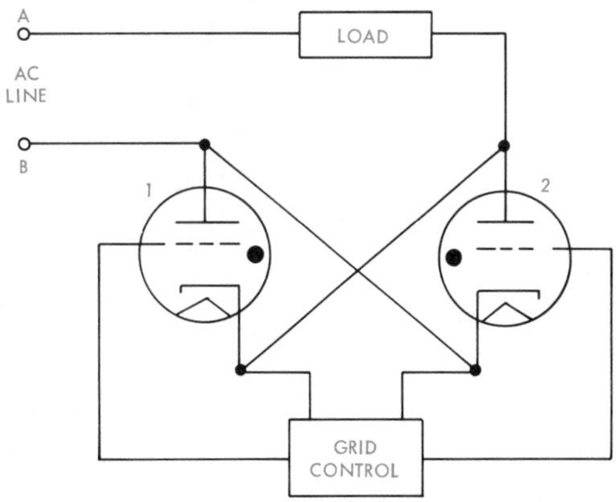

Fig. 41. *Thyratrons connected back-to-back for ac control.*

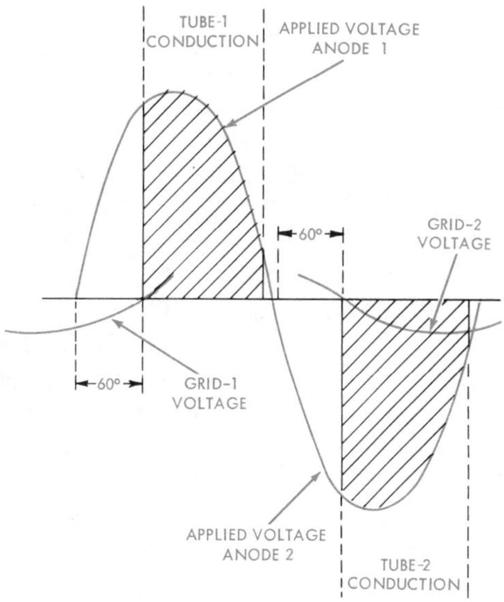

Fig. 42. *Operation of back-to-back thyratrons as controlled ac switch.*

tube is conducting the other tube has a negative anode. The amount of conduction is controlled by the grid-control circuit. Operation is illustrated in Fig. 42 which shows the grid voltage of each tube lagging the applied anode voltage by 60°. The shad-ing indicates the amount of ac conduction during one cycle of applied voltage.

Thyratrons have been used extensively in control circuits designed to maintain constant dc motor speeds. Fig. 43 shows thyratron control of a separate-field motor. (A

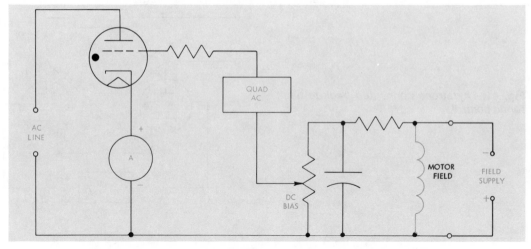

Fig. 43. *Thyratron circuit maintains constant speed of dc motor.*

separate-field motor is one in which the field and armature are energized from different sources. In a true shunt motor the field and armature are connected in parallel to the same source.)

In Fig. 43 the armature is the load in a half-wave thyratron rectifier circuit supplied from the ac line. Grid control is determined by a fixed-quadrature ac voltage from the phase-shifter, adjustable dc bias and the counter-voltage developed in the rotating armature. The bias potentiometer is used to preset the motor speed.

When the motor load decreases and the rotor speed starts to increase, the counter-voltage in the armature (which is relative to rotor speed) increases, making the cathode more positive. This acts to retard firing to a point in the conducting half-cycle later than the preset time. Later firing results in less average current, maintaining the speed at the preset level.

If the load increases, the rotor speed decreases, reducing the counter-voltage. The

cathode becomes less positive and the tube fires earlier in the half-cycle. The resulting increase in current maintains the rotor speed at the preset level (within limits) although the load is greater. In this manner the counter-voltage in the armature of a dc motor adjusts the firing time of a thyratron to maintain constant rotor speed under changing load conditions.

The circuit in Fig. 44 shows thyratron control of current in the magnetic coupling coil of a drive mechanism. In this unit the amount of coupling and speed of the shaft vary with the coil current.

DC bias for the thyratron is developed across the potentiometer by the back-to-back diode circuit. Adjustment of the potentiometer sets the speed of the drive. A tachometer-generator senses the shaft speed and develops an ac output voltage proportional to the speed. This output, rectified by D_3 and filtered by C_1, appears across R_1, negative at the grid end. The potential across R_1 opposes the dc bias and

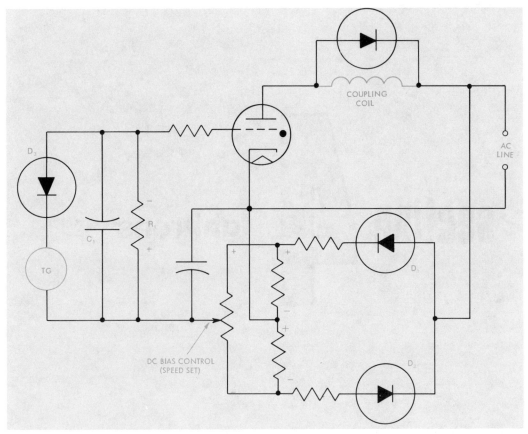

Fig. 44. *Tachometer-generator and thyratron maintain constant speed of drive mechanism.*

the difference is the thyratron control signal.

This circuit operates automatically to maintain a constant preset shaft speed when the shaft load changes. When the shaft speed starts to increase the tachometer-generator output increases, thereby increasing the negative component of the grid bias. This results in reduced current through the thyratron and coupling coil, causing the shaft speed to return to approximately the preset value. When the tachometer-generator senses a decrease in shaft speed, it provides a reduced negative voltage to the bias circuit. The average current through the thyatron and coil increases, maintaining the preset shaft speed. The commutating diode across the coupling coil provides a path for self-induced coil current during non-conducting half-cycles.

141

Unit 3

section 4 Ignitrons

Ignitrons are controlled mercury-pool rectifiers designed to meet the high-current control and rectification requirements of industrial processes and large dc equipment. They make possible the precise control of very high (thousands of amperes) short-duration welding currents. They are also used in continuous-duty power-rectifier service, high-voltage switching and power-conversion applications.

An ignitron does not have some of the limitations of the thyratron. The cathode does not require heating and is not subject to destruction, maximum tube current does not depend on cathode capacity, and no warm-up time is required. A disadvantage of the ignitron, when compared with the thy-

ratron, is the requirement of a relatively large turn-on current, whereas a low-power signal triggers the thyratron.

The ignitron shown in Fig. 45, the 1051A, is a size B water-cooled tube used in ac-control and welding applications. It has a length of 13 inches and a diameter of 3¼ inches. It operates at ac voltages between 250 and 600 volts and has a direct-current rating of 56 amperes. It is approximately equivalent to a 300-ampere magnetic contactor. The 5550 ignitron, shown in Fig. 46, is a clamp-cooled, size A tube (length: 10 inches; diameter: 2½ inches). A pair of 5550's control 300 KVA on a demand basis at voltages from 250 to 600 volts—half the capacity of a pair of 1051A's.

Fig. 45. *Water-cooled ignitron for welding and ac-control applications. (Courtesy of National Electronics, Inc.).*

Fig. 46. *The 5550 ignitron is a clamp-cooled type used in resistance-welding control. (Courtesy of RCA Corp.).*

Ignitron Construction

The general construction of a water-cooled ignitron is illustrated in Fig. 47. It is a three-electrode structure, consisting of an anode, a mercury-pool cathode and an ignitor. These electrodes are mounted in a vacuum-tight envelope, part of which is a double-walled, stainless-steel jacket. Cooling coils carrying water are brazed to the inner wall of the jacket. Some units do not have cooling coils. In these, water circulates between the walls of the jacket.

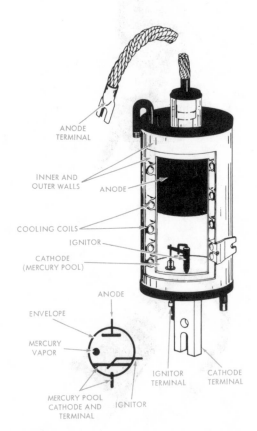

Fig. 47. *General construction of typical water-cooled ignitron. (Courtesy of National Electronics, Inc.).*

The cathode is a pool of mercury at the bottom of the tube. In some tubes the diameter of the pool is five inches or more. The ignitor is a rod with a cone-shaped tip which extends into the surface of the mercury. It is made of heat-resistant material such as silicon carbide. The tip of the ignitor is formed into a rough surface which has many fine, sharp points. The kind of material used to form the ignitor and the shape of the tip create a resistance between the ignitor and the mercury pool ranging from about 10 ohms to 300 ohms.

The anode is made of graphite, which radiates heat very well, does not normally emit electrons and has a negative temperature-coefficient-of-resistance (as temperature increases, resistance decreases). The ability of the graphite anode to radiate heat is a significant factor in ignitron operation since the current is usually high and heat dissipation is an important consideration. Some rectifiers, especially models used in power-rectifier service, have an additional anode, known as a "holding anode." This electrode, which has its own ac supply, is used to maintain an arc to the mercury-pool cathode when the main-anode current is very low.

Fig. 48 is a cross-section of a typical water-cooled ignitron. The copper cooling coil through which water is circulated is indicated at 1. A concentration of coil turns in the lower part of the tube is indicated by 2. This produces a cooler wall for condensation of mercury near the pool. The wider spacing in the upper part does not promote mercury condensation on the upper walls near the anode where arc-back could occur. The stainless-steel jacket is designated by 3. The inner wall is covered with an insulating coating. This, together with the outer wall, prevents air contact with the cooled materials—eliminating moisture condensa-

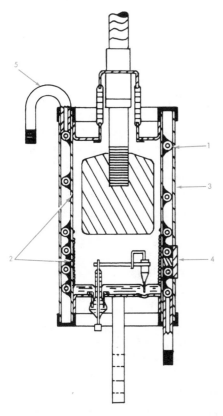

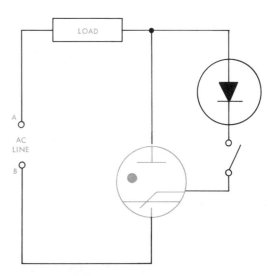

Fig. 49. *Basic ignitron circuit.*

Fig. 48. *Cross-section showing constructional details of water-cooled ignitron. (Courtesy of National Electronics, Inc.).*

tion on the tube. A copper thermal block and thermostat mount are indicated by 4. This assembly makes contact with the inner wall to sense temperature for water-flow regulation. Connection to the water supply is made at 5.

Ignitron Operation

When the circuit in Fig. 49 (switch open) is connected to the ac supply, the full line voltage appears across the ignitron. Although a peak positive potential is applied

to the anode when line A is positive, the tube does not conduct. Conduction cannot occur because electrons are not emitted from a cold mercury-pool cathode.

If the switch is closed, line voltage is applied to the ignitor-cathode circuit. When the ignitor is positive an arc is formed between the ignitor tip and the mercury cathode. An arc is formed because the rough tip does not make a good ohmic contact with the mercury. A high voltage gradient exists between the rod and the mercury, resulting in a field strong enough to pull electrons out of the mercury. The top of the rod becomes highly positive and attracts the electrons. These electrons ionize some of the mercury vapor which was produced by the heat of the arc. The positive ions formed by the ionization accelerate toward the cathode pool where they free electrons from the mercury by secondary emission. The secondary-emission electrons are attracted to the anode, which is positive at this time.

These accelerated electrons ionize the mercury vapor between the cathode and anode, forming the main arc, which now has an ample supply of electrons from the mercury-pool cathode.

After the main arc (cathode to anode) is formed, the service of the ignitor circuit is not required until the next conducting half-cycle. In Fig. 49 the ignitor circuit is in parallel with the cathode-anode circuit. When the main arc is formed the voltage across the parallel combination decreases to the arc-drop level of the ignitron. This places a comparatively low voltage across the ignitor circuit—perhaps one-tenth of that required for firing. Consequently, the ignitor-circuit current decreases to a very low, or zero, value during ignitron conduction.

The diode in the ignitor circuit prevents reverse current through the circuit during non-conducting half-cycles, when the cathode line is positive and the anode line is negative. Reverse current can damage the ignitor and shorten the life of the ignitron.

Operation of the circuit in Fig. 49 is illustrated by the waveforms in Fig. 50. Positive potential applied to the anode and ignitor circuits increases until the ignitor fires the tube. At that time the voltage across the tube decreases to the arc-drop level, current starts flowing through the tube and load and continues to flow for the remainder of the conducting half-cycle. During the alternate half-cycle the anode is negative, the tube does not conduct and the diode prevents reverse current flow through the ignitor circuit.

Ignitron Ratings

Five main ratings are ordinarily applied to ignitrons. Each of these is defined and described in paragraphs which follow.

Temperature. Temperature is a factor in the proper operation of ignitrons. However, unlike mercury-vapor rectifiers and thyratrons, low-temperature operation is not a problem. The mercury-pool cathode can support conduction until the tube reaches operating temperature.

Ignitron thermal problems occur at high temperatures. Since ignitrons carry high currents and dissipate large amounts of power, maximum temperature limits must be established for proper operation. Because it is difficult to measure the condensed-mercury temperature (as in the thyratron) the maximum-operating-temperature rating applies to the cooling water. The cooling-water maximum temperature for the 1051A (shown in Fig. 45) ranges from 45°C at an operating voltage of 600 volts ac to 55°C at 250 volts ac. The minimum inlet water temperaure is 0°C.

Maximum Ignitor Voltages and Currents. For proper operation and safety, ignitor voltage and current levels should not

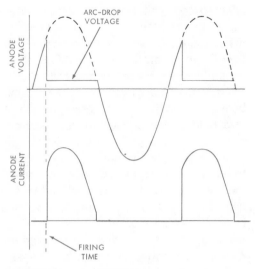

Fig. 50. *Anode voltage and current waveforms of ignitron shown in Fig. 49.*

exceed established maximums. For the 1051A the maximum allowable instantaneous positive ignitor voltage is the rated anode voltage. The maximum negative limit is 5 volts. The maximum instantaneous ignitor current is 100 amperes. The maximum allowable rms current is 10 amperes and the average allowed is 1 ampere.

Arc Drop. In mercury-vapor rectifiers and thyratrons the arc drop remains relatively constant with changes in load. This is not true of ignitrons. Because of the very high peak currents through the ignitron, arc drop increases with the load. This is shown in Fig. 51, where the arc drop of a typical ignitron is plotted as a function of anode current.

The occurrence of high arc drops in conjunction with high currents produces large amounts of heat which must be dissipated. The peak arc drop of the 1051A ignitron is 13 volts at a peak current of 176 amperes. It increases to 26 volts at a peak current of 3400 amperes.

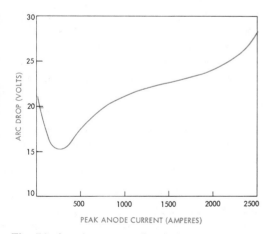

Fig. 51. *Arc drop vs peak anode current for a typical ignitron.*

Maximum Anode Voltages and Currents. The anode voltage and current ratings of ignitrons relate to applications. In control applications the 1051A has an average-anode-current rating of 56 amperes dc. The maximum averaging time is 11.25 seconds at 600 volts and 27 seconds at 250 volts. For intermittent duty as a controlled rectifier, the 1051A has a maximum-peak-anode-current rating of 700 amperes at a maximum peak anode voltage of 500 volts. At 1200 volts the maximum peak current is 600 amperes and at 1500 volts it is 480 amperes. The maximum-average-anode-current rating at 700 amperes peak is 40 amperes dc, at 600 amperes it is 22.5 amperes dc and at 480 amperes it is 18 amperes dc. The averaging times are 6 seconds for 700 amperes and 10 seconds for 600 and 480 amperes.

Percent Duty. Since ignitrons are used extensively in welding applications, where currents flow intermittently, an important ignitron parameter is "percent duty." This is an index of the percentage of time an ignitron can carry certain currents at specified anode voltages. It is the ratio of maximum "on" time to maximum averaging time. For rating purposes the currents are known as "demand currents" and are specified in ac amperes.

Rating charts provided by tube manufacturers usually show the allowable range of demand currents and corresponding percent duty values of ignitron tubes connected inverse-parallel. The data are given for tubes connected in this manner because this circuit configuration is used in most applications. Fig. 52 shows demand current vs. percent duty for the 1051A ignitron.

As indicated by the data in the rating chart, the 1051A can carry about 1250 amperes (rms) at 500 volts (rms) up to almost a 6% duty cycle. At 250 volts the

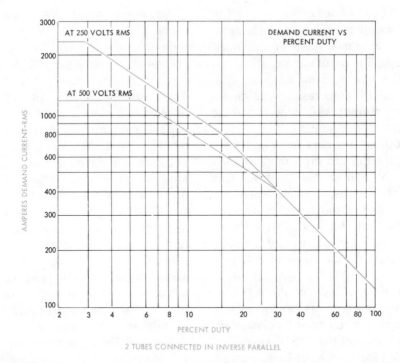

Fig. 52. *Demand current vs. percent duty for the 1051A ignitron. (Courtesy of National Electronics, Inc.).*

1051A can carry this current for a longer duty cycle—about 9%. At 30% duty cycle the capacity of this ignitron drops to 400 amperes and at 60% it is 200 amperes. Since this is a maximum characteristic, any operating point falling to the left of the line indicates that the ignitron is operating safely below its maximum.

Ignitron Applications

Ignitron applications include power rectification, welding-current control, power conversion and high-voltage switching. The most extensive use of ignitrons is in welding service.

Ignitron circuitry is relatively simple. Fig.

53 shows a pair of ignitrons in the most widely used configuration: inverse-parallel. This is basically the circuit used in most commercial ignitron contactors. In this circuit the ignitrons do not rectify the line current. When the switch is closed they conduct alternately as the line voltage changes polarity, allowing controlled alternating current to flow through the transformer primary.

When line A is positive the polarity of the potential from ignitor rod to cathode of tube A is correct for firing. (The cathode is connected to negative line B and the ignitor rod is connected to positive line A through resistor R_A, diode 3, fuse, switch, diode 2

148

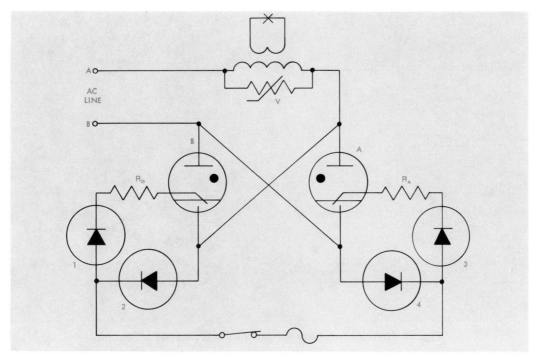

Fig. 53. *Circuit of ignitron contactor (controlled high-current ac switch).*

and transformer primary.) The ignitor fires and electrons flow from line B through the ignitor section of tube A, resistor R_A, diode 3, fuse, switch, diode 2 and transformer primary to line A. The ignitor action turns on the anode section of tube A and line current flows from line B through ignitron A and the transformer primary to line A.

During the alternate half-cycle, when line B is positive, firing polarity appears across the ignitor circuit of tube B. (The cathode is connected to negative line A through the transformer primary and the ignitor rod to positive line B through resistor R_B, diode 1, switch, fuse and diode 4.) The ignitor fires and tube B conducts, allowing line current to flow through the transformer primary from line A to line B. The diodes are included in the circuit to prevent reverse current flow through the ignitors.

The resistor across the transformer primary is a non-linear silicon-carbide unit. It is used to protect circuit components from high-voltage surges (inductive kicks) produced in the primary. Under normal voltage conditions it has very high resistance and passes little current. At high voltages its resistance decreases rapidly, providing a current path across the excessive voltage, thereby preventing the flow of damaging current through other circuit components.

The control switch can be replaced by a pair of contacts in a thyratron-controlled relay circuit or in some other form of

149

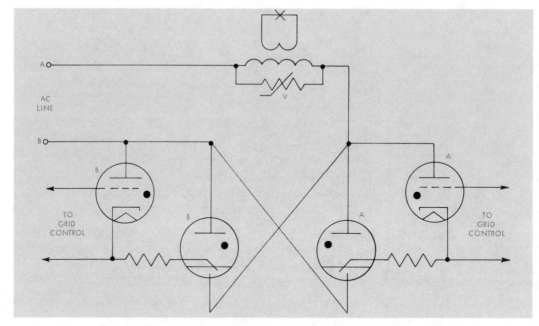

Fig. 54. *Thyratrons trigger ignitrons in "anode-control" circuit.*

control circuit. Thermostatic and water-flow switches can be added to provide for turn-off when the temperature is excessive or water supply is inadequate.

The circuit in Fig. 54 illustrates a form of ignitron control known as "anode control." The thyratron-controlled ignitor circuit is connected across the ignitron, making the ignitor-circuit voltage and current dependent upon the anode potential; hence the name *anode control.*

When line A is positive the anodes of thyratron A and ignitron A are positive. If a turn-on signal is applied to the thyratron grid at this time the thyratron conducts, completing the ignitor circuit of ignitron A. This, in turn, fires the ignitron and current flows through the load from line B to line A. During the next half-cycle when line A is

negative the A tubes are off. Line B makes the anodes of the B tubes positive. A trigger voltage at the grid of thyratron B causes it to conduct, completing the ignitor circuit of ignitron B. Current now flows through the load from line A to line B.

Accurate control over much of each half-cycle of line voltage can be achieved with the circuit in Fig. 54. However, for early and late firing there may not be enough voltage to operate the ignitor circuits. Removal of the ignitor circuits from the anode supply and reconnection to separate supplies overcomes this disadvantage and provides more precise control.

The advantages of three-phase systems in providing large amounts of power are utilized in some ignitron applications. A three-phase circuit is shown in Fig. 55. The

150

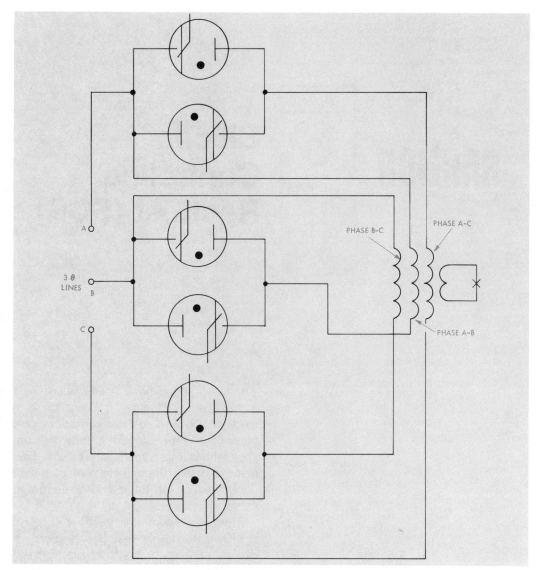

Fig. 55. *Ignitrons in three-phase system provide large amounts of controlled welding current.*

ignitor firing circuits are not shown. The transformer is a special-purpose unit with three primaries and one secondary, designed for high-current welding applications. As the ignitrons conduct in sequence they provide high-heat welding current to the load.

151

Unit 3

section 5

Silicon Controlled Rectifier (SCR)

In many applications solid-state devices have replaced bulky, power-dissipating electron tubes, rheostats, contactors, and other control and switching units. In some applications these solid-state devices have made possible the achievement of results unobtainable with tubes and other components.

The silicon controlled rectifier (SCR) is a solid-state device that has replaced its earlier counterpart, the thyratron, in many industrial and commercial applications. It is a three-junction semiconductor unit which can replace relays, power switches and thyratron tubes. Because the SCR operates like a thyratron it has been called a "solid-state thyratron" although it differs greatly from the thyratron in construction.

As a controlled rectifier the SCR's conduction can be easily started and timed. It has the advantage of high switching speed and instant conduction (no warm-up). The unit is rugged and static (no moving parts), efficient (low voltage drop), and comparatively small in size and weight. Also, it can be sealed and is free from the effects of vibration and shock. Unlike mechanical switches and relays, the SCR has unlimited life when operated according to specifications. A few microwatts input to an SCR can control a several-hundred-watt load—a power gain of millions.

SCR's are available in a full range of forms and sizes to meet the requirements of a great variety of industrial, commercial and military applications. Presently, they are available in current ratings from less than one ampere to 1400 amperes and over

a voltage range of fifteen to 2600 volts.

Fig. 56 shows a general-purpose, low-current (1.0 to 4.0 amperes) hermetically-sealed SCR. The SCR in Fig. 57 is a silicone-encapsulated, planar-passivated unit designed for low-current volume applications. The SCR's in Figs. 58 and 59 are representative of a class of devices with voltage ratings of 25-500 volts and a current range of seven to 25 amperes. The SCR's in Figs. 60 and 61 are typical of two forms used to control currents ranging from 55 to 200 amperes at voltages of 500 to 1200 volts. The SCR in Fig. 60 is a 55-ampere unit and that in Fig. 61 has a 200 ampere rating.

SCR's in the 200-500 ampere range are generally fabricated as shown in Fig. 62. The voltage range for this class of device is usually 100-1700 volts.

The SCR unit in Fig. 63 is the General Electric "Press Pak," designed for use in the 800-1400 ampere range. This form of construction allows for double-sided water,

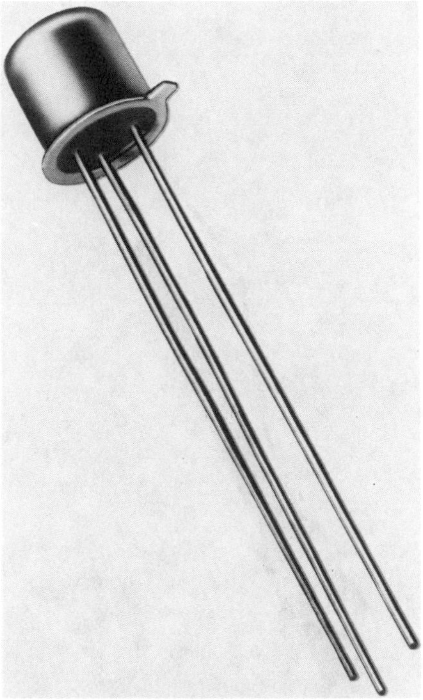

Fig. 56. *General-purpose low-current SCR. (Courtesy of General Electric Co.).*

Fig. 57. *Low-current, encapsulated, planar SCR. (Courtesy of General Electric Co.).*

153

Fig. 60. *SCR for currents up to 55 amperes and voltages to 1200 volts. (Courtesy of General Electric Co.).*

Fig. 58. *SCR in 7-25 ampere range. (Courtesy of General Electric Co.).*

Fig. 59. *SCR in medium-current, 25-500 volt range. (Courtesy of General Electric Co.).*

Fig. 61. *SCR with 200 ampere, 1200 volt rating. (Courtesy of General Electric Co.).*

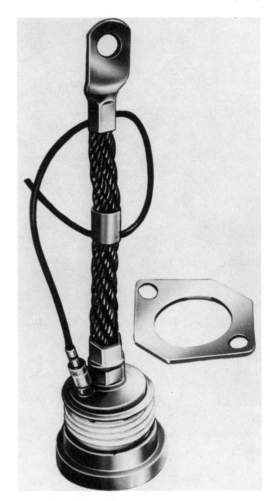

Fig. 62. SCR for currents up to 500 amperes and voltages up to 1700 volts. (Courtesy of General Electric Co.).

Fig. 63. "Press-Pak" SCR, for currents in 800-1400 ampere range and voltages from 100-2600 volts. (Courtesy of General Electric Co.).

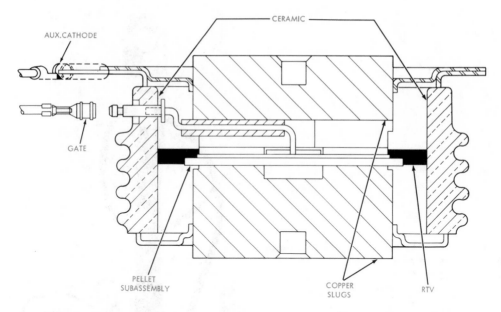

Fig. 64. *Construction of Press-Pak SCR. (Courtesy of General Electric Co.).*

or forced-air, cooling. A cross-section of the unit in Fig. 63 is shown in Fig. 64. The voltage range of these high-current SCR's extends from 100 volts to 2600 volts.

Construction of the SCR

An SCR consists of four layers of P- and N-type materials, as illustrated in Fig. 65. Three PN junctions are formed by the four layers. Each SCR has three terminals: anode, cathode, and gate. The gate corresponds to the control grid of the thyratron tube.

The SCR structure can be considered as a combination of two transistors, a PNP and an NPN. This model is shown in Fig. 66. In this configuration N_1 is the base of the upper transistor and collector of the lower. P_2 is the base of the lower transistor and collector of the upper. Fig. 67 shows an equivalent two-transistor circuit.

Operation of the SCR

With rated anode-to-cathode voltage (anode +) junctions J_1 and J_3 (Fig. 66) are forward-biased, but junction J_2 is reverse-biased, preventing conduction. However, if voltage is applied gate-to-cathode (gate +) a small cathode-gate current flows. By transistor action the reverse bias of junction J_2 is overcome and a flow of electrons moves through junctions J_2 and J_1 to the anode. The SCR now conducts like a conventional rectifier.

If the potential applied to the gate is removed, the SCR continues to conduct. Thus the gate can initiate conduction but cannot stop it. This function of the gate is the same as that of the thyratron grid. SCR conduction is stopped by opening the anode-load circuit or by reducing the supply voltage so that the anode current decreases to a value

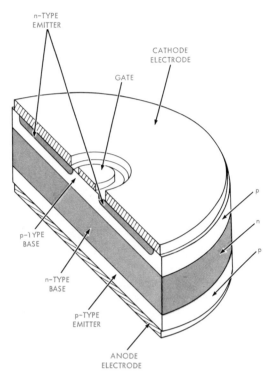

Fig. 65. Cross-section of a typical SCR pellet. (Courtesy of RCA Corp.).

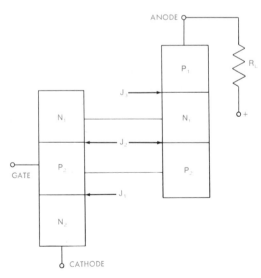

Fig. 66. Two-transistor model of SCR structure.

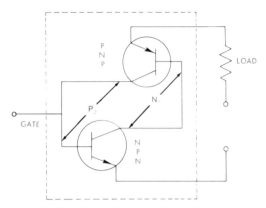

Fig. 67. Two-transistor equivalent circuit of SCR.

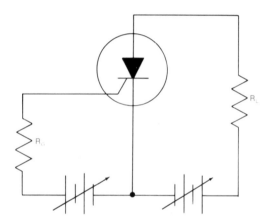

Fig. 68. Experimental SCR circuit.

below a certain "holding current" which is necessary to maintain conduction.

An experimental SCR circuit having adjustable dc supplies for the anode and gate circuits is given in Fig. 68. If the gate current (I_G) is set at a relatively low value and the anode voltage (V_{AK}) is increased from zero it reaches a value called the "breakover voltage" (V_{BR}), at which the SCR conducts.

Fig. 69 shows the voltage distribution in

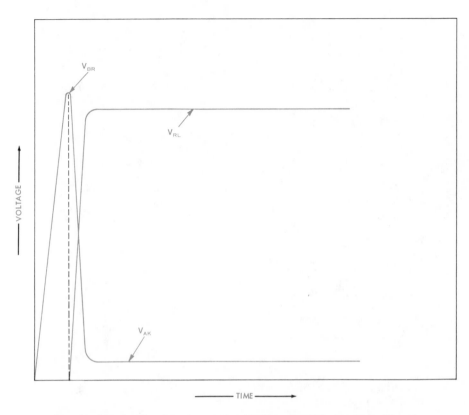

Fig. 69. *Anode-circuit voltage distribution of SCR circuit in Fig. 68.*

the anode circuit. Before firing, the full supply voltage is across the SCR, anode-to-cathode. After firing, V_{AK} drops to about one volt and the remainder of the supply voltage appears across the load. If the supply voltage is reduced so that the anode current decreases below the holding value, the SCR ceases to conduct. If the gate current is reset to a higher value and the anode voltage is again increased from zero, the SCR will conduct at a lower breakover voltage. Thus V_{BR} varies inversely with I_G.

The volt-ampere curves of an SCR given in Fig. 70 show anode currents and breakover voltages for different values of gate current. With a low value of gate current (I_{G1}) the anode current is minimum (leakage) until the anode voltage (V_{AK}) reaches V_{BR1}. At this point the SCR fires, V_{AK} decreases to the after-firing value and the anode current (I_A) increases rapidly to a value determined by the supply voltage and the load resistance.

At higher values of gate current (I_{G2} and I_{G3}) breakover occurs at lower anode potentials. Although gate currents and anode voltages may vary, anode current is determined by the supply voltage and load resistance.

Fig. 71 shows breakover voltage as a

158

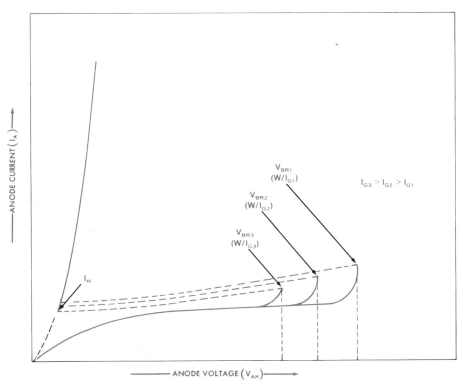

Fig. 70. *Volt-ampere characteristic of SCR for three values of gate current.*

function of gate current for a small SCR. The rapid decrease in breakover voltage for small changes in gate current indicates the extent to which gate current determines the firing point of an SCR.

In the SCR circuit in Fig. 72, a low-voltage, low-current dc gate circuit controls half-wave direct current through the load. When the switch is closed, gate current flows, triggering the SCR on at the point in the conducting half cycle when breakover voltage occurs. If a variable resistance is added to the gate circuit, gate current and breakover voltage can be adjusted to make changes in the load current. The load-current waveform in Fig. 72 indicates trig-

gering of the SCR during the first part of the conducting half-cycle.

In Fig. 73 a diode eliminates the separate dc gate supply. Gate current is supplied from the ac line during each half-cycle that the anodes are positive. When the SCR triggers on, the anode voltage drops to its very low conduction value and the anode-load current is determined by the source voltage and the load resistance. The resistor in series with the diode limits the gate current to a safe value.

If the resistance in Fig. 73 is replaced by a variable resistance, as in Fig. 74, control of load current can be varied over essentially a 90° range. With the resistance at

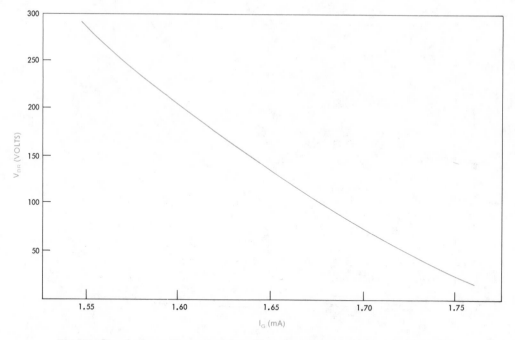

Fig. 71. *Breakover voltage as a function of gate current for a small SCR.*

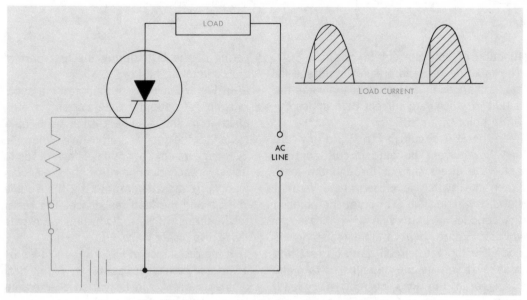

Fig. 72. *DC control of SCR half-wave rectifier.*

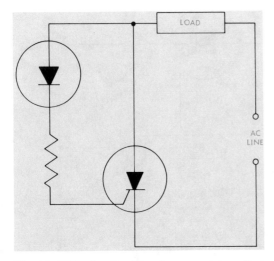

Fig. 73. *SCR circuit with gate current supplied from the ac line.*

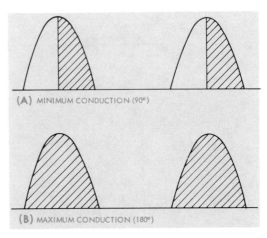

(A) MINIMUM CONDUCTION (90°)

(B) MAXIMUM CONDUCTION (180°)

Fig. 75. *Minimum and maximum conduction achievable in circuit of Fig. 74.*

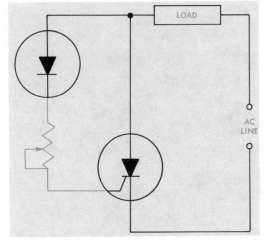

Fig. 74. *Variable resistance adjusts SCR triggering.*

minimum the SCR triggers on at the beginning of the conducting half-cycle. This results in maximum load current (full half-cycle conduction). As the resistance is in-

creased, gate current decreases and higher breakover voltages are required to fire the SCR.

To obtain minimum load current the gate-circuit resistance must be increased sufficiently to limit the gate current to a value which requires a breakover voltage equal to the available peak anode voltage. Under these conditions the SCR fires when the anode voltage peaks and conducts during the next quarter-cycle. This is the minimum amount of conduction (other than zero) possible with this form of control circuit. The two extremes of conduction are illustrated in Fig. 75.

Applications of the SCR

Control of battery charging is a common application of the SCR. This is illustrated in Fig. 76, where the SCR is used in conjunction with a full-wave dc power supply. The battery voltage is applied to the gate-control circuit so that, when the voltage is low, SCR conduction is maximum and the battery potential (charge) increases. As the

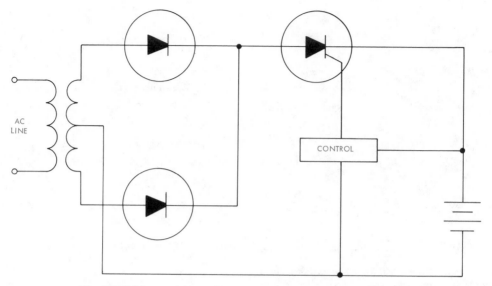

Fig. 76. SCR provides automatic control of battery charging.

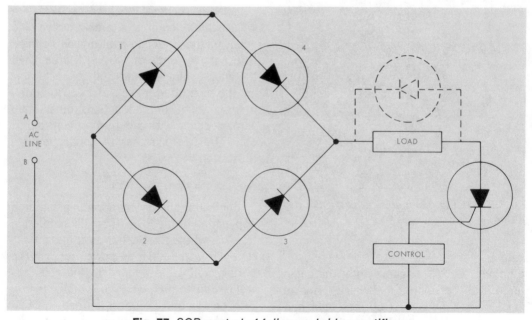

Fig. 77. SCR control of full-wave bridge rectifier.

battery potential increases, the gate circuit limits conduction until, at full charge, there is no further conduction.

SCR control of a full-wave bridge rectifier and load circuit is shown in Fig. 77. During one half-cycle, electron flow is from line A through diode 1, SCR, load, and diode 3, to line B. During the alternate half-cycle, electron flow is from line B through diode 2, SCR, load, and diode 4, to line A. The amount of direct current through the load during each half-cycle of applied voltage depends on the setting of the SCR gate-control circuit. If the load is inductive, a "free-wheeling" diode, connected as shown, helps to maintain proper switching of the SCR.

The circuit in Fig. 78 provides variable full-wave alternating current to a load. When terminal A is negative and the SCR is con-ducting, electron flow is from line A through the load, diode 1, SCR and diode 3, to terminal B. During the alternate half cycle, electron flow is from terminal B, through diode 2, SCR, diode 4 and the load, to terminal A. The amount of current through the load is determined by the gate-control.

Two SCR's can be connected "back-to-back" or "inverse-parallel" to act as a high-current switch in an ac circuit. This configuration, illustrated in Fig. 79, allows the SCR's to conduct on alternate half cycles. When the gate-circuit switch is closed and line A is positive, there is a small flow of electrons from line B through the cathode and gate of SCR_1, resistor R and diode D_1, to line A. This triggers SCR_1, completing the load circuit for all or part of one half cycle. During the half cycle when line B is positive, gate current flows through the

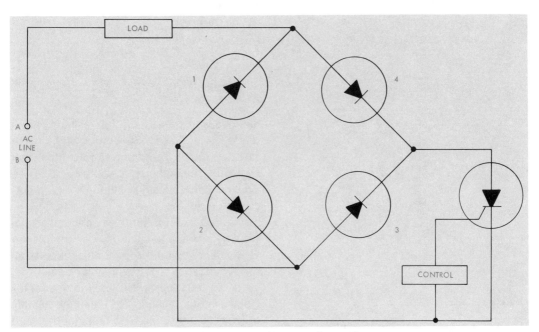

Fig. 78. *SCR control of full-wave alternating current.*

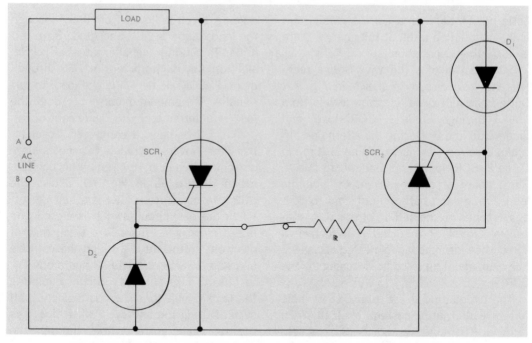

Fig. 79. *Inverse-parallel SCR's form contactless, high-current ac switch.*

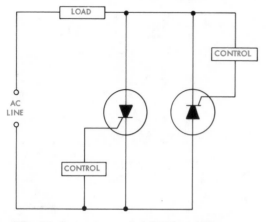

Fig. 80. *Inverse-parallel SCR's with separate gate controls.*

cathode and gate of SCR$_2$, resistor R and diode D$_2$, to line B. SCR$_2$ fires and current flows through the load during this half cycle. In this manner back-to-back SCR's provide contactless switching of high-current ac circuits.

Fig. 80 shows another ac circuit controlled by back-to-back SCR's. In this arrangement separate gate-control circuits allow for independent regulation of each half cycle of load current. Separate variables (temperature, speed, etc.) can be readily utilized to make adjustments in the load current.

Unit 3

section 6

Gate-Controlled AC Switch (Triac)

One method of controlling ac load currents utilizes two SCR's connected inverse-parallel. A device which combines the functions of the two SCR's in one unit is a gate-controlled semiconductor switch called a *triac*. It is so named because it is a three-terminal (triode) ac switch— "tri-ac." It is known generically as a *bidirectional triode thyristor*.

The triac is a versatile, easily-connected "static switch" which can be used in a wide range of ac-control applications. It has a number of advantages over other switching devices. It can control high-current load circuits with minimum control power. There are no contact problems— bounce, arcing, wear, corrosion, etc. Triac control also requires fewer components than other semiconductor switching methods. Triacs are available with current ratings up to 25 amperes and voltage ratings up to 500 volts. Common forms of triacs are shown in Figs. 81, 82, 83, and 84.

The triac in Fig. 81 is a molded silicone plastic unit. Triacs in this form have current ratings up to ten amperes. The unit in Fig. 82 is designed for press-fit mounting. This package is used for many medium-current (10-15 amperes), and some 25 ampere, triacs. Fig. 83 shows a stud-mounted form of triac in which the stud serves as the anode connection. The unit in Fig. 84 has an anode terminal and isolated stud. Stud types are available in currents up to 25 amperes. All the triacs shown have voltage ratings of 200-500 volts.

Fig. 81. *Silicone plastic triac unit for currents to 10 amperes. (Courtesy of General Electric Co.).*

Fig. 83. *Triac with mounting stud as anode terminal. (Courtesy of General Electric Co.).*

Fig. 82. *Press-fit form of triac used in 10-25 ampere range. (Courtesy of General Electric Co.).*

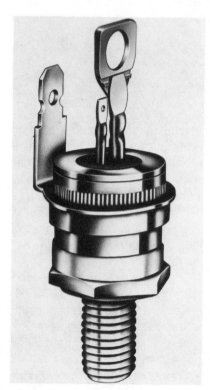

Fig. 84. *Stud-mounted triac with separate anode terminal. (Courtesy of General Electric Co.).*

Construction of the Triac

The triac is essentially two four-layer switches in parallel—a PNPN and an NPNP. One form of construction is illustrated in Fig. 85. A similar sketch showing electrode terminals is given in Fig. 86. Also shown is the triac symbol, consisting of back-to-back SCR's and a gate lead—suggesting the bilateral function of the triac. Since the triac conducts in both directions, the terminals are designated by numbers instead of names as in the SCR. Terminal 1 is used as the reference terminal for measurement and circuit-diagram purposes. Fig. 87(A) shows the NPNP switch structure and Fig. 87(B) the PNPN switch.

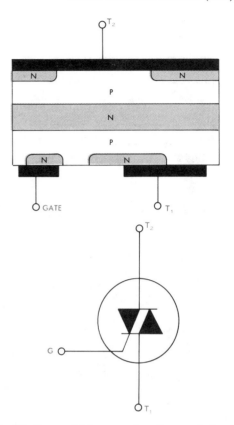

Fig. 86. *Form of triac construction and circuit symbol.*

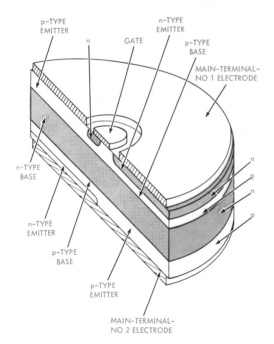

Fig. 85. *Cross-section of a typical triac pellet. (Courtesy of RCA Corp.).*

Operation of the Triac

When potential is applied to a triac, making terminal T_2 positive and terminal T_1 negative, operation is in the first quadrant of the volt-ampere characteristic given in Fig. 88. This characteristic shows voltage and current changes without a gate signal. Turn-on is accomplished by the applied voltage. When this voltage reaches the breakover value (V_{BR}) the PNPN section switches on and electron flow is from Terminal T_1 to terminal T_2. As the triac conducts, current rises from the switching level to a value de-

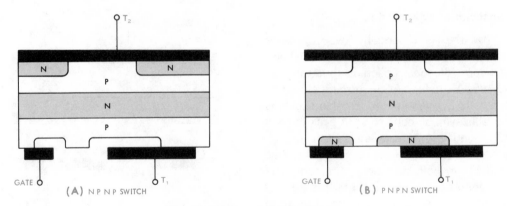

Fig. 87. *Triac switch structures.*

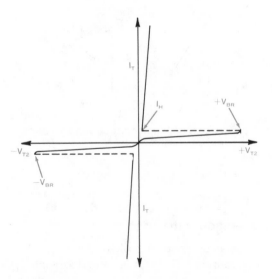

Fig. 88. *Triac volt-ampere characteristic.*

termined by the supply voltage and load impedance. The voltage across the triac drops from the breakover point to a low conduction value. As shown by the characteristic curve, the conduction voltage re-mains almost constant as the current increases.

When the applied potential reverses polarity, making terminal T_2 negative and terminal T_1 positive, operation is in the third quadrant. As the voltage across the triac reaches $-V_{BR}$, the NPNP section conducts and electrons now flow from terminal T_2 to terminal T_1. Although the polarity of the voltage and the direction of the current are reversed, the variations in voltage and current are the same as in the first quadrant. The third-quadrant curve is a mirror image of the first-quadrant curve.

Normal operation of a triac requires that the device be triggered into conduction by a gate signal. Consequently, a triac and its supply voltage must be matched so that the supply voltage does not peak at a value equal to, or greater than, the triac break-over voltage. If the triac is triggered by the terminal potential it conducts until the current decreases below the holding value (I_H). (This turn-on action usually protects the triac from the effects of damaging voltage transients.)

When correct voltage is applied to a triac (less than V_{BR}) the device is turned on by a gate signal, as in SCR control. However, because of its unique structure, the triac can be triggered by a positive or negative gate signal in either the first or third quadrant. This capability allows for four polarity configurations:

1. Quadrant I: T_1-, T_2+, gate $+$
2. Quadrant I: T_1-, T_2+, gate $-$
3. Quadrant III: T_1+, T_2-, gate $-$
4. Quadrant III: T_1+, T_2-, gate $+$

The triac operates efficiently in the first three configurations. The fourth is used only in special applications. Fig. 89 shows operation of a triac in the first and third quadrants for two values of gate current. Operation in the first quadrant is similar to SCR operation (T_2 positive). In the third quadrant T_2 is negative.

If an alternating voltage is applied to the triac with gate current, I_{G1}, flowing, the triac operates as shown in quadrant I during one half-cycle (T_2+) and in quadrant III during the alternate half-cycle (T_2-). When the applied voltage reaches V_{BR1} the triac triggers on. The voltage across the triac drops to the conducting value and the current increases rapidly. On the alternate half cycle the triac triggers and conducts in the opposite direction when the applied voltage reaches $-V_{BR1}$. If the gate current is increased the triac turns on at a lower breakover voltage. When I_{G2} flows the triac conducts at V_{BR2}. In this manner the gate signal controls triac conduction.

Since triac triggering can be accomplished when terminal T_2 is positive or negative by either positive or negative gate signals, such signals can be provided from several sources, such as an ac or dc supply, unijunction transistor, diac or silicon bilateral switch.

Triac Commutation (Turn-Off)

When back-to-back SCR's are used to control ac circuits each SCR has a half cycle in which to turn off. However, the triac must turn off in a much shorter time— when the current goes to zero. Actually, with a resistive load, the time for turn-off starts when the current drops below the holding level and continues until the next half cycle of applied voltage reaches the breakover value. In most applications this is sufficient time.

With an inductive load, triac commutation is affected by the inductively-produced phase shift. The triac current approaches zero after the applied voltage changes polarity. When the current reaches zero and the triac tries to turn off, a rapidly-increasing voltage appears across the terminals. The rate of voltage rise (dv/dt) is sometimes sufficient to fire the triac during this time. The dv/dt factor is aided by an exces-

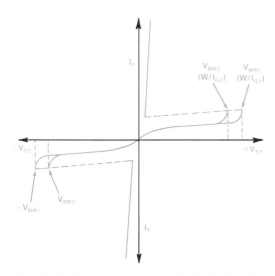

Fig. 89. *Volt-ampere characteristic of triac for two values of gate current.*

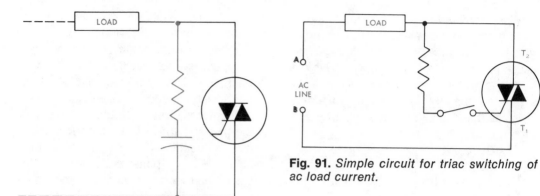

Fig. 91. *Simple circuit for triac switching of ac load current.*

Fig. 90. *RC circuit improves triac switching.*

sive, short-duration reverse current, called recovery current, which flows at this time (immediately after the forward current reaches zero.) Thus, the current lag created by an inductive load can interfere with the switching of a triac.

To improve switching performance an RC snubber circuit can be used, as shown in Fig. 90. The resistor limits the discharge of the capacitor when the triac conducts and also limits the ringing (overshoot) of the LC circuit (load and capacitor). Values of 0.1 μF and 100 ohms will generally limit the triac dv/dt factor to about one volt per microsecond for most inductive loads. Manufacturers recommend that, in addition to utilizing RC snubbers, triacs be selected which have dv/dt ratings of at least two volts per microsecond. Many commercially-available triacs (5- 10- 15-ampere units) have dv/dt ratings of four volts per microsecond. Some 25-ampere triacs have ratings of five volts per microsecond.

Applications of the Triac

The ease with which a triac can be used to control a large ac load current is illus-

trated in Fig. 91. The switch could be replaced by a microswitch, magnetic-reed switch or other small switching device. When the switch is closed and line terminal A is positive, both T_2 and the gate are positive. The triac triggers on and allows current through the load. During the alternate half-cycle, when T_2 and the gate are negative, the triac conducts in the opposite direction. In this manner a miniature device can be used to switch a high-current ac circuit.

A triac circuit which allows for half-power and full-power operation is shown in Fig. 92. With the switch in the off position no gate current flows, the triac is in the blocking state and there is no load current. When the switch is in position 1 the triac operates as in Fig. 91, conducting on both half cycles. With the switch in position 2 the diode allows gate current only during the half cycle when line A is positive. When line A is negative the diode blocks gate current and the triac is turned off. Thus the load operates at half power when the switch is in position 2.

DC control of a triac is illustrated in Fig. 93. During one half-cycle this circuit operates in the first quadrant of the triac char-

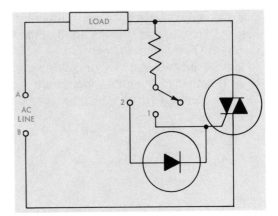

Fig. 92. *Triac circuit for full- and half-power operation.*

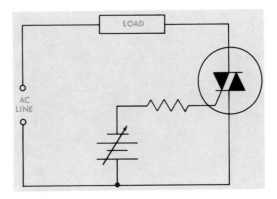

Fig. 93. *DC triac triggering.*

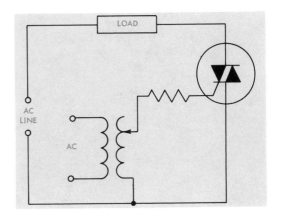

Fig. 94. *Variable ac triggering of triac.*

acteristic (T_2+, gate$-$). During the alternate half cycle operation is in the third quadrant (T_2-, gate$-$).

Fig. 94 shows variable ac-triggering of a triac. If both load and gate supplies are the same frequency, such as 60 Hz, they can be phased to avoid the gate being positive when T_2 is negative. This mode of operation is not recommended, except for special purposes. Phasing to produce like polarities at T_2 and the gate assures proper operation.

Unit 3

section 7 Pulse-Triggering

To limit SCR conduction to less than a quarter-cycle, triggering must occur when the anode voltage is between 90° and 180° of the conducting half-cycle. This can be accomplished by using a pulse of gate current to trigger the SCR. With proper timing, a gate-current pulse can start SCR conduction at any desired point over practically the full 180° range of the conducting half-cycle.

Gate-pulse triggering of SCR's and triacs has other advantages. In many applications, wherein the gate-current source is a dc supply or the anode supply, gate current continues to flow after conduction has started, causing unnecessary power dissipation which can overheat the gate junction. Prevention of overheating can be accomplished by using a pulse of gate current which flows for a short time—just long enough for triggering.

Variations in gating requirements between units can usually be overcome by overdriving with strong pulses. Where capacitors are used in trigger-control circuits, the trigger energy can be stored slowly. Consequently, control-circuit power can be comparatively low.

Trigger pulses for SCR's and triacs can be provided by a number of small, low-cost, low-power semiconductor devices, such as: unijunction transistor (UJT), silicon unilateral switch (SUS), silicon bilateral switch (SBS), bilateral trigger diode (diac) etc. These devices will be described and illustrated in sections which follow.

Unit 3

section  Unijunction
Transistor (UJT)

The unijunction transistor is a simple and versatile semiconductor device. When used to trigger an SCR gate it can also serve as a step-up device between low-level signals and the SCR. Output from photocells, thermocouples and other transducers can be used to trigger UJT's which, in turn, fire SCR's. Used in this manner, UJT's make possible turn-on power gains of billions—microvolt signals controlling hundreds of watts of load power. UJT's are also used in oscillators, timers and voltage- and current-sensing applications.

Several features of the UJT make it an important semiconductor device. It has low trigger current and stable trigger voltage, relatively high pulse-current capability and low cost. It has a negative-resistance characteristic which permits its use in oscillators and bistable circuits.

Construction of the UJT

The unijunction transistor is a three-terminal, single-junction device which is quite different from the conventional two-junction transistor. As illustrated in Fig. 95(A), a small bar of N-type silicon is mounted on a ceramic base. Leads are attached to each end of the bar. These are called the base 1 (B_1) and base 2 (B_2) connections. A rectifying contact is formed by alloying an aluminum wire into the bar near the base 2 connection. This contact becomes the PN emitter junction.

Another form of UJT construction is illustrated in Fig. 95(B). The N-type silicon is shaped into a cube and mounted on a gold-plated base. The base 2 connection is at the junction of the cube and the base. A wire alloyed into the upper surface of the cube becomes the base 1 connection. The

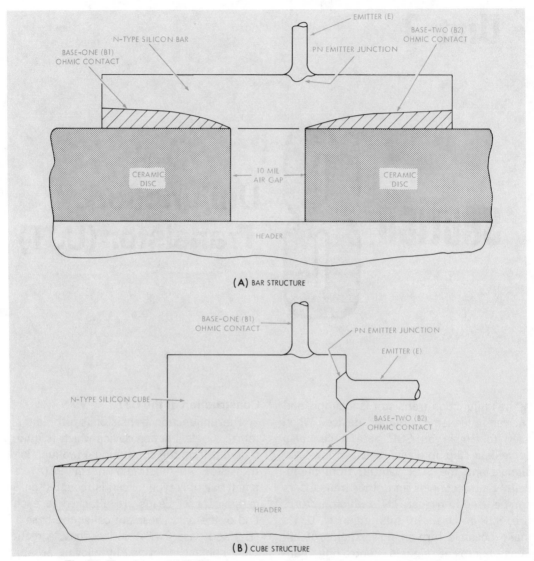

Fig. 95. *Two forms of UJT construction. (Courtesy of General Electric Co.).*

PN emitter junction is formed by alloying an aluminum lead into the side of the cube. This form of construction results in a number of good features, such as: low peak-point current, short turn-on time, low val-ley current, low operating voltage and good pulse output for triggering SCR's.

Operation of the UJT

The circuit symbol and equivalent circuit

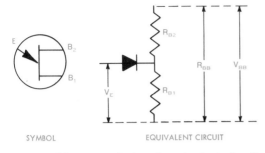

SYMBOL   EQUIVALENT CIRCUIT

Fig. 96. *Circuit symbol and equivalent circuit of unijunction transistor. (UJT).*

of the UJT are given in Fig. 96. The direction of the arrow in the symbol indicates a P-type emitter and N-type base. The equivalent circuit shows the interbase resistance (resistance of the pellet) divided into two parts, R_{B2} and R_{B1}. The interbase resistance (R_{BB}) is usually between 4-10 kilohms. V_{BB} is the interbase voltage and V_E signifies the applied emitter potential.

In operation, when no emitter current is flowing the UJT acts like a simple voltage divider. The fraction of V_{BB} which appears across R_{B1} is known as the "intrinsic standoff ratio" (η). This ratio (usually between 0.45 and 0.85) determines the emitter firing voltage for a constant interbase voltage.

If a positive potential (V_E) applied to the emitter is less than ηV_{BB} (the voltage across R_{B1}) the emitter junction is reverse-biased and only a small leakage current flows through the junction. When the emitter voltage is greater than ηV_{BB} the junction is forward-biased and a forward current flows through the emitter-base 1 circuit. Holes are injected into the silicon at the junction and electrons move upward through R_{B1}. The abundance of carriers through R_{B1} effectively reduces its resistance. This, in turn, changes the voltage-divider propor-

tions, thereby reducing the emitter-to-base 1 voltage.

The relationship between the decreasing voltage and increasing current is the negative-resistance characteristic. This is shown by the maximum-to-minimum slope of the emitter characteristic curve given in Fig. 97. The base 1 resistance of a typical UJT can decrease from about 4500 ohms at zero emitter current to about 50 ohms at an emitter current of 50 milliamperes.

Two important points on the UJT characteristic curve are the "peak point" and "valley point." The peak-point emitter voltage (V_P) is the potential at which the UJT triggers on. Peak-point current (I_P) is the minimum emitter current required for triggering. Valley voltage (V_V) and valley current (I_V) are the values at the point where R_{B1} ceases to be negative. Beyond the valley point the UJT saturates and R_{B1} becomes positive. The portion of the curve to the left of the peak point is the cutoff region, where the emitter voltage is not sufficient to fire the UJT. During cutoff the emitter junction is reverse-biased and only leakage current (I_{EO}) flows.

To obtain "flip-flop" operation the UJT emitter can be biased at a point in the cutoff region and a pulse applied to produce operation through the negative-resistance portion of the characteristic to a point in the saturated region. Operation will remain at this point until the pulse decays and the emitter junction is again reverse-biased. Thus the application of repetitive pulses to a UJT can produce operation in two stable states (flip-flop action).

Applications of the UJT

For triggering purposes the UJT is usually combined with an RC unit to form a relaxation oscillator, as illustrated in Fig. 98. When the switch is closed the dc supply

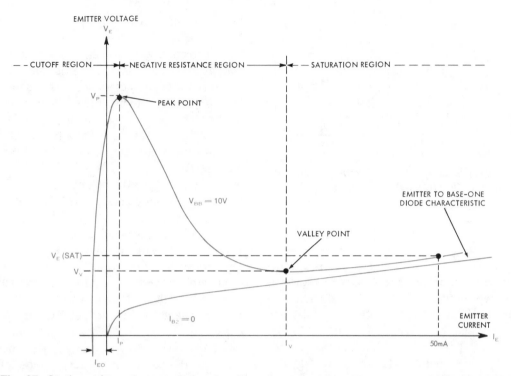

EMITTER VOLTAGE
V_E

— – CUTOFF REGION —— ←— NEGATIVE RESISTANCE REGION ——→ ←— SATURATION REGION — — — — — — —

V_P —

PEAK POINT

$V_{BB} = 10V$

EMITTER TO BASE–ONE
DIODE CHARACTERISTIC

VALLEY POINT

V_E (SAT)—

V_V —

$I_{B2} = 0$

EMITTER
CURRENT

I_P

I_V

50mA

I_E

I_{EO}

Fig. 97. *Static emitter characteristic of unijunction transistor. (Courtesy of General Electric Co.).*

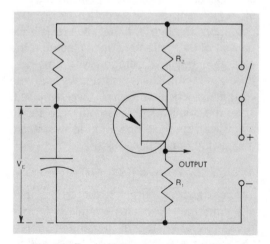

R_2

V_E

OUTPUT

R_1

+

—

Fig. 98. *Basic UJT relaxation oscillator.*

charges the capacitor. Charge time is determined by the resistance and capacitance values. When the charge voltage across the capacitor (which is also V_E) reaches V_P (peak-point emitter voltage) the UJT turns on. As it conducts it allows the capacitor to discharge through R_1. Fast discharge through the low resistance of R_1 (perhaps 50 ohms or less) creates a pulse of voltage across this resistor.

When the capacitor discharges to the point where V_E reaches a certain minimum value, typically two volts, the UJT turns off, the capacitor starts to recharge and a new cycle begins. This action continues until the

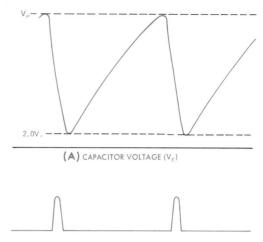

Fig. 99. *Sawtooth and output-pulse waveforms produced by UJT relaxation oscillator.*

(**A**) CAPACITOR VOLTAGE (V$_E$)

(**B**) OUTPUT PULSE (V$_{R1}$)

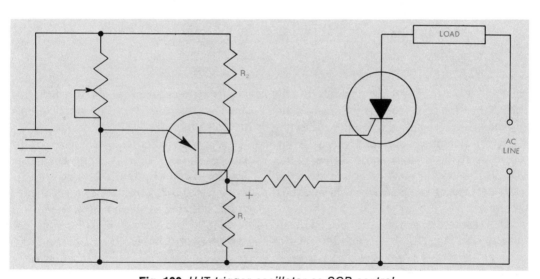

Fig. 100. *UJT trigger oscillator as SCR control.*

switch is opened. Fig. 99(A) shows the sawtooth-voltage waveform produced by the relaxation oscillator. The output-pulse waveform is shown in Fig. 99(B).

Fig. 100 shows UJT control of an SCR. Adjustment of the variable resistance determines the time constant of the RC combination. This, in turn, sets the oscillator fre-

179

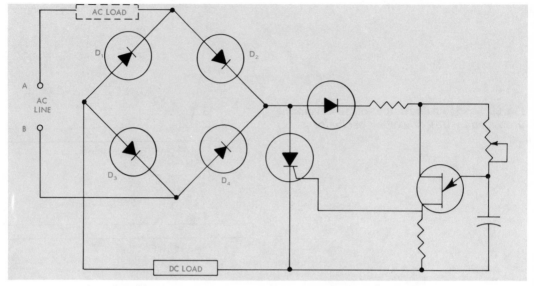

Fig. 101. *UJT triggering of full-wave SCR control circuit.*

quency, which is the triggering rate of the UJT. When the capacitor charge reaches the V_P value and discharges through R_1 and the UJT, the potential developed across R_1 is negative at the bottom and positive at the top. This places a positive potential at the SCR gate, firing the SCR when its anode is positive.

UJT control of a full-wave circuit is illustrated in Fig. 101. When line terminal A is negative and B is positive, load current flows through diode D_1, the dc load, the SCR and diode D_4, to terminal B. The point

in this half-cycle at which the SCR conducts is determined by the application of the pulse from the UJT control circuit.

During the alternate half-cycle of line voltage, current flow is from terminal B through diode D_3, the DC load, the SCR and diode D_2, to terminal A. Again, the UJT circuit determines the amount of SCR conduction. In this manner a UJT can be used in control of full-wave direct current. This circuit can also be used for full-wave ac control by connecting the ac load as indicated in Fig. 101.

Unit 3

section 9

Silicon Unilateral Switch (SUS)

The SUS is a simple form of integrated circuit used primarily in triggering and timing applications. It is basically a small SCR with an anode gate. The equivalent circuit, shown in Fig. 102, consists of two transistors, a diode and a resistor. The SUS symbol is also shown.

Since the transistor configuration in Fig. 102 is the same as that in the SCR equivalent circuit (Fig. 67) the SUS is comparable to a small SCR with a breakdown diode from gate to cathode, as illustrated in Fig. 103.

Operation of the SUS

Operation of the SUS is similar to operation of the SCR. This is indicated by the similarity between the SUS volt-ampere

181

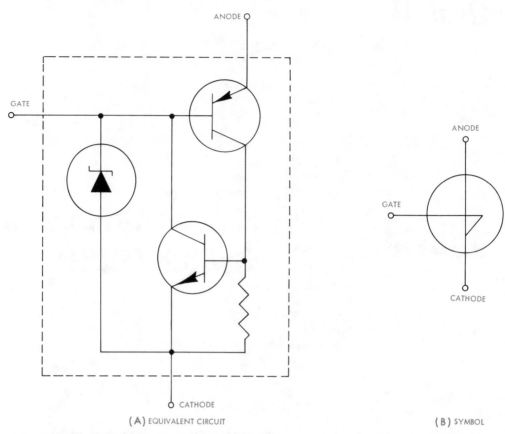

(A) EQUIVALENT CIRCUIT   (B) SYMBOL

Fig. 102. *Equivalent circuit and circuit symbol of silicon unilateral switch. (SUS).*

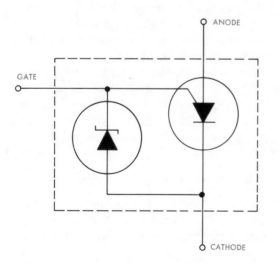

Fig. 103. *SCR-diode equivalent of SUS.*

characteristic (Fig. 104) and the SCR characteristic (Fig. 70).

A typical SUS is in the off state when the applied potential (positive anode, negative cathode) is less than six volts. (Most available units have switching voltages between six and ten volts). When the SUS is in the off state the resistor provides a path for leakage current. In this state the breakdown diode does not conduct because the potential across it is less than its breakdown value.

If the anode-to-cathode voltage is increased to the rated switching value of the SUS, the breakdown diode starts to conduct. When the diode conducts, base current flows in the PNP transistor, turning it on. The NPN transistor also turns on. Both transistors saturate, providing a "closed switch" from anode to cathode. This action is like the turn-on action of the SCR.

The SUS volt-ampere characteristic given in Fig. 104 shows switching at $7\frac{1}{2}$ volts (V_s). At this time the current rises from a minimum (leakage) to the switching value (I_s). (Leakage current is usually less than one μA and switching current between 150 and 500 μA.) The voltage across the SUS drops to its conduction value, (V_F), called the forward voltage—generally about 1.5

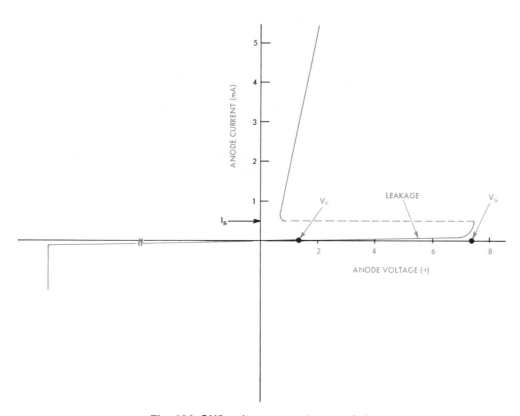

Fig. 104. *SUS volt-ampere characteristic.*

volts. The current changes from the switching value to a level determined by the supply voltage and the load. The maximum continuous forward current of a typical SUS is about 200 mA. The maximum peak recurrent value is about one ampere for a 10 microsecond pulse on a one percent duty cycle. The holding current (minimum required to maintain conduction) ranges from about 0.5 to 1.5 mA.

After the SUS starts to conduct it can only be turned off by reversing the anode voltage or disconnecting the supply. Reversing the anode voltage reverse-biases the emitter-base junction of the PNP transistor, thereby preventing conduction. (The maximum reverse-voltage rating of most available SUS's is 30 volts.) When a reverse potential is applied to an SUS in order to return it to the blocking state, the device must be held at a negative value or zero for a certain minimum time before a positive potential can be reapplied to the anode. This is known as turn-off time and is in the range of five to ten microseconds, depending on circuit-current level.

Applications of the SUS

An application of the SUS is shown in Fig. 105. Here it is used to reshape a pulse to a form more suitable for fast, positive triggering of an SCR. As the voltage of the input pulse increases gradually the capacitor charges. When the charge voltage reaches the turn-on level of the SUS it conducts, allowing the capacitor to discharge quickly through the SUS and resistor R_1. The discharge action develops a fast-rising voltage across the resistor. This becomes the output pulse which is used to trigger an SCR.

As a triggering device the SUS is generally used in a relaxation-oscillator circuit, as illustrated in Fig. 106. When the charge on the capacitor reaches the switching voltage of the SUS, the SUS turns on and the capacitor discharges through R_2. The pulse of voltage developed across R_2 fires the SCR during half-cycles when the SCR anode is positive. During negative half-cycles diode D_1 protects the SUS and the SCR gate circuit from the effects of reverse potential.

A pulse transformer can be used to isolate the SUS trigger generator from the SCR gate circuit. This is shown in Fig. 107. When the voltage across the capacitor turns on the SUS, a pulse of capacitor-discharge

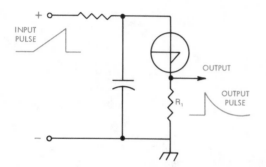

Fig. 105. *Application of SUS in pulse-shaping circuit.*

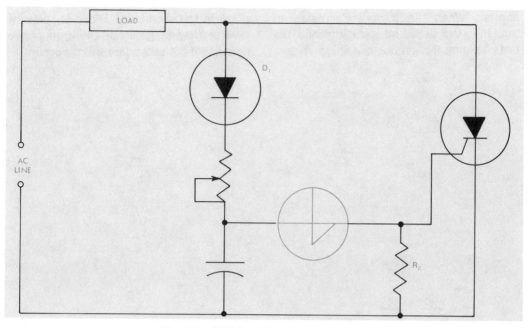

Fig. 106. *SUS in SCR trigger circuit.*

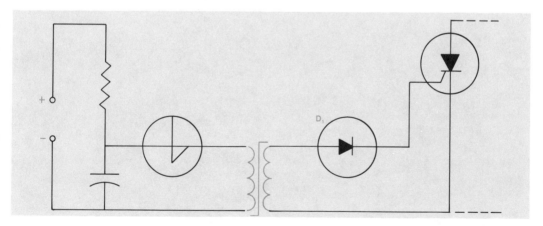

Fig. 107. *Pulse transformer isolates SUS trigger generator from SCR gate circuit.*

current flows through the primary of the transformer.

A good pulse output from the secondary is assured because of the special construction of the core. A pulse-transformer core saturates quickly when current flows in the primary. When the current decreases to zero the core desaturates rapidly and the fast-changing flux produces a sharp voltage pulse in the secondary. Diode D_1 prevents reverse flow of gate current if ringing or reversal of the secondary voltage occurs.

Unit 3

section 10

Silicon Bilateral Switch (SBS)

The SBS is an integrated circuit which is useful for phase-triggering SCR's controlling ac loads. It can also be used as a phase control for the triac.

Construction of the SBS

The SBS consists of two unilateral switches connected "inverse-parallel," as illustrated by the equivalent circuit in Fig. 108. (The circuit symbol is also shown in this figure.)

The anode of one switch and the cathode of the other are connected together as one SBS anode. The remaining unilateral anode and cathode are connected as the other bilateral anode. Just as the SUS is equivalent to a small SCR with a breakdown diode from gate to cathode, the SBS is com-

parable to a pair of small inverse-parallel SCR's with a common gate lead and gate-to-cathode breakdown diodes. This equivalent circuit is shown in Fig. 109.

Operation of the SBS

Since the SBS is essentially a pair of inverse-parallel SUS's, it can respond to an alternating driving voltage and provide both positive and negative outputs. This full-cycle operation is illustrated by the volt-ampere characteristic curve given in Fig. 110. As indicated by the curve, the variation in SBS current as a function of anode voltage is the same during both half-cycles.

When anode 1 in Fig. 108 is positive, switch A is reverse-biased and does not conduct. However, when the positive potential

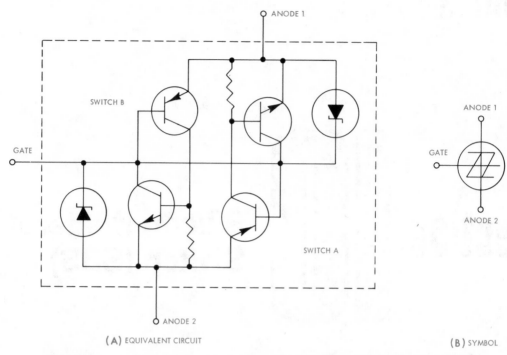

(A) EQUIVALENT CIRCUIT

(B) SYMBOL

Fig. 108. *Equivalent circuit and circuit symbol of silicon bilateral switch (SBS).*

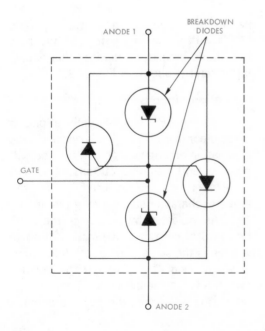

Fig. 109. *SCR-diode equivalent of SBS.*

188

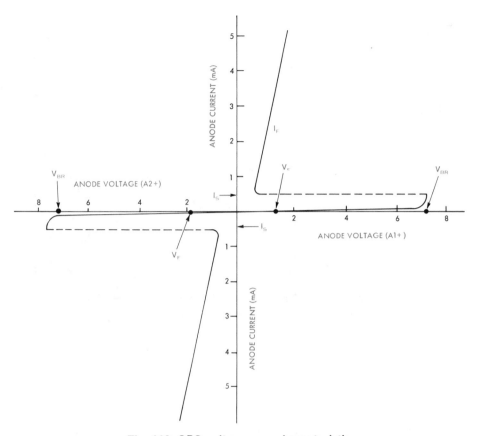

Fig. 110. *SBS volt-ampere characteristic.*

at anode 1 increases to the breakover value, switch B conducts.

During the alternate half-cycle when anode 1 is negative and anode 2 is positive switch B turns off. Switch A conducts when the applied potential reaches the breakover level. The volt-ampere characteristic shows that, as each switch turns on, the current increases to the switching value and then changes to a conduction value. The anode-to-anode voltage decreases to the conducting level. The SBS can be switched on when the anode voltage is less than the breakover value with a signal to the gate.

The electrical specifications of the bilateral switch are generally the same as those of the unilateral switch except for the forward voltage. This may be a little higher for the SBS—about 1.7 volts. Also, since the SBS conducts in both directions, it does not have a reverse-voltage rating.

Applications of the SBS

The SBS can be used in control of SCR's and triacs. In Fig. 111 an SBS is part of a relaxation oscillator controlling the conduction of an SCR. When the capacitor voltage reaches the switching value of the SBS the

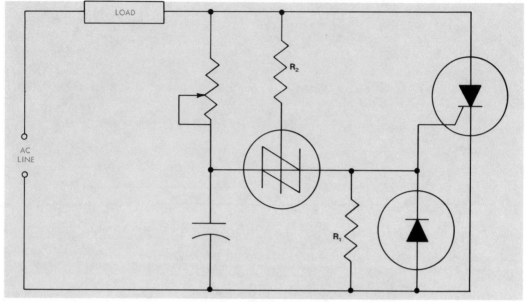

Fig. 111. *SCR controlled by SBS trigger oscillator.*

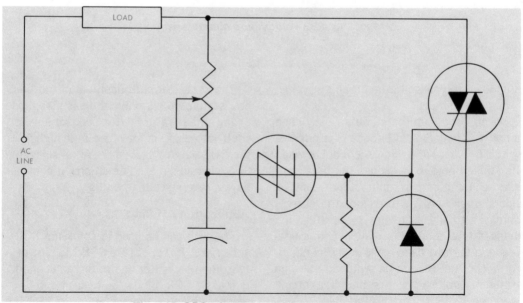

Fig. 112. *SBS trigger oscillator control of triac.*

SBS turns on. The capacitor discharges through resistor R_1 and the SBS. The pulse of voltage developed across R_1 turns on the SCR. The point in the conducting half-cycle (anode positive) at which the SCR conducts depends on the time constant of the RC combination. Since this is dependent on the setting of the variable resistance, SCR turn-on time is adjustable.

In Fig. 106 a high-voltage diode was used to protect the SUS and the SCR gate circuit during the non-conducting half-cycle (SCR anode negative). In Fig. 111 the SBS does not require this protection. It is a bilateral switch which can turn on in response to reverse voltage, thereby protecting itself. However, the SCR gate needs protection from the reverse voltage. This is provided by the diode from gate to cathode. This diode can be a less-expensive, lower-voltage type than that required in the SUS circuit.

The SBS gate is connected to the anode line through resistor R_2 to assure triggering of the SBS each time the line goes negative. This eliminates any hysteresis which might otherwise develop as the SBS switches on and off during alternate half-cycles.

SBS control of a triac is illustrated in Fig. 112. Since both triac and SBS conduct on both half-cycles of the supply voltage, these units work very well together in controlling the amount of full-wave current through an ac load. Operation from off to full-on is possible with this circuit. Turn-on time for each half-cycle is adjusted by the variable resistance. Since the SBS switches in both directions at approximately the same voltage, the angle between switching times of the two half cycles is close to 180°.

Unit 3

section 11

Bilateral Trigger Diode (Diac)

A rather simple form of triggering device is the bilateral trigger diode, commonly called a *diac*. It can be used in conjunction with a triac to form a full-wave ac control.

Construction of the Diac

The diac is a two-terminal semiconductor unit which can carry current in either direction—hence the name "diac" (di-ode ac). As the symbol (Fig. 113) suggests, the diac is similar in construction to the transistor. The symbol indicates an NPN structure.

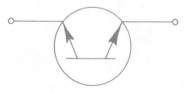

Fig. 113. *Diac circuit symbol.*

Operation of the Diac

When a potential is applied across a diac it does not conduct until the potential reaches the breakover value of the device—V_{BR} in Fig. 114. (The type ST2 diac manufactured by the General Electric Co. has a breakover voltage of 28 to 36 volts.) When turn-on occurs, current through the diac increases from leakage to the breakover level—I_{BR}. (Maximum breakover current of the type ST2 diac is 200 μA.).

After breakover, the voltage across the diac decreases but not as rapidly as the voltage across the SUS or SBS. As the diac conducts it exhibits negative resistance (as current increases voltage decreases). The negative slope of the characteristic curve (Fig. 114) indicates that the negative-resis-

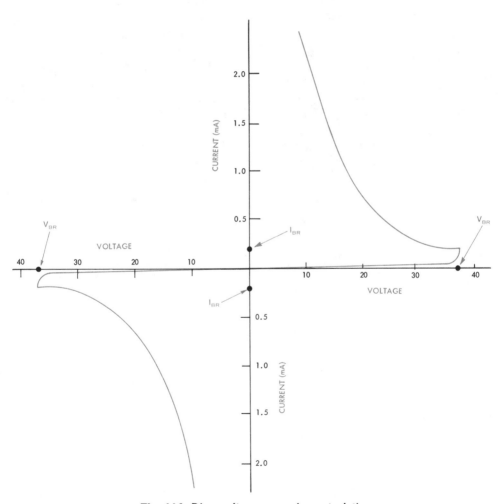

Fig. 114. *Diac volt-ampere characteristic.*

tance property of the diac extends over the full operating range. Since the current increases from the breakover level to a higher conduction value directly, the diac does not have a holding current requirement (minimum current necessary for conduction).

According to the characteristic, operation is the same when the polarity of the applied voltage is reversed. Operating and switching currents and breakover voltage are the same in both directions; therefore the device is a symmetrical bilateral diode. Since the diac is a bilateral device it can be used with an ac supply to provide an alternating output.

Applications of the Diac

One of the simplest full-wave ac controls consists of a diac trigger circuit and a triac. Such a control is shown in Fig. 115. As in other relaxation-oscillator circuits, when the charge on the capacitor reaches the diac breakover voltage, the diac switches on and

the capacitor discharges through the triac gate circuit and the diac. The charge time, and consequently the turn-on time in each half cycle, is determined by the setting of the variable resistance. To improve triac commutation when the load is inductive, a resistor-capacitor combination (RC snubber) can be connected across the triac (as shown in Fig. 115).

The circuit in Fig. 115 exhibits a hysteresis effect, which can cause the triac to trigger before the desired turn-on time. Such early turn-on does not allow for small conduction angles. This disadvantage can be minimized by constructing the trigger circuit with a double time constant as shown in Fig. 116. Because it has reduced hysteresis this circuit can be adjusted to trigger triac conduction over a wide range—from small angles to full-on. If the load is a universal motor its speed can be varied from minimum to maximum.

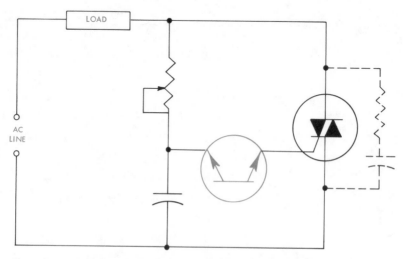

Fig. 115. *Triac controlled by diac trigger circuit.*

194

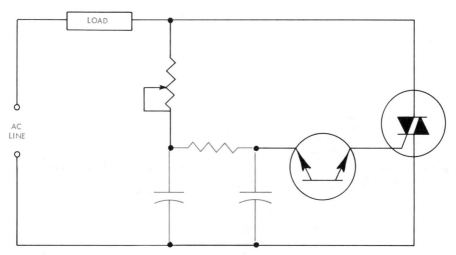

Fig. 116. *Double RC circuit provides greater control range for triac controlled by diac trigger.*

Unit 3

section 12

Laboratory Procedures

The laboratory procedures outlined in this Section assume that the student has access to the devices and equipment listed for each experiment, is familiar with basic circuits and circuit diagrams, and performs the work under the supervision of an instructor.

Some of the devices and circuits require 120 V ac. Adequate precautions should be observed.

Mercury-Vapor Rectifier: Basic Operation

Purpose: To study basic operation of a mercury-vapor rectifier.

Devices and Equipment: Rectifier, mercury-vapor, (866A or equivalent); transformer, filament, 2.5 V, 5 A, for 866A; power supply, 0-200 V dc; VTVM; 2 switches, SPST; load resistance—to be determined.

Procedure:
1. Study specifications and ratings of selected rectifier.
2. Determine a load resistance which will limit tube current to rated average value or less at selected maximum supply voltage. Examples: for 866A, using a 200 V supply: 2 kΩ, 40 W; 5 kΩ, 20 W; 8 k Ω, 12 W; 10 kΩ, 10 W.
3. Wire circuit as shown in Fig. 117. Have wiring approved.
4. Set anode supply voltage at zero. Close switch S_F (S_A open).
5. After recommended warm-up time (866A—30 seconds) close switch S_A.
6. Adjust anode supply voltage to low value (below firing potential). Measure and record tube and load voltages.
7. Connect VTVM across tube. Increase anode supply voltage until tube fires. Record firing voltage and tube voltage after firing (arc drop).

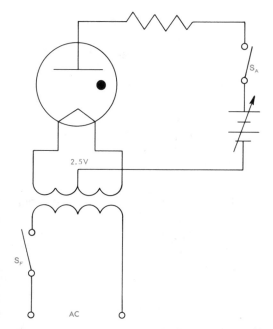

Fig. 117. *Mercury-vapor rectifier dc test circuit.*

mer, filament, 2.5 V, 5 A, for 866A; oscilloscope; load resistance—to be determined.

Procedure:
1. Study specifications and ratings of selected rectifier.
2. Determine a load resistance which will limit tube current to rated average value or less with 120 V ac supply. Examples: for 866A: 1 kΩ, 30 W; 2 kΩ, 20 W.
3. Wire circuit as shown in Fig. 118. Have wiring approved.
4. Close switch S_F to preheat filament (S_A open).
5. Connect scope across ac line. Adjust waveform to one or two cycles.
6. Connect scope across tube. Close switch S_A and record tube-voltage waveform.

8. Measure load voltage and calculate anode-load current. Record values.
9. For several values of supply voltage record arc drop, load voltage and current.
10. Change load and repeat step 9.
11. Write a statement describing operation of a mercury-vapor rectifier in terms of firing potential, arc drop and load variation.

Mercury-Vapor Rectifier: Half-Wave Operation

Purpose: To study operation of half-wave mercury-vapor rectifier circuit.
Devices and Equipment: Rectifier, mercury-vapor (866A or equivalent); transfor-

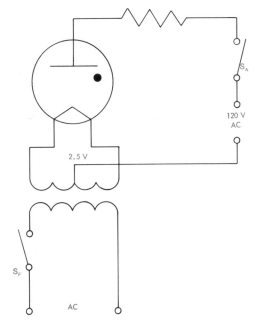

Fig. 118. *Half-wave mercury-vapor rectifier circuit.*

7. Open switch S_A and connect scope across load.
8. Close switch and record load-voltage waveform.
9. Write a statement describing operation of a half-wave mercury-vapor rectifier. Explain waveforms.

Thyratron: Basic Operation

Purpose: To study basic operation of a thyratron and develop a grid-control characteristic.

Devices and Equipment: Thyratron (884); filament supply, 6.3 V, 1 A, ac; power supply 0-300 V dc; power supply, 0-24 V dc; 2 VTVMs; milliammeter, 0-100 mA dc; resistor, 100 kΩ, ½ W; resistor, 3-4 kΩ, 40-30 W.

Procedure:
1. Study specifications and ratings of thyratron.
2. Wire circuit as shown in Fig. 119. Connect VTVMs grid-to-cathode and anode-to-cathode. Have wiring approved.
3. Set anode supply voltage at zero and preheat cathode (884 - 10 seconds minimum).
4. Set grid voltage at −20 volts. Increase

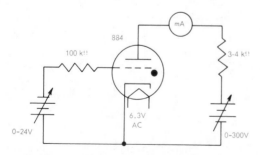

Fig. 119. *Thyratron dc test circuit.*

anode supply voltage until thyratron fires. Record firing voltage.
5. Record arc drop, load voltage and current.
6. Return anode supply voltage to zero to allow deionization and return of tube control to grid.
7. Repeat steps 4 and 5 at several reduced grid potentials, such as: 17.5 V, 15 V, 12.5 V, 10 V, 7.5 V, 5 V, 2.5 V, 0 V.
8. Plot anode firing voltage as a function of grid voltage.
9. Write a statement describing firing of thyratron in terms of grid and anode potentials.

Thyratron as a Controlled Rectifier

Purpose: To study operation of a thyratron as a controlled rectifier.

Devices and Equipment: Thyratron (884); filament supply, 6.3 V, 1 A, ac; power supply 0-24 V dc; VTVM; milliammeter, 0-100 mA dc; switch, SPST; resistor, 100 kΩ, ½ W; resistor, 3-4 kΩ, 40-30 W; oscilloscope.

Procedure:
1. Study specifications and ratings of thyratron.
2. Wire circuit as shown in Fig. 120. Connect scope across load. Have wiring approved.
3. Preheat cathode (884—10 seconds minimum)—switch S_A open.
4. Set grid voltage at −20 volts. Close switch S_A.
5. Measure and record tube voltage (A to K) and load voltage.
6. Decrease grid voltage until thyratron fires. Record load-voltage waveform.
7. Measure and record tube voltage, load voltage and current.
8. Decrease grid voltage in steps. Record

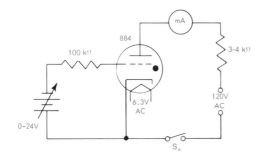

Fig. 120. *Thyratron as controlled half-wave rectifier.*

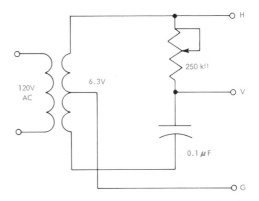

Fig. 121. *Experimental phase-shift circuit.*

corresponding voltage and current readings and waveforms.

9. Write a statement describing operation of thyratron as a grid-controlled rectifier. Explain waveforms.

Phase-Shift Circuit

Purpose: To study operation of a bridge-type RC phase shifter.

Devices and Equipment: Transformer, 117 V / 6.3 V c.t., low-current; potentiometer, 250 kΩ, 2 W; capacitor, 0.1 μF; VTVM; oscilloscope.

Procedure:

1. Wire circuit as shown in Fig. 121. Connect terminal H to scope horizontal input, terminal V to vertical input and terminal G to scope ground. Have wiring approved.
2. Set potentiometer at zero and energize transformer.
3. Record scope pattern and voltage V-G.
4. Step-increase resistance of potentiometer to maximum. Record corresponding V-G voltage values and scope patterns.
5. Write a statement relating recorded scope patterns to operation of phase shifter.

Phase-Shift Control of Thyratron

Purpose: To study control of a thyratron by an RC phase-shift circuit.

Devices and Equipment: Thyratron (884); filament supply, 6.3 V, 1 A, ac; transformer, 117 V / 25-35 V, c.t., low current; potentiometer, 250 kΩ, 2 W; capacitor, 0.1 μF, 50 V; resistor, 100 kΩ, ½ W; resistor, 3-4 kΩ, 40-30 W; VTVM; oscilloscope.

Procedure:

Note: To achieve control, anode and point X on diagram must be of same polarity.

1. Wire circuit as shown in Fig. 122. Connect oscilloscope across load. Have wiring approved.
2. Preheat cathode—10 seconds minimum.
3. Apply anode supply voltage and observe scope. (Control circuit deenergized.)
4. Set potentiometer at zero and energize control transformer.
5. Gradually increases potentiometer resistance to maximum. Record waveform and load voltage at several steps.
6. Write a statement evaluating effectiveness of the phase-shift control circuit.

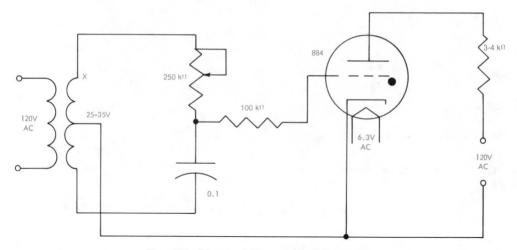

Fig. 122. *Phase-shift control of thyratron.*

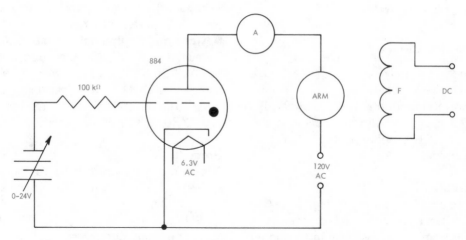

Fig. 123. *Experimental thyratron motor-control circuit.*

Thyratron Application: Motor Control

Purpose: To study application of a thyratron as a motor-control device.

Devices and Equipment: Thyratron (884); filament supply, 6.3 V, 1 A, ac; power supply, 0-24 V dc; small, shunt-type, 100-125 V dc motor; power supply, dc, for motor field; resistor 100 kΩ, ½ W; ammeter, 0-1 A, dc.

Procedure:

1. Wire circuit as shown in Fig. 123. Have wiring approved.

2. Preheat cathode—10 seconds minimum.
3. Apply —20 volts to grid.
4. Apply 120 V ac to anode circuit and rated voltage to motor field, F.
5. Decrease grid voltage until thyratron fires and rotor turns. Do not allow tube current to exceed 0.3 A.
6. Vary grid voltage and note effect on rotor speed.
7. Write a statement describing two practical applications of thyratrons as motor-control devices.

Thyratron Application: Speed Change as Control Signal

Purpose: To observe how speed changes can be utilized by a thyratron to produce desired changes in load operation.

Devices and Equipment: Thyratron (884); filament supply, 6.3 V, 1 A, ac; power supply, 0-24 V dc; small, shunt-type, 100-125 V dc motor; power supply, dc, for motor field; ammeter, 0-1 A, dc; resistor, 100 kΩ,

½ W; tachometer generator, dc (Servo-Tek Products Co. type SA-740A-7); VTVM.

Procedure:
1. Wire circuit as shown in Fig. 124. Have wiring approved.
2. Preheat cathode—10 seconds minimum.
3. Apply —20 volts to grid.
4. Apply 120 V ac to anode circuit and rated voltage to motor field.
5. Set grid voltage so rotor turns at less than maximum speed. Do not allow tube current to exceed 0.3 A.
6. Apply rotational force to tachometer-generator shaft (power drill, rotating wheel, etc.). Monitor generator output voltage. Do not exceed rated output.
7. Vary shaft speed and record effect on rotor speed.
8. Interchange tachometer-generator connections. Apply rotational force and record effect on rotor speed.
9. Write a statement explaining operation of grid-control circuit in steps 7 and 8.

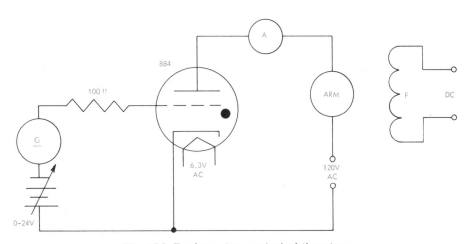

Fig. 124. *Tachometer control of thyratron.*

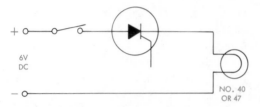

Fig. 125. *Experimental dc SCR circuit.*

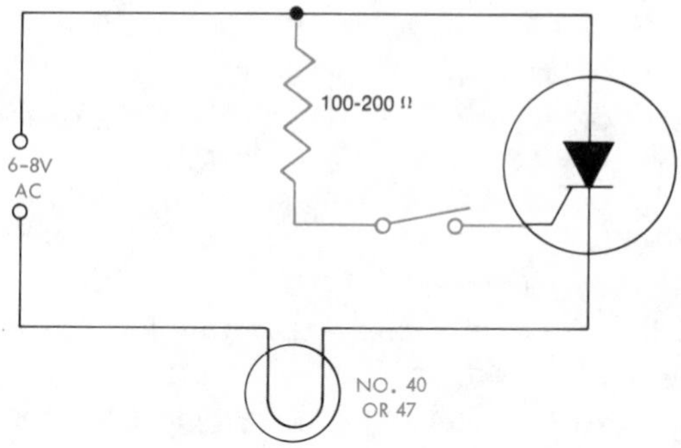

Fig. 126. *Experimental controlled-rectifier circuit.*

Silicon Controlled Rectifier: Basic Operation

Purpose: To study basic operation of a silicon controlled rectifier (SCR).

Devices and Equipment: SCR, low power (2N3228, General Electric GE-X1, Motorola HEP 302, RCA S2600B, or equivalent); power supply, low-voltage, dc; VTVM; switch, SPST; lamp, No. 40 or 47.

Procedure:
1. Study specifications and ratings of selected SCR.
2. Wire circuit as shown in Fig. 125. Have wiring approved.
3. Set supply voltage at 6 volts. Close switch.
4. Record SCR and lamp voltages.
5. Momentarily connect jumper from anode to gate. Remove quickly. Record effect. Record SCR and lamp voltages.
6. Momentarily connect jumper from anode to cathode. Remove quickly. Record effect.
7. Reverse power–supply polarity and test operation.
8. Write a statement explaining observed effects and voltage values.

SCR as Gate-Controlled Rectifier

Purpose: To study operation of an SCR as a controlled rectifier.

Devices and Equipment: SCR, low power (2N3228, General Electric GE-X1, Motorola HEP 302, RCA S2600B, or equivalent); ac supply, 6-8 V; VTVM; switch, SPST; oscilloscope; lamp, No. 40 or 47; resistor, 100-200 ohms.

Procedure:
1. Study specifications and ratings of selected SCR.
2. Wire circuit as shown in Fig. 126. Have wiring approved.
3. Apply ac potential (switch open). Record SCR and lamp voltages.
4. Close switch and note effect. Record SCR and lamp voltages.
5. Open switch and note effect. Check SCR and lamp voltages.
6. Connect oscilloscope across lamp and record waveform.
7. Write a statement describing operation of the SCR as a controlled rectifier.

SCR Operation: DC Anode, DC Gate

Purpose: To study operation of an SCR over a range of anode and gate potentials.
Devices and Equipment: SCR, low power,

(2N3228, General Electric GE-X1, Motorola HEP 302, RCA S2600B, or equivalent); power supply, 0-150 V dc; power supply, low-voltage dc; VTVM; resistor, load, 2-3 kΩ, 10 W; resistor, gate, to be calculated.

Procedure:

1. Study specifications and ratings of selected SCR. Calculate gate resistor which limits gate current to operating value of SCR.
2. Wire circuit as shown in Fig. 127. Have wiring approved.
3. Set gate supply voltage at zero and anode supply voltage at 100 volts. Record voltage across SCR.
4. Increase gate supply voltage slowly until SCR fires.
5. Record voltages across gate resistor, load resistor and SCR.
6. Calculate and record gate and anode currents.
7. Reduce gate and anode supply voltages to zero.
8. Repeat steps 4, 5, and 6 using other anode supply voltages (90, 80, etc.)
9. For several values of gate current determine and record corresponding breakover voltages.
10. Display graphically the data accumulated in step 8.

SCR Operation: AC Anode, DC Gate

Purpose: To study operation of an SCR as a controlled rectifier.

Devices and Equipment: SCR, low power (2N3228, General Electric GE-X1, Motorola HEP 302, RCA S2600B, or equivalent); power supply, low-voltage dc; ac supply, 0-120 V; oscilloscope; VTVM; resistor, load, 2-3 kΩ, 10 W; resistor, gate, to be calculated.

Note: With ac applied to the anode and dc to the gate, gate current flowing when the anode is negative can increase SCR leakage considerably, causing increased power dissipation. This effect can be minimized by operating the SCR well below maximum ratings.

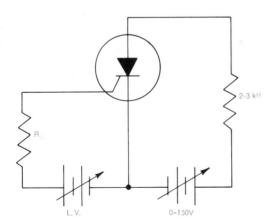

Fig. 127. *Experimental SCR circuit—dc anode, dc gate.*

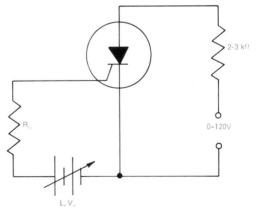

Fig. 128. *Experimental SCR circuit—ac anode, dc gate.*

Procedure:

1. Study specifications and ratings of selected SCR.
2. Calculate gate resistor which limits gate current to operating value of SCR.
3. Wire circuit as shown in Fig. 128. Connect oscilloscope across load. Have wiring approved.
4. Set gate supply voltage at zero and anode supply at 100 volts.
5. Increase gate supply voltage slowly until SCR fires. Observe waveform.
6. Set gate potential for early firing. Determine and record: gate current, load current, load voltage and load waveform.
7. Set gate potential for late firing and repeat step 6.
8. Write a statement explaining the relationship between early and late firings

and corresponding gate and anode parameters.

SCR Application: Motor Control

Purpose: To study application of an SCR as a motor-control device.

Devices and Equipment: SCR, 2N3228 or equivalent; 2 diodes, 1N3755 or equivalent; resistor, 5.6 kΩ, 2 W; potentiometer, 1 kΩ, 2 W; small universal motor; fuse, 4 A; VTVM; oscilloscope.

Note: Circuit suggested in RCA Application Note SMA-34.

Procedure:

1. Wire circuit as shown in Fig. 129. Connect VTVM across load. Have wiring approved.

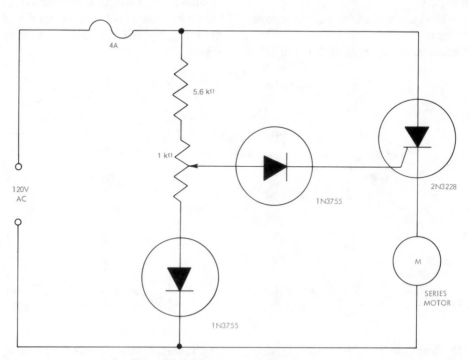

Fig. 129. *SCR motor-control circuit.*

2. Apply line voltage. Vary potentiometer setting. Record speed and voltage changes.
3. Connect oscilloscope across motor. Vary potentiometer setting. Record resulting waveforms of load voltage.
4. Write a statement relating speed, load voltage and waveforms under early and late firing conditions.

Solid-State Motor Control

Purpose: To study circuitry and operation of a commercial solid-state motor control.
Devices and Equipment: Motor control (Heathkit GD 973A (15A), Speedial MK 15 (15A), MK 10 (10A), MK 5 (5A), or equivalent); VTVM; oscilloscope; load: universal motor—current requirement less than control rating.

Procedure:

1. Circuit-trace unit. Sketch layout and circuit diagram.
2. Connect motor to control and VTVM across motor.
3. Apply line voltage and increase speed gradually. Record range of voltage developed across motor.

4. Connect scope across motor. Record low-speed and high-speed waveforms.
5. Load motor shaft and note waveform and load voltage.
6. Apply full line voltage to unloaded motor. Note speed, load voltage and waveform.
7. Write a statement describing operation of motor control at low and high speeds. Compare operation of motor at highest adjustable speed with direct line voltage operation.

Triac: Basic Operation

Purpose: To study operation of a triac in a simple circuit.
Devices and Equipment: Triac (General Electric SC240. GE-X12, RCA 40638, RCA 40485, or equivalent); diode, low-current, silicon; power supply, low-voltage, dc; VTVM; switch, SPST; lamp, No. 40 or 47; resistor, 47 ohm, $\frac{1}{2}$-1 W; ac supply, 6 V.

Procedure:

1. Study specifications and ratings of selected triac.
2. Wire circuit as shown in Fig. 130. Have wiring approved.

Fig. 130. *Experimental basic triac circuit.*

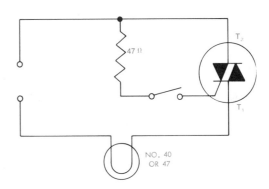

3. Apply 6 volts dc to circuit (switch open).
4. Record triac and lamp voltages.
5. Close switch and note effect. Record triac and lamp voltages.
6. Open switch and change supply polarity. Close switch and record effect.
7. Connect diode in series with gate resistor.
8. Apply 6 volts ac and record effect.
9. Write a statement listing some conclusions about triac triggering and conduction.

Triac Operation: AC Load, DC Trigger

Purpose: To study operation of a triac as a dc-controlled ac switch.
Devices and Equipment: Triac (General Electric SC240, GE-X12, RCA 40638, RCA 40485, or equivalent); power supply, low-voltage, dc; VTVM; resistor, 100 ohm, ½ W; load: lamp, motor, etc.—up to 600 W.

Procedure:
1. Study specifications and ratings of selected triac.
2. Wire circuit as shown in Fig. 131. Connect oscilloscope across load and VTVM from gate to T_1.

3. Set gate supply voltage at zero and apply load-circuit voltage.
4. Increase gate voltage slowly until triac fires.
5. Record gate voltage and load-voltage waveform.
6. Read gate-resistor voltage. Calculate and record gate current.
7. Set gate supply voltage for early firing. Record gate current, load voltage and load-voltage waveform.
8. Write a statement evaluating the triac as a dc-controlled ac switch.

Triac Operation: AC Load, AC Trigger

Purpose: To study operation of a triac with ac gate control.
Devices and Equipment: Triac (General Electric SC240, GE-X12, RCA 40638, RCA 40485, or equivalent); power supply, low-voltage ac; VTVM; oscilloscope; resistor, 100 ohms, ½ W; load: lamp, motor, etc.— up to 600 W.

Procedure:
1. Study specifications and ratings of selected triac.
2. Wire circuit as shown in Fig. 132. Set

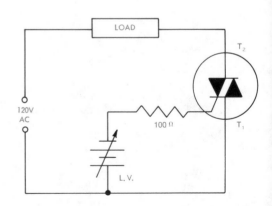

Fig. 131. *Triac with ac load and dc trigger.*

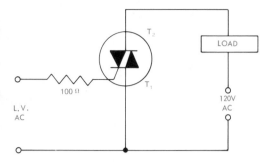

Fig. 132. *Triac with ac load and ac trigger.*

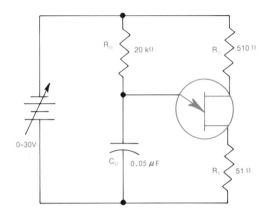

Fig. 133. *Experimental UJT relaxation oscillator circuit.*

gate and T_2 in phase. Connect scope across load. Have wiring approved.
3. Set gate supply voltage at zero and apply load-circuit voltage.
4. Observe scope and record load and triac (T_2-T_1) voltages.
5. Increase gate voltage until triac conducts. Record triac voltage, load voltage and load waveform.
6. Write a statement concerning the effectiveness of the triac as an ac-controlled ac switch.

Unijunction Transistor (UJT) Operation

Purpose: To study operation of a UJT in a relaxation-oscillator circuit.
Devices and Equipment: UJT (2N2160, Motorola HEP 310, or equivalent); power supply, 0-30 V dc; oscilloscope; capacitor, 0.05 μF, 50 V; resistors: 51Ω, 510Ω, 20 kΩ, ½ W.

Procedure:
1. Wire circuit as shown in Fig. 133. Connect oscilloscope across R_1. Have wiring approved.
2. Increase supply voltage slowly and observe oscilloscope for triggering.
3. Set supply voltage to maintain oscilla-

tion and record waveform of R_1 voltage (oscillator output).
4. Change values of R_0 and C_0. Record effects on output.
5. Write a statement describing operation of UJT oscillator. Explain effects of R_0 and C_0 values.

UJT Application: Phase Control of SCR

Purpose: To study application of UJT relaxation oscillator as a variable SCR-trigger control.
Devices and Equipment: SCR (2N1773 or equivalent); UJT (2N2646 or equivalent); capacitor, 0.1 μF, 50 V; resistors: 47Ω, 3.3 kΩ (minimum) 33 kΩ, ½ W; potentiometer, 50 kΩ, 2 W; load (440 W maximum)—lamps, small motor, etc.
Note: Circuit suggested in General Electric Transistor Manual, 7th Edition.

Procedure:
1. Wire circuit as shown in Fig. 134. Connect oscilloscope across load. Have wiring approved.

207

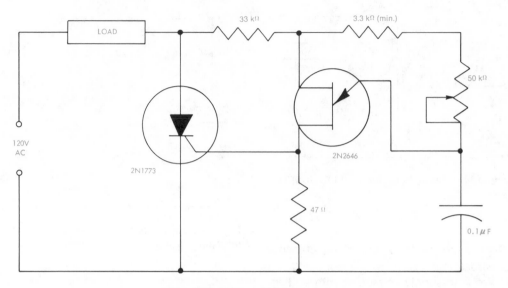

Fig. 134. *UJT as SCR control.*

2. Set potentiometer at maximum. Apply line voltage and record effect at load.
3. Decrease potentiometer resistance gradually and record effect at load.
4. Change value of capacitor and record effect on circuit operation.
5. Write a statement evaluating the effectiveness of the UJT relaxation oscillator as an SCR control.

Silicon Unilateral Switch (SUS) Operation

Purpose: To study operation of an SUS in a relaxation-oscillator circuit.

Devices and Equipment: SUS (2N4987 or equivalent); power supply 0-30 V dc; oscilloscope; capacitor, 0.1 μF, 50 V; resistors: 22Ω, 1 W, 10-20 kΩ, $\frac{1}{2}$ W.

Procedure:

1. Study specifications and ratings of selected SUS.

2. Wire circuit as shown in Fig. 135. Connect oscilloscope across output resistor, R_2.

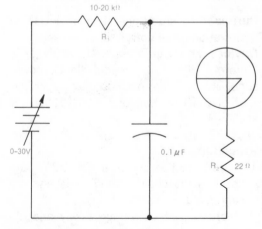

Fig. 135. *Experimental SUS relaxation-oscillator circuit.*

3. Increase supply voltage slowly until SUS triggers on. Record output waveform.
4. Determine output voltage from scope calibration.
5. Replace 0.1 µF capacitor and 22 ohm resistor with other values and test circuit operation.
6. Write a statement describing SUS oscillator operation with various resistance and capacitance values.

SUS Application: Phase Control of SCR

Purpose: To study application of an SUS as an SCR-triggering device.
Devices and Equipment: SUS (2N4987 or equivalent); SCR (General Electric C20B or equivalent); diode (General Electric A14 or equivalent); potentiometer, 500 kΩ, 2 W; capacitor, 0.2 µF, 50 V; resistors: 100Ω,

220 kΩ, ½ W; oscilloscope; load, up to 440 W—lamps, etc.
Note: Circuit suggested in General Electric SCR Manual, 5th Edition.

Procedure:
1. Wire circuit as shown in Fig. 136. Connect scope across load. Have wiring approved.
2. Set potentiometer at maximum. Apply line voltage and record effect at load.
3. Decrease resistance of potentiometer gradually and record effect at load.
4. Write a statement evaluating SUS control of an SCR.

Silicon Bilateral Switch (SBS) Operation

Purpose: To study operations of an SBS in a relaxation-oscillator circuit.

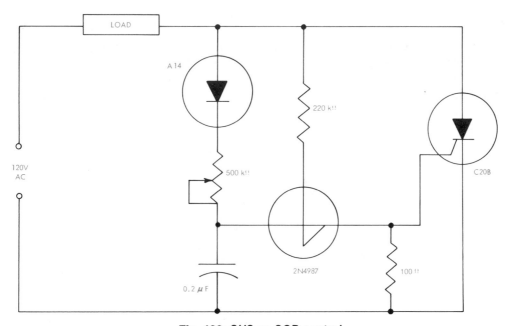

Fig. 136. *SUS as SCR control.*

Devices and Equipment: SBS (2N4991, 2N4992, 2N4993, or equivalent); power supply, 0-30 V dc; oscilloscope; capacitor, 0.1 μF, 50 V; resistors, 22Ω, 1 W, 10-20 kΩ, ½ W.

Procedure:
1. Study specifications and ratings of selected SBS.
2. Wire circuit as shown in Fig. 137. Connect scope across output resistor (R_2). Have wiring approved.
3. Increase supply voltage until SBS triggers on. Record output waveform.
4. Determine output voltage from scope calibration.
5. Reverse polarity of applied voltage and repeat steps 3 and 4.
6. Replace 0.1 μF capacitor and 22Ω resistor with other values and test circuit operation.
7. Write a statement comparing operation of the SBS under two polarity modes.

SBS Application: Phase Control of Triac

Purpose: To study application of an SBS as a triac-triggering device.

Devices and Equipment: SBS (2N4991, 2N4992, 2N4993 or equivalent); triac (General Electric SC240, GE-X12, RCA 40638, RCA 40485, or equivalent); diode, low-voltage (1N599 or equivalent); potentiometer, 2 megohm, 2 W; resistors: 1.2 kΩ, 5.1 kΩ, ½ W, capacitor, 0.1 μF, 50 V; oscilloscope; load, up to 440 W—lamps, etc.

Procedure:
1. Wire circuit as shown in Fig. 138. Connect scope across load. Have wiring approved.
2. Set potentiometer at maximum. Apply line voltage and record effect at load.
3. Decrease resistance of potentiometer gradually and record effect at load.
4. Change value of capacitor and record effects at load.
5. Write a statement explaining SBS phase control of triac.

Diac Operation

Purpose: To study operation of a diac in a relaxation-oscillator circuit.
Devices and Equipment: Diac (General Electric ST-2, GE-X13, RCA 45411, RCA

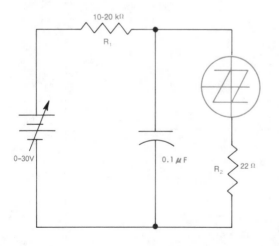

Fig. 137. *Experimental SBS relaxation-oscillator circuit.*

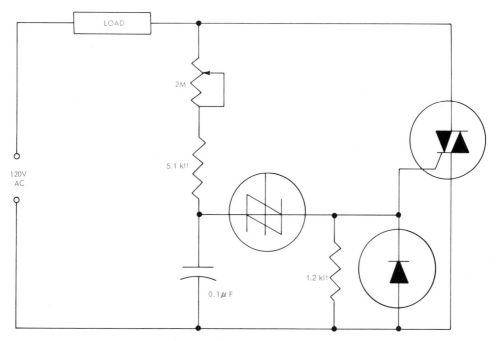

Fig. 138. *SBS as triac control.*

45412); power supply, 0-50 V dc; oscillo-scope; capacitor, 0.1 μF, 50 V; resistors: 22Ω, 1 W, 10-20 kΩ, $\frac{1}{2}$ W.

Procedure:

1. Study specifications and ratings of se-lected diac.
2. Wire circuit as shown in Fig. 139. Con-nect oscilloscope across output resistor R_2. Have wiring approved.
3. Increase supply voltage until diac trig-gers on. Record output waveform.
4. Determine output voltage from scope calibration.
5. Reverse polarity of applied voltage and repeat steps 3 and 4.
6. Replace 0.1 μF capacitor and 22 ohm

resistor with other values and test cir-cuit operation.
7. Write a statement concerning diac out-put under various circuit conditions.

Diac Application: Phase Control of Triac

Purpose: To study operation of a diac as a triac-triggering device.

Devices and Equipment: Diac (General Electric ST-2, GE-X13, RCA 45411, RCA 45412, or equivalent); triac (General Elec-tric SC240, GE-X12, RCA 40638, RCA 40485, or equivalent); oscilloscope; capaci-tor, 0.1 μF, 50 V; potentiometer, 200-500 kΩ, 2 W; resistor, 2700Ω, $\frac{1}{2}$ W; load, up to 440 W—lamps, etc.

211

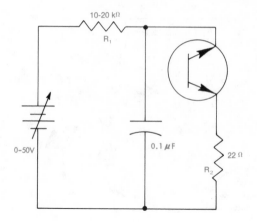

Fig. 139. *Experimental diac relaxation-oscillator circuit.*

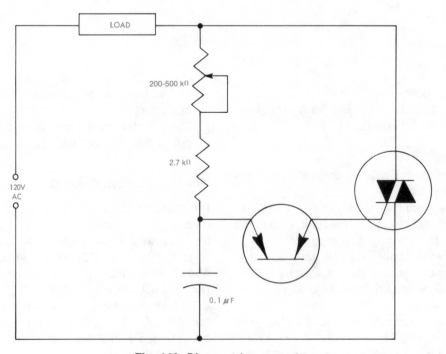

Fig. 140. *Diac as triac control.*

Procedure:

1. Wire circuit as shown in Fig. 140. Connect scope across load. Have wiring approved.
2. Set potentiometer at maximum. Apply line voltage and record effect at load.
3. Decrease potentiometer resistance gradually. Record effects at load.
4. Change load and check circuit operation. Record results.
5. Write a statement on the effectiveness of a diac as a triac phase control.

Try writing out the answer
to each question before look-
ing up the answer.

Review Questions

Power Tubes

1. Define ionization potential of a gas or vapor tube.
2. How does the anode-to-cathode voltage (arc-drop) in a gas tube differ from that in a vacuum tube?
3. What is the purpose of current-averaging?
4. What are the effects of firing a cold mercury-vapor rectifier?
5. Why are capacitor-input filters not recommended for use with gaseous rectifier tubes?
6. What are the advantages of a three-phase rectifier system over a single-phase system?
7. When does a tube fire in a three-phase gaseous rectifier circuit?
8. What is the purpose of the shield grid in the tetrode thyratron?
9. How is the grid current of a thyratron held to a value below the maximum rating?
10. Define the "maximum peak forward-voltage" of a thyratron. What occurs when it is exceeded?
11. What is indicated by the non-linearity of the curves in Figs. 24 and 25?
12. What is a thyratron "control locus"?
13. What is an advantage of phase-shift control?
14. What effect does increasing the variable resistance in Fig. 35 have on the anode-grid phase angle?
15. How is late-firing achieved in the circuit of Fig. 36?
16. Is phase or amplitude control utilized in Fig. 39?
17. Why are two thyratrons used in Fig. 41?
18. List the voltage sources which combine to produce the grid-control potential in Fig. 43.
19. In Fig. 43 what effect does an increase in armature speed have on the grid-control voltage?
20. Why is the output of the tachometer generator in Fig. 44 rectified and filtered?
21. List some applications and advantages of ignitron tubes.
22. Why is the ignitron anode made of graphite?

214

23. Why are ignitron cooling coils spaced as shown in Fig. 48?
24. In the circuit of Fig. 49 where is the remainder of the supply voltage when the anode potential drops to the arc-drop level?
25. How does arc-drop in an ignitron differ from arc-drop in a thyratron?

Solid-State Controls

26. What features of the SCR make it an important control device?
27. Describe the SCR structure.
28. What is "holding current"?
29. How does an increase in gate current affect the voltage at which an SCR fires?
30. To achieve late-firing of the SCR in Fig. 74, should the resistance be increased or decreased? Explain.
31. Why is the SCR configuration in Fig. 79 called "inverse-parallel"?
32. What is a triac?
33. What constructional feature of the triac allows it to switch ac circuits?
34. Why are triac terminals designated T_1 and T_2 rather than anode and cathode?
35. How does the triac characteristic differ from that of the SCR?

36. How is turn-on time of a triac varied?
37. What precaution should be observed in operation of the triac circuit in Fig. 94?
38. What operational features of the UJT make it a useful device?
39. Describe the UJT equivalent circuit.
40. Explain the term *intrinsic stand-off ratio?*
41. Describe briefly the operation of the UJT relaxation oscillator in Fig. 98.
42. In Fig. 100, how does adjustment of the variable resistance vary the SCR firing rate?
43. Describe SUS construction.
44. How is the SUS switched on?
45. How does reversing the polarity of the anode potential turn off an SUS?
46. In Fig. 106, what is the purpose of diode D_1?
47. What determines the switching rate in Fig. 107?
48. How is full-range control possible in the circuit of Fig. 112?
49. Explain the significant difference between the characteristic curves of the diac and the SBS.
50. In Fig. 115, how does adjustment of the variable resistance affect diac turn-on time?

Answers to Review Questions

Power Tubes

1. Ionization potential is the anode-to-cathode voltage at which ionization of a gas or vapor occurs.

2. The arc-drop in a gas tube remains relatively constant with changes in tube current; in a vacuum tube the anode-cathode voltage varies inversely with tube current.

3. Current-averaging is used to determine how the average value of an intermittent tube current compares with the maximum dc-amperes output rating of the tube.

4. Firing a cold mercury-vapor rectifier can result in excessive arc-drop, high rates-of-change of current, damaging circuit voltages, cathode damage and increased ionization time.

5. Charging of the input capacitor could cause excessive current flow through the rectifier tube.

6. Advantages of a three-phase rectifier system over a single-phase system are:

more power output with comparable devices, reduced wiring for equal amounts of power, smoother dc output.

7. In a three-phase system a gas tube begins conduction as its increasing anode voltage becomes equal to the decreasing anode voltage of the conducting tube.

8. The shield grid in a tetrode thyratron minimizes control-grid current.

9. A resistor is placed in series with the grid to limit grid current to a safe operating value.

10. Maximum-peak-forward-voltage is the maximum allowable anode potential for normal operation. Higher values fire the tube prematurely causing the grid to lose control.

11. The non-linearity of the curves in Figs. 24 and 25 indicates that, as the thyratron grid voltage is increased, increasingly larger anode voltages are required for firing.

12. A thyratron control locus is a curve

216

plotted from control-characteristic bias values and corresponding firing potentials on the anode-voltage waveform.

13. An advantage of phase-shift control is the capacity for firing a thyratron over most of the conducting half cycle.

14. Increasing the variable resistance in Fig. 35 increases the anode-grid phase angle.

15. In Fig. 36 late-firing is achieved by increasing the dc control voltage.

16. Amplitude control is the form used in Fig. 39.

17. Two thyratrons are used in the circuit of Fig. 41 to provide control of both half cycles of the ac load current.

18. Sources of grid-control potential in Fig. 43 are the armature winding, dc supply and phase shifter.

19. In Fig. 43 an increase in armature speed results in an increased grid-control voltage.

20. The output of the tachometer generator in Fig. 44 is rectified and filtered to provide a dc voltage which combines with the applied bias to determine the thyratron control potential.

21. Some applications of ignitrons are: welding-current control, high-voltage switching, and high-power rectifier service. Some advantages of ignitrons are: no warm-up time is required, the cathode is not subject to destruction, and maximum tube current is not determined by cathode capacity.

22. The ignitron anode is made of graphite because graphite does not normally emit electrons, has a negative temperature-coefficient-of-resistance, and is a good heat radiator.

23. The ignitron cooling coils are spaced as shown in Fig. 48 to minimize mercury condensation in the upper part of the tube and maximize it in the lower part.

24. When the anode potential in Fig. 49 drops to the arc-drop level the remainder of the supply voltage appears across the load.

25. Unlike arc-drop in a thyratron, which is fairly constant with load changes, arc-drop in an ignitron can increase with load changes which produce high peak currents through the ignitron.

Solid-State Controls

26. Among the features of the SCR which make it an important control device are: rugged construction, instant conduction, high switching speed, good efficiency, long life, and high power gain.

27. An SCR is made up of four layers of P-type and N-type silicon which form three PN junctions. It has three terminals: cathode, anode, and gate.

28. Holding current is the minimum value necessary to maintain SCR conduction.

29. An increase in gate current reduces the firing voltage of an SCR.

30. To achieve late-firing of the SCR in Fig. 74 the resistance is increased. This limits the gate current to a value which requires a larger breakover voltage. Such voltages occur late in the first quarter cycle of the applied anode voltage.

31. The SCR configuration in Fig. 79 is called "inverse-parallel" because the two SCR's are connected in parallel, anode-to-cathode.

32. A triac is a bidirectional, three-terminal, solid-state, ac switch.

33. The triac can switch ac circuits because it consists of two four-layer switches connected in parallel (PNPN and NPNP)—the equivalent of back-to-back SCR's.

34. Triac terminals are designated T_1 and

T_2 because the triac conducts in both directions, with the terminals (T_1 and T_2) acting alternately as anode and cathode.

35. The triac characteristic shows operation in the first and third quadrants; the SCR characteristic shows operation in the first quadrant.

36. Turn-on time of a triac can be varied by changing the gate current.

37. The gate signal and T_2 voltage should be in phase for proper operation of the circuit in Fig. 94.

38. The UJT operates at low trigger current and stable trigger voltage, has good pulse-current capacity and a useful negative-resistance characteristic.

39. Two resistors in series and a diode at their junction form the equivalent circuit of a UJT.

40. The intrinsic stand-off ratio is the ratio of the voltage across R_{B1} to the interbase voltage (V_{BB}).

41. The dc supply charges the capacitor. When the charge equals the peak-point emitter voltage the UJT triggers on and the capacitor discharges through R_1 creating an output voltage pulse across R_1. When the capacitor voltage drops below a certain minimum value the UJT turns off and the capacitor recharges, repeating the cycle.

42. Increasing the variable resistance in Fig. 100 increases the time constant of the RC combination, thereby decreasing the triggering rate of the UJT. This, in turn, decreases the firing rate of the SCR. Decreasing the variable resistance has the opposite effect.

43. The SUS is constructed essentially as a small SCR with an anode gate and a breakdown diode from gate to cathode.

44. When the rated switching voltage of an SUS is applied anode-to-cathode the breakdown diode conducts and base current flows in the NPN section, turning it on. The PNP section also turns on.

45. Reversing the polarity of the SUS anode potential reverse-biases the emitter-base junction of the PNP structure, thereby turning off the SUS.

46. In Fig. 106 diode D_1 protects the SCR gate circuit and the SUS from reverse-voltage effects.

47. The switching rate in Fig. 107 is determined by the time constant of the resistor-capacitor combination.

48. Full-range control is possible in the circuit of Fig. 112 because both triac and SUS can conduct during both half-cycles of the applied ac.

49. A comparison of the diac and SBS characteristic curves shows that, while the voltage across the SBS decreases rapidly after breakover, the voltage across the diac decreases more slowly as the current increases, thereby exhibiting negative resistance.

50. In Fig. 115 diac turn-on time is decreased as the variable resistance is decreased and increased as the resistanc is increased.

UNIT 4

Saturable Reactors and Magnetic Amplifiers

Contents

Unit 4

List of Illustrations

Unit 4

Unit 4

section 1 Introduction

4

Saturable reactors and magnetic amplifiers are devices in which low-power input circuits electromagnetically control high-
power load circuits. Although the names
suggest equipment which is technically com-
plicated, saturable reactors and magnetic
amplifiers are relatively simple units.

In some applications a single saturable
reactor is the control element. In other applications saturable reactors are combined
with additional components to form magnetic amplifiers. Because the saturable
reactor is the main component of the magnetic amplifier, these devices are considered together in the following sections.

Before about 1940 such control equipment was used only to a limited extent.
Since World War II, due to improvements
in magnetic core materials and rectifiers,
saturable reactors and magnetic amplifiers
have become important in increasing numbers of industrial applications.

A saturable reactor consists of a ferromagnetic core and two or more windings, much like a transformer. The load to be controlled is connected in series with one or more windings. Control is accomplished by current in another winding. A saturable reactor for dc motor control is shown in Fig. 1.

A magnetic amplifier is a combination of saturable reactor and other components, such as rectifiers, transformers, and resistors. Fig. 2 shows a group of amplifier and reactor units.

Fig. 1. *Saturable reactor for dc motor control. (Courtesy of General Electric Co.)*

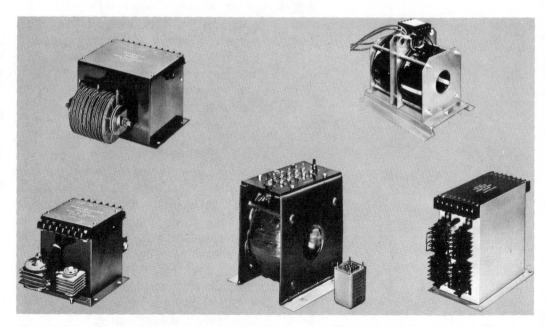

Fig. 2. *Magnetic-amplifier and saturable-reactor units. (Courtesy of General Electric Co.)*

Unit 4

section 2

Saturable Reactors

Because the saturable reactor can operate as an independent control and is also the principal element in the magnetic amplifier, the construction and operation of saturable reactors is presented first—followed by the circuitry of magnetic amplifiers and applications of both devices.

Principle of Operation

The operation of a saturable reactor is based on the principle that a changing flux produced by a coil on a steel or iron core creates opposition to the changing current in the coil (inductive reactance). The strength of the flux, and consequently the opposition to current flow, depends to a great extent on the magnetization of the core material.

Fig. 3 shows the change in magnetization of a steel core during one cycle of alternating current through the coil. This curve is known as the "B-H curve" or "hysteresis loop" of this particular type of material.

225

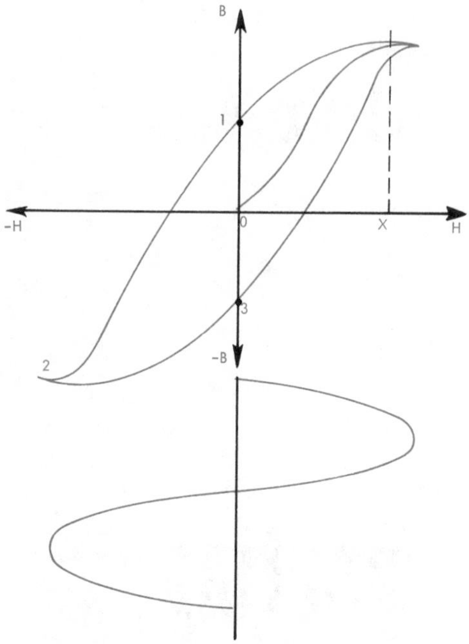

Fig. 3. *Magnetization of mild steel as a function of magnetizing force for one cycle of alternating current.*

In Fig. 3 the magnetizing force H (produced by the alternating current) is on the horizontal axis and the magnetization B is on the vertical axis.

When the magnetizing force increases from zero the magnetization of the core (flux density) also increases from zero. As the magnetizing force continues to increase, the magnetization increases rapidly. If the force is sufficient to completely magnetize the core, the core is said to be *saturated*.

Any increase in magnetizing force beyond this point (X in Fig. 3) does not increase the magnetic flux in the core. When the magnetizing force returns to zero the flux does not decrease accordingly. It decreases to point 1.

This lag, known as "hysteresis lag," is due to the fact that when a material is magnetized in a certain direction, or polarity,

it tends to retain some of the magnetism when the magnetizing force is removed. This characteristic is known as the *retentivity* of the material. The magnetic flux remaining in the core when the magnetizing force decreases to zero is known as *residual magnetism*.

As the magnetizing force increases in the opposite direction, ($-$H), the residual magnetism decreases to zero. (The force required to remove residual magnetism is known as *coercive force* and is an indication of the retentivity of a material). As the magnetizing force continues to increase, core magnetization again rises from zero to saturation (2). When the magnetizing force decreases to zero the core flux decreases to 3.

As the magnetizing force begins a second cycle the core flux decreases to zero and the magnetizing sequence begins again.

As alternating current continues to flow through the coil the magnetization of the core varies according to the hysteresis loop.

The reactance of a coil is proportional to the rate of change of the flux threading the coil. On the hysteresis curve the greatest rate of change of flux occurs on the straight, sloping portion. The steeper the slope the greater the reactance. During saturation the curve is almost horizontal and the coil reactance is minimum. This changing-reactance characteristic is the control mechanism in saturable reactors. Varying the degree of magnetization varies the reactance, which, in turn, varies the load-circuit current.

Saturable-Reactor Core Materials

Materials suitable for saturable-reactor cores have several characteristics. They are highly permeable (easily magnetized), with almost rectangular hysteresis loops, as in Fig. 4. They have reduced eddy-current and hysteresis losses and high saturation flux density. (Eddy-current and hysteresis losses are power losses caused by the creation of eddy currents in the core material and the

energy required to overcome the hysteresis lag.)

Silicon-iron and nickel-iron alloys are generally used for saturable-reactor cores. Among the commercially-available silicon-iron alloys are Corosil, Hipersil, Silectron and Trancor. These are 97% iron and three percent silicon. Available nickel-iron alloys include Deltamax, Orthonol, Hipernik and Copernik (about 50% nickel and 50% iron).

Saturable-Reactor Construction and Circuit Operation

The simplest saturable reactor consists of two windings on a common core. One winding (load coil) is connected in series with a load to an alternating-current supply. The other winding (control coil) is connected to a direct-current supply. This form of saturable reactor is illustrated in Fig. 5. (The saturable reactor symbol is also shown.) With no current in the control coil and a less-than-saturable value of current in the load circuit, the load coil develops maximum reactance. Under these condi-

Fig. 4. *B-H curve of steel alloy used in satur-able-reactor cores.*

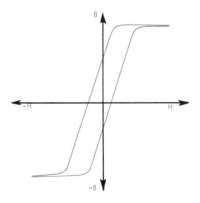

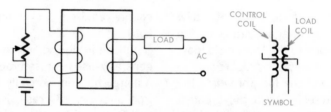

Fig. 5. *Application of simple saturable reactor and circuit symbol.*

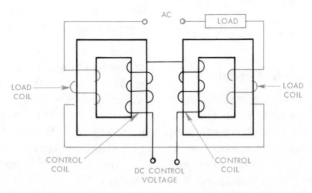

Fig. 6. *Two reactors series-connected to eliminate unwanted voltages in control coils.*

tions load-coil voltage is maximum, load voltage and load current are minimum.

If a small amount of direct current is applied to the control coil it partially magnetizes the core. If the current is increased sufficiently the core becomes saturated (completely magnetized) and is held in this state by the current. With the core completely magnetized the alternating current in the load coil cannot create a flux in the core. Consequently, load-coil reactance is minimum and load voltage and load current are maximum. This form of saturable reactor is seldom used because the alternating current in the load coil can induce voltages into the control coil which can damage the

control circuit or interfere with its operation.

Unwanted voltages in control coils may be eliminated in several ways. A method utilizing two reactors is illustrated in Fig. 6. Here both load and control coils are connected in series. When relative polarities are observed the coils can be connected so that voltages induced into the control coils cancel. Series-connected coils can also be placed on the two-legged core shown in Fig. 5. As in Fig. 6, the coils are connected to effect cancellation of voltages induced into the control circuit. Another form of saturable reactor which eliminates induced voltages from the control coils consists of

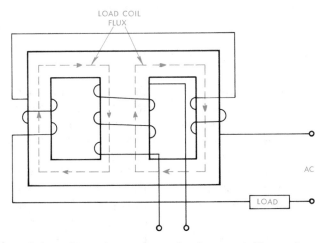

Fig. 7. *Magnetization of three-legged core by ac load current. Fluxes in center leg cancel.*

two two-legged cores mounted as a single unit.

The most common form of saturable-reactor core construction is the three-legged core shown in Fig. 7. In this unit the load coils are wound on the outer legs and the control coil on the center leg. The load coils are connected in series or parallel depending on load requirements. They are wound and wired so that their fluxes are in opposition in the center leg. This is shown by the dashed lines, which represent the ac flux for one half-cycle. (During the other half-cycle the flux directions are reversed.) The fluxes in opposition in the center leg cancel, thereby eliminating the induction of unwanted voltages in the control coil.

Fig. 8 shows the core flux when direct current flows in the control coil with no current in the load coils. If the current is sufficient the core becomes saturated.

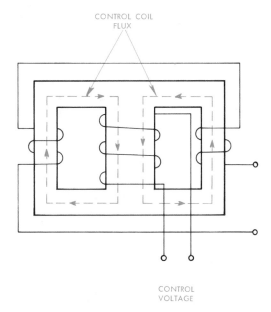

Fig. 8. *Magnetization of three-legged core by dc control current. Fluxes in center leg add.*

229

Fig. 9 shows the fluxes present in the core when both alternating and direct currents are flowing in the reactor. The center-leg flux is due to control-coil current and the flux in the outer legs is produced by both control and load currents. During one half-cycle the direct-current and alternating-current fluxes are additive in one leg and subtractive in the other. During the alternate half-cycle the reverse is true.

Under additive conditions saturation may be approached or achieved, resulting in a reduced or minimum rate of change of flux and a corresponding reduction in load-coil impedance. At the same time reduced resultant flux in the other outer leg allows for a high rate of change and substantial load-coil impedance.

The total impedance in the load coils is the sum of the two coil impedances. This can be varied by the control current. As this current is increased, core saturation is achieved and load-coil impedance decreases, allowing maximum load-current flow. When the control current is reduced, the core becomes unsaturated and the load coils develop normal impedance, reducing the load current. Thus, the flow of current through an ac load can be varied by adjustments in a dc control current without the induction of objectionable voltages into the control coil.

Operation of a saturable reactor with different values of control current is illustrated in Fig. 10. Initially, a small amount of direct current magnetizes the core to point A on the magnetization curve. The alternating current in the load coil increases the magnetization to the saturation level (B-C). Variation of the magnetization is shown by the sine-wave sections. The shaded areas indicate the time of core saturation—minimum load-coil impedance and maximum load current.

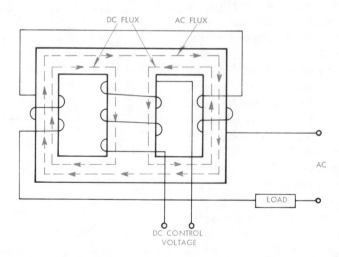

Fig. 9. *Core magnetization produced by control and load currents.*

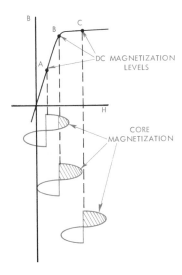

Fig. 10. *Operation of saturable reactor at three levels of dc magnetization.*

If the control current is increased a certain amount the operating point shifts to point B on the curve. Operation from this point produces minimum load-coil impedance and maximum load current and voltage during a full half-cycle of applied voltage.

When the control current is increased sufficiently to set the dc magnetization at point C the core is saturated at all times—resulting in minimum coil impedance and maximum load current and voltage during both halves of the ac cycle.

For some purposes saturable reactors are operated with the load coils connected in parallel, as illustrated in Fig. 11. This configuration permits a reactor to control a larger current than when the coils are wired in series. However, the response of parallel coils to changes in control current is slower than that of the same coils connected in series. This is due to the fact that voltages induced into parallel-connected coils by changes in control-coil flux set up fluxes which are additive and oppose the changing control-coil flux, delaying the control action. In series-connected load coils the induced voltages are equal and opposite, thereby cancelling, causing no time delay.

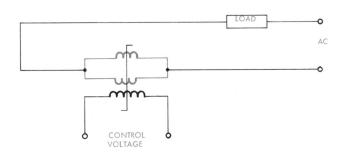

Fig. 11. *Load coils connected in parallel to control larger currents.*

Unit 4

section 3

Magnetic Amplifiers

Although saturable reactors are valuable devices for low-level dc control of ac power circuits, their use can be greatly extended when combined with rectifiers and other components to form magnetic amplifiers. It can be said, then, that magnetic amplifiers are circuits in which the saturable reactor is the chief component.

Magnetic-Amplifier Circuits and Operation

A simple form of magnetic amplifier is shown in Fig. 12. This circuit provides a controllable direct current to the load. As in normal half-wave rectifier operation, when terminal A is negative and B is positive no current flows through the load. When A is positive and B is negative, electron flow is from B through the load, the load coils and the rectifier to terminal A. However, with no current in the control coil the load coils produce maximum impedance during the

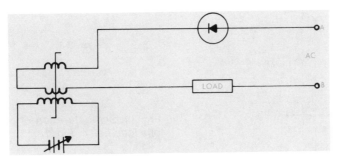

Fig. 12. *Simple magnetic amplifier.*

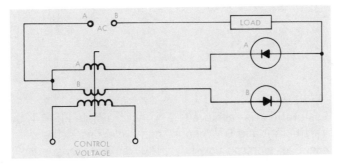

Fig. 13. *Self-saturating magnetic amplifier.*

conducting half-cycle and limit the current to a minimum. The voltage across the load coils is maximum and that across the load is minimum.

When direct current is applied to the control coil it tends to saturate the core. Consequently, the load coils cannot develop full impedance and the load current increases. The voltage across the load coils decreases and that across the load increases. When the control current is sufficient to completely saturate the core both load voltage and load current are maximum during the conducting half-cycle. A good power gain is possible with this circuit since a small control current can control a large load current.

Self-Saturation. In a simple saturable reactor the magnetism created in the core by one half-cycle of alternating current is cancelled or "reset" by the following half-cycle flowing in the opposite direction through the load coils. Thus the overall average value of magnetization due to the alternating current is zero. Rectifiers can be utilized to prevent the reversal of current through the load coils and thus retain magnetic flux produced by the alternating current. The result is a "self-saturating" effect, as illustrated in Figs. 13 and 14.

233

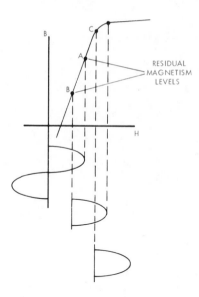

Fig. 14. *Self-saturation of core section under one load coil in Fig. 13.*

In Fig. 13 self-saturation is achieved through the use of rectifiers A and B. When line terminal B is negative, electron flow is from B through the load, rectifier B and load coil B to terminal A. During the next half-cycle electron flow is from terminal A through load coil A, rectifier A and the load to terminal B. Each section of the core is magnetized by a half-cycle of current.

During the half-cycle when coil A is conducting, rectifier B prevents the flow of current through coil B. Thus the core flux produced by coil B is not reset by a reverse current. When coil B is conducting, rectifier A prevents any flow of "reset" current through coil A. In this manner the core retains some flux after each half-cycle of conduction.

The magnetic condition of the section of core under one load coil is shown in Fig. 14. The same effect occurs in the other section during alternate half-cycles.

According to Fig. 14, the first conducting half-cycle raises the core flux to point A. The residual magnetism left in the core after this half-cycle is indicated at point B. During the next conducting half-cycle the load current increases the core flux starting at level B. The residual magnetism after the second conducting half-cycle is shown at C. With each succeeding conducting half-cycle the residual core flux increases until the core becomes saturated. When saturation is achieved the impedance of both coils is minimum and the load current is maximum.

Control of Self-Saturated Magnetic Amplifier. If no control current is present in the circuit of Fig. 13 the magnetic amplifier saturates in a few cycles and an uncontrolled maximum current flows through the load. If direct current is made to flow through the control coil in such a direction that its flux adds to the load-coil flux, the

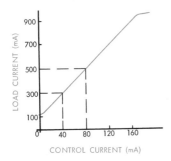

Fig. 15. *Control characteristic of reactor without self-saturation shows current gain of five.*

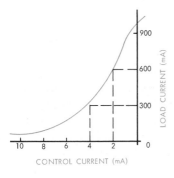

Fig. 16. *Control characteristic of self-saturated reactor shows current gain of 150.*

core is more quickly saturated and no control is possible.

To achieve control of the load current, the control current must flow so that its flux opposes that of the load coils. In this mode control-current flux cancels some of the load-current flux, removing the core from saturation. When the core is removed from saturation and operation is on the sloping portion of the magnetization core, the load coils develop impedance and limit the load current.

The advantage of self-saturation in terms of current gain is shown by the characteristic curves given in Figs. 15 and 16. In Fig. 15 the control characteristic of a small reactor without self-saturation shows that a control-current change of 40 mA produces a load-current change of 200 mA—a current gain of five. In Fig. 16 the control characteristic of the same reactor with self-saturation shows a much greater current gain. A control-current change of 2 mA causes a load-current change of 300 mA—a current gain of 150. Depending upon circuit impedances, a current gain of 150 could result in a power gain of several thousand.

The value of the control current in a magnetic amplifier is usually low. Consequently, the control coil is made of small-size wire and occupies little space. This allows the placement of additional coils on the control leg of the saturable reactor.

235

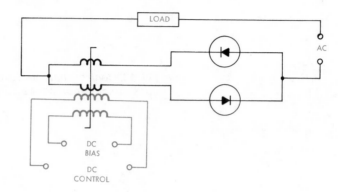

Fig. 17. *Self-saturating magnetic amplifier with control and bias coils.*

Such coils can serve various purposes: carry a bias current which sets the operating point of the magnetic amplifier; allow for "feedback" from the load circuit; provide inputs for control signals from thermocouples, photocells and other transducers. Fig. 17 shows control and bias coils.

Bias. In the circuit of Fig. 13, load current varies inversely with control current. The addition of a bias current can allow the control and load currents to vary directly and, at the same time, set the operating point of the magnetic amplifier at some desired point on the control characteristic. This is done by applying direct current to the bias coil in such a direction that its flux opposes that of the load coils and prevents complete self-saturation, thereby setting the operating point below saturation.

With the bias set, current can be made to flow in the control coil so that its flux adds to the load-coil flux, increasing the core magnetization toward full saturation. This, in turn, lowers the load-coil reactance and increases the load current. A decrease in control current results in less core flux, more load-coil reactance and less load cur-

rent. In this manner changes in control current produce like changes in load current.

Magnetic Amplifiers with DC Outputs. In the circuit of Fig. 13 the magnetic amplifier provided controlled alternating current to the load. Magnetic amplifiers can also provide controlled direct-current outputs. A simple, half-wave circuit is shown in Fig. 18. Voltage induced into the control coil from the load coil is suppressed by the series-connected high impedance.

With no control current the core saturates and the load current becomes maximum during the conducting half-cycle. With current in the control coil the core magnetism is reset to a point below saturation. When operating below saturation the load coil limits the load current to a reduced value during the conducting half-cycle until the core reaches saturation. The point in the half-cycle at which saturation occurs and consequently, increased current, depends on how far down the characteristic curve the control current resets the core. Thus, the amount of direct current in the load depends on the amount of direct current in the control coil.

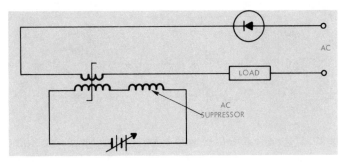

Fig. 18. *Basic magnetic amplifier with dc load and ac suppressor in control circuit.*

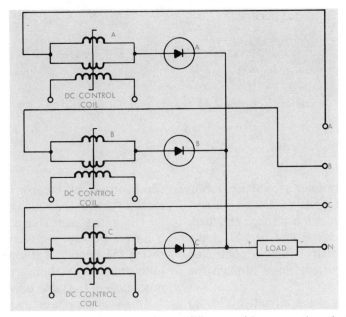

Fig. 19. *Three-phase, half-wave magnetic amplifier provides smoother dc load current.*

Basic half-wave magnetic amplifiers can be used with a three-phase source, as illustrated in Fig. 19. During the phase-A conducting half-cycle, electron flow is through the load, rectifier A and load coils A, to line A. During phase-B and phase-C conducting half-cycles, current flows in these branches in a similar manner.

Practical magnetic amplifiers providing dc output usually incorporate full-wave rectification. This is illustrated by the circuit in Fig. 20, which utilizes a center-tapped transformer and two rectifiers to provide full-wave output. During one half-cycle a controlled current flows from the center tap through the load, rectifier A, load coil A and

237

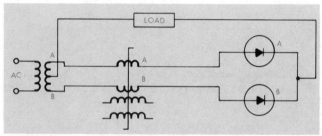

Fig. 20. *Magnetic amplifier with controlled full-wave dc output.*

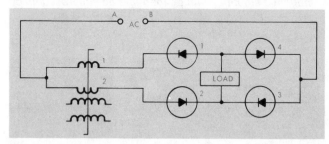

Fig. 21. *Magnetic amplifier incorporating bridge rectifier minimizes instability of inductive load.*

part A of the transformer secondary. During the alternate half-cycle controlled current flows from the center tap through the load, rectifier B, load coil B and part B of the transformer secondary. Thus, a controlled, full-wave direct current flows through the load.

A disadvantage of the circuit in Fig. 20 is that, when the load is inductive, counter emf set up in the load can cause unstable operation of the amplifier. This disadvantage is not present in the bridge circuit shown in Fig. 21. During one half-cycle controlled current flows from line A through load coil 1, rectifier 1, the load and rectifier 3 to line B. The flow of controlled current during the alternate half-cycle is from line B through rectifier 4, the load, rectifier 2 and load coil 2 to line A. If the load is inductive the resulting load-flux change

which occurs as the current tends to decrease (before saturation) creates a counter-emf in the load. This potential produces a current through rectifiers 3 and 4, dissipating the energy of the inductive "kick." In this manner the bridge circuit eliminates this cause of unstable operation.

Three single-phase magnetic amplifiers incorporating bridge rectifiers can be used with a three-phase supply to provide a controlled, low-ripple dc output. This circuit arrangement is illustrated in Fig. 22. In accordance with three-phase operation, rectifiers 1 and 2 conduct alternately for line A, rectifiers 3 and 4 for line B and rectifiers 5 and 6 for line C. Although three single-phase units can be combined to form a three-phase magnetic amplifier, complete assemblies are available from some manufacturers.

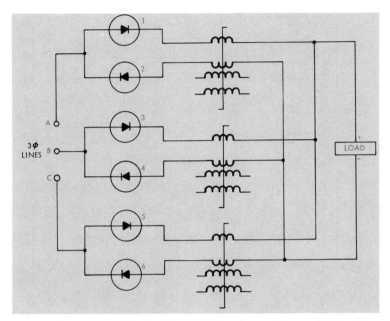

Fig. 22. *Low-ripple, three-phase magnetic amplifier.*

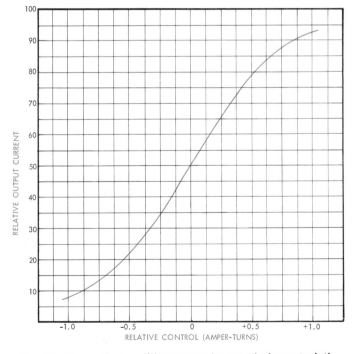

Fig. 23. *Magnetic-amplifier general control characteristic.*

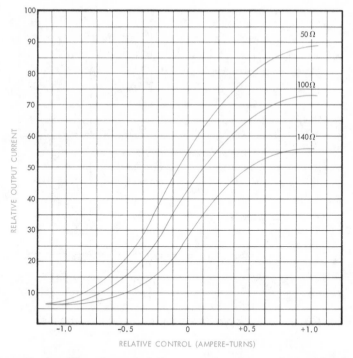

Fig. 24. *Magnetic-amplifier characteristic curves for three values of load resistance.*

Magnetic-Amplifier Control Characteristic. The output of a magnetic amplifier as a function of control is shown by the control characteristic curve, also called the *transfer characteristic.* A general control characteristic is shown in Fig. 23. Since the flux produced by the control coil is due to the magnetomotive force developed by the coil, the control variable used to plot the characteristic is the ampere-turn, the unit of magnetomotive force. Amplifier output is given in terms of output voltage, output current, or percent of rated output.

A family of characteristic curves is shown in Fig. 24. Here output current is plotted as a function of control ampere-turns for three values of load resistance. According

to the data, output current is minimum when the ampere-turns are highly negative (core unsaturated) and maximum when the ampere-turns are positive (core saturated). Also, for a given value of control ampere-turns, output current increases as load resistance decreases.

Fig. 25 shows typical control-characteristic curves of a general-purpose 75 VA magnetic amplifier (G.E. Model 9T95Y24). Here dc output voltage is plotted as a function of control ampere-turns with a 120 volt supply. As indicated by the curves, the output voltage is minimum when the control ampere-turns are negative (core unsaturated) and maximum when the ampere-turns are positive (core saturated). For a

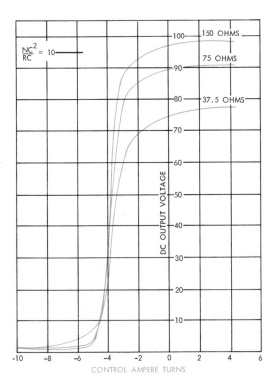

$\frac{NC^2}{RC} = 10$

150 OHMS

75 OHMS

37.5 OHMS

DC OUTPUT VOLTAGE

CONTROL AMPERE TURNS

Fig. 25. *Control characteristic of a general-purpose 75 VA magnetic amplifier: G.E. Amplistat, model 9T95Y24. (Courtesy of General Electric Co.)*

set value of ampere-turns, output voltage increases as the load resistance increases.

As in other supply-and-load configurations, the optimum value of load resistance is that which allows maximum transfer of power to the load. This occurs when the load resistance equals the internal impedance of the amplifier at saturation. This is not always possible in high-power magnetic amplifier circuits, where the impedance of the amplifier is usually low. In such cases the load impedance must be sufficient to limit the load-coil current to a safe operating value. However, in low-power amplifiers the internal impedance is usually high enough to allow for matching the load impedance to the source, thereby obtaining maximum power transfer without exceeding load-coil current ratings.

241

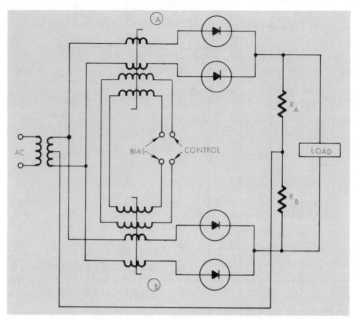

Fig. 26. *Push-pull magnetic amplifier can provide zero and reversible outputs.*

Push-Pull Magnetic Amplifier. The magnetic amplifiers in previous illustrations are "single-ended" amplifiers, and, as such, exhibit certain properties. According to the control characteristic (Fig. 23), with zero ampere turns of control, a quiescent load current flows. Also, a single-ended magnetic amplifier controls its output in one polarity direction only. Zero load current and an output of reversible polarity can be obtained by connecting two single-ended units in a push-pull mode, as illustrated in Fig. 26. Each unit in Fig. 26 contains control and bias coils, two load coils, two rectifiers and an output resistor, and operates as a single-ended, full-wave amplifier. The output of amplifier A is developed across R_A and that of amplifier B across R_B. The control characteristic of each amplifier and the composite characteristic are shown in Fig. 27.

With current in the bias coil and no current in the control coil the operating point of each amplifier is at X. Equal currents flow through the load coils of amplifiers A and B and through resistors R_A and R_B. Equal voltages are developed across R_A and R_B. Since these equal voltages are of opposite polarity, the resultant load voltage and load current are zero.

The relationship between the control coils and the load coils is such that when current in the control coils flows in one direction it increases the core flux in one amplifier and decreases it in the other. When the control current causes the load current in amplifier A to increase from X to Y (Fig. 27) it causes the load current in amplifier B to decrease from X to Z. The current through resistor R_A is now greater than that through R_B and the sum of the voltages across the two resistors is no

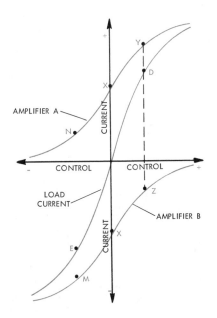

Fig. 27. *Control characteristics of push-pull magnetic amplifier.*

longer zero. The resultant voltage creates a current in the load equal to point D.

If the direction of the control current is reversed an opposite effect occurs. As the load current in amplifier B increases from X to M, the load current in amplifier A decreases from X to N. The current in resistor R_B is now greater than the current in resistor R_A. The resultant output voltage changes polarity and current through the load (point E) is in the opposite direction. Thus the push-pull magnetic amplifier can provide zero quiescent load current and reversible output. Also, any fluctuations in supply voltage do not affect the output since changes in the potentials across R_A and R_B due to the fluctuations are of opposite polarity and therefore cancel.

The slope of the composite characteristic indicates that the push-pull amplifier has twice the amplification of a single-ended unit and the longer straight portion indicates a greater linear range.

Feedback. In the self-saturated magnetic amplifier, magnetization of the core by the load current is known as internal, or intrinsic, feedback. Feedback is also accomplished externally by passing the load current through an additional coil on the control leg of the magnetic amplifier. Such a coil is shown in Fig. 28.

In operation, when the load current flows through the feedback coil in such a direction that its ampere-turns aid the ampere-turns of the control coil, the feedback is *regenerative* (also called positive). When the ampere-turns of the two coils are in opposition the feedback is *degenerative* (negative). When regenerative feedback is utilized, fewer turns are required on the

243

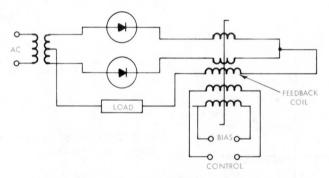

Fig. 28. *Magnetic amplifier with feedback coil.*

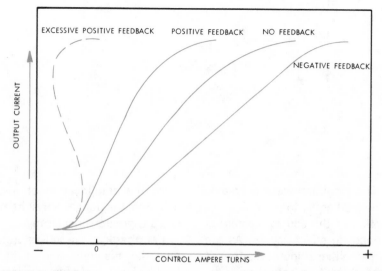

Fig. 29. *Characteristic curves of magnetic amplifier with and without feedback.*

control coil to control a particular load current. Since load currents are usually relatively large, the required feedback ampere-turns can be produced with a few turns of heavy wire.

The control characteristic in Fig. 29 illustrates the operation of a magnetic amplifier with and without feedback. Without feedback, the load current is a small quiescent value when the control current is zero. As the control current is increased in a positive direction, load-coil flux decreases and load current increases gradually toward maximum at saturation. However, with positive feedback the quiescent (zero control current) value of load current

244

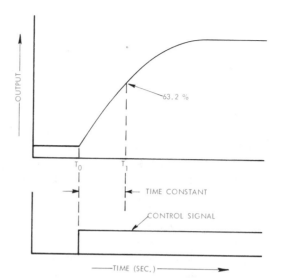

Fig. 30. *Magnetic-amplifier time constant.*

is increased. This is because positive-feed-back ampere-turns have the same effect on the core flux as control-coil ampere-turns.

As the control current is increased from zero the load current rises rapidly toward maximum since the feedback and control currents act together to increase core saturation. The increased steepness of the slope of the feedback-amplifier characteristic indicates that a certain change in control current can produce a greater change in load current in an amplifier with feedback than in one without feedback. Therefore greater gain can be realized with positive feedback. However, as in other forms of amplifiers, regenerative feedback results in decreased stability and linearity. In order to maintain reasonable stability the flux produced by regenerative feedback should not exceed about 80% of the combined control and feedback fluxes.

Negative feedback produces opposite effects. Since its action opposes that of the control circuit a larger control-current change is required to produce a certain change in load current than is required in a non-feedback amplifier. Although this results in less gain, there is an increase in stability and more linearity of response with negative feedback.

Magnetic-Amplifier Time Constant and Response Time. Since magnetic amplifiers contain inductive reactors, there is an inherent time delay between a change in the control signal and the resultant change in output. (An inductance opposes any change in current flowing through it.) Two terms, *time constant* and *response time*, are used to indicate the delay of a saturable reactor or magnetic amplifier. These terms can be expressed in seconds or cycles of applied voltage.

The time constant of a magnetic amplifier is the time required for the output to reach 63.2% of its final value in response to an instantaneous, or step, change in the control signal. This is illustrated in Fig. 30. When the control signal rises from zero to maximum the output current begins a gradual increase. T_1 indicates the time at which the current reaches the 63.2% point. The time constant is the time elapsed between T_0 and T_1.

Response time is the time required for the output of a magnetic amplifier to reach a selected percentage of its final value when reacting to an instantaneous control-signal change. The response time of a certain amplifier might be expressed as 0.08 seconds (95%).

The response delay of a magnetic amplifier is determined by the action of both input and output circuits. Output-circuit factors which contribute to the delay are (a) inductive loads and (b) the occurrence of core saturation during the non-conducting half-cycle. When the core saturates during the non-conducting half-cycle, output-circuit response does not occur until the conducting half-cycle.

Control-circuit delay is that of a series resistive-inductive (RL) circuit. The time constant of this circuit is directly proportional to the inductance and inversely proportional to the resistance. Inductance is proportional to the square of the turns. Therefore, if many turns are wound on a highly-permeable core, the delay can be appreciable. Where larger reactors are used it may be several cycles of the line frequency.

While the delay contributed by the load circuit is more or less fixed, the time constant of the control circuit can be changed by varying the circuit resistance. The addition of a resistor in series with the control coil decreases the L/R ratio and reduces the time constant. However, this necessitates an increase in control-circuit power to maintain control at the level required for effective operation. An increase in control-circuit power with no change in load power results in lower power gain. Lower power gain is also realized if a resistor is added to the control circuit without increasing the control-circuit power.

The response time of a saturable reactor or magnetic amplifier can be reduced by using a higher-frequency supply voltage. If the response of a unit to a 60-Hz line voltage reaches 95% at the end of six cycles the delay is 6/60 or 0.10 seconds. If the supply frequency is changed to 400 Hz (used in many military applications) the delay is still six cycles but the time is shorter —6/400 or 0.015 second. Thus a change in frequency from 60 Hz to 400 Hz decreases response time almost seven times. Another advantage of a higher supply frequency is the reduction in size and weight of the required magnetic core.

Unit 4

section 4

Applications, Advantages and Disadvantages

Saturable reactors and magnetic amplifiers are used extensively in control of such high-current equipment as electric furnaces, superheaters, pasteurizers, theater lights and battery chargers. They can replace large rheostats, variable transformers, high-wattage resistors and large, high-current switches.

Rheostats and resistors are inefficient. They dissipate power and create heat problems. Switches carrying large currents develop contact problems. Saturable reactors and magnetic amplifiers, in contrast, have no moving contacts and dissipate little power. When operated at rated capacity they function indefinitely and usually outlast the equipment they control. Because they have no moving parts they are highly reliable and can be fabricated for pot-type packaging. Saturable reactors and magnetic amplifiers are stable in operation, can carry heavy overloads and withstand extreme shock and vibration. They can operate in explosive atmospheres and can be hermetically sealed for use under extreme environmental conditions.

Saturable-reactor construction provides electrical isolation between control and load circuits. Such isolation is a requirement in many power-control applications. Saturable-reactor construction also allows for the application of several separate control signals.

A typical magnetic amplifier has an efficiency rating of 70% or higher. This exceeds the rating of the electron-tube amplifier, which generally has a maximum of about 50%. Magnetic amplifiers are excellent power-control amplifiers. Gains of a million or more are possible in a single unit. Greater gains can be achieved by cascading. Some magnetic amplifiers are very sensitive, handling input signals of less than a microwatt.

A large range of magnetic-amplifier input impedances is possible, from a few ohms to over 100,000 ohms. Most commercial units have input impedances between 200 and 6,000 ohms. Because the magnetic amplifier can be designed with low input impedance it is quite appropriate for use with transducers which have low output impedance—applications for which the high input impedance of the electron-tube amplifier is not suitable.

In addition to the advantages listed above, saturable reactors and magnetic amplifiers have some disadvantages relating to response time, frequency response, and size.

Concerning response time, there is a definite delay between the time an input-signal change is applied to one of these electromagnetic units and the time when the resultant change in output occurs. Generally, the response times of these devices are longer than those of comparable solid-state and electron-tube controls.

Such time lags set limitations on the use of saturable reactors and magnetic amplifiers in applications where fast response is a requirement, as in some servo and automatic-control systems. However, magnetic-reactor time delay is not considered a disadvantage in applications wherein other circuit components have longer response times.

In normal operation the frequency of the control signal applied to a saturable reactor or magnetic amplifier must be a fraction of the load-supply frequency. This requirement severely limits the highest frequency to which these devices can respond. With the possible future development of units which will operate at higher frequencies, the effects of this limitation will be reduced. However, high-frequency operation introduces additional limitations, namely: losses due to increased eddy currents and distributed-capacity effects.

Because inductive reactance is directly proportional to frequency, a much larger coil is required to develop a certain amount of reactance in a lower-frequency circuit than in a higher-frequency circuit. As a result, saturable reactors and magnetic amplifiers are generally larger than comparable solid-state and electron-tube units—especially for 60 Hz applications.

Recent developments in magnetic materials and construction methods have overcome some of the disadvantage of size, especially in regard to 400 Hz units. Some 400 Hz units are smaller and more compact than other forms of controls of equal capacity.

A variety of common industrial control applications can be satisfactorily handled by the use of commercial general-purpose magnetic amplifiers such as the one shown in Fig. 31.

Two industrial control applications which

combine magnetic amplifiers and saturable reactors are illustrated in Figs. 32 and 33. The magnetic amplifier utilized in both applications is the General Electric "Amplistat" shown in Fig. 31.

In Fig. 32 the equipment under control is a high-current electric furnace. A thermocouple supplies temperature information to a unit which provides current to a control coil in the magnetic amplifier. The magnetic amplifier, in turn, furnishes current to a control coil in the saturable reactor. In this manner, changes in temperature are utilized to adjust the heating current automatically.

Fig. 31. *General-purpose magnetic amplifier. (Courtesy of General Electric Co.)*

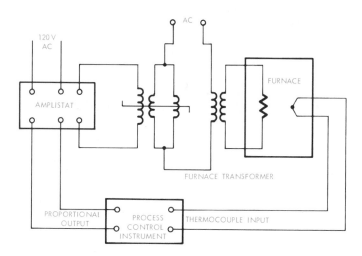

Fig. 32. *Magnetic-amplifier control of saturable reactor in electric-furnace application. (Courtesy of General Electric Co.)*

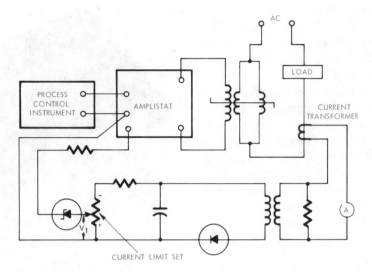

Fig, 33. *Magnetic amplifier-saturable reactor control of high-current load incorporating automatic feedback. (Courtesy of General Electric Co.)*

The circuit in Fig. 33 also illustrates magnetic amplifier-saturable reactor control of a high-current load. In this application a process-control instrument provides a control signal to the magnetic amplifier. The magnetic-amplifier load is the control coil of the saturable reactor.

A feedback circuit is used to limit the load current to a predetermined maximum. The current is sensed by a current transformer which provides input to a half-wave rectifier. Rectifier output is developed across a potentiometer which is used in setting the load-current limit. When the voltage, V_1, exceeds the breakdown voltage of the diode, the diode conducts and V_1 appears across the magnetic-amplifier control coil opposing the signal from the process instrument—thus limiting the current through the saturable reactor and load. Since control currents can be bucked in a single coil, this form of load-current regulation requires the use of only one magnetic-amplifier control coil.

Unit 4

section 5

Laboratory Procedures

The laboratory procedures outlined in this Section assume that the student has access to the devices and equipment listed for each experiment, is familiar with basic circuits and circuit diagrams, and performs the work under the supervision of an instructor.

Some of the devices and circuits require 120 V ac. Adequate precautions should be observed.

Saturable Reactor: Elementary Form

Purpose: To study operation of an isolation transformer as a saturable reactor.
Devices and Equipment: Transformer, isolation, 120 V/120 V, 150 VA; rheostat, 300 ohm, 100 W; switch, SPST; VTVM; lamp, 50-75 W; small universal motor, 120 V.

251

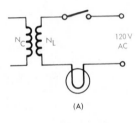

(A)

(B)

Fig. 34. *Test circuit to study operation of an isolation transformer as a saturable reactor.*

Fig. 35. *Test circuit for studying induced ac in saturable-reactor control winding.*

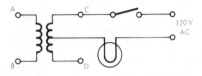

Procedure:
1. Wire circuit as shown in Fig. 34(A), with lamp as load. Have wiring approved.
2. Connect VTVM across lamp.
3. Apply voltage. Close switch. Record lamp condition and lamp voltage.
4. Open switch and connect leads of open winding (N_c) together.
5. Close switch and record lamp condition and lamp voltage.
6. Open switch and connect rheostat into "control" winding circuit as in Fig. 34(B).
7. Vary control current with rheostat and record effects on lamp voltage and brightness.
8. Substitute a small universal motor for lamp load. Vary control current and record effect on motor speed.

9. Write a statement evaluating an isolation transformer as a saturable reactor.

Induced AC in Saturable-Reactor Control Winding

Purpose: To observe undesirable voltage induced in control winding by load-winding flux. To prevent the induction of this voltage.

Devices and Equipment: Transformer, filament, 120/6.3 V, c.t., 1 A; switch, SPST; VTVM; lamp, 75-100 W.

Procedure:
1. Wire circuit as shown in Fig. 35, with lamp as load. Have wiring approved.
2. Energize circuit. Record lamp voltage and condition and V_{AB}.

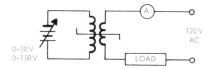

Fig. 36. *Test circuit for studying operation of an industrial saturable reactor.*

3. Open switch and connect C to D.
4. Close switch and record lamp voltage and condition and V_{AB}.
5. Redraw Fig. 35 and show with arrows a set of currents and fluxes. Explain their effects on V_{AB}.

Industrial Saturable Reactor

Purpose: To study operation of an industrial saturable reactor.

Devices and Equipment: Saturable reactor, 120 V ac, 25 V dc (General Electric SX-G2), 120 V ac, 125 V dc (General Electric SX-G5); power supply, 0-30 V dc; power supply, 0-150 V dc; ammeters, ac, 2-15 A; VTVM; load resistance, 8-12 ohms, 1200-1800 W, such as a heating element.

Procedure:

Part A

1. Check maximum ratings of SX-G2 saturable reactor.
2. Connect saturable reactor and load as shown in Fig. 36. Have wiring approved.
3. Set control voltage at zero and apply line voltage to load circuit.
4. Record load voltage and current.
5. Increase control voltage from zero in 5-volt steps. (Observe rated maximum.) Record corresponding load-voltage and load-current values. (Observe rated maximum load current.)

6. Plot load voltage as a function of control voltage.

Part B

1. Repeat procedure in Part A using a General Electric SX-G5. Use 10-volt step-increases in control voltage. Do not exceed rated maximums of saturable reactor.
2. Plot load current as a function of control voltage.

Elementary Saturable-Reactor and Magnetic-Amplifier Circuits

Purpose: To study (A) an elementary two-reactor control circuit and (B) an elementary, self-saturating, magnetic-amplifier circuit.

Devices and Equipment: Two transformers, filament, 120/6.3 V, 10 A; two rectifiers, 1 A, 200 V, PVR; dc supply, 0-20 V, 10 A; ammeter, 0-10 A, dc; VTVM; lamp 75-100 W.

Procedure:

Part A

1. Wire circuit as shown in Fig. 37; high-voltage windings in parallel as load coils, low-voltage windings in series as control coils. Have wiring approved.
2. Apply 120 V ac to load circuit.

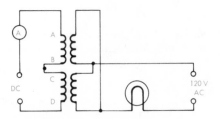

Fig. 37. *Two-reactor control circuit.*

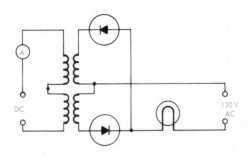

Fig. 38. *Elementary self-saturating magnetic amplifier.*

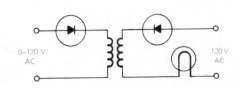

Fig. 39. *Basic Ramey magnetic-amplifier circuit.*

3. With no dc applied to control circuit check control coils for induced voltage. Measure V_{AD}. If V_{AD} is 12-14 V interchange A and B or C and D (not both). Recheck for zero induced voltage.
4. Record lamp condition and load voltage.
5. Apply dc control current, increasing from zero to approximately saturation (indicated by load voltage). Record lamp condition and load voltage.
6. Change control-voltage polarity. Repeat step 5.

Part B

1. Add two rectifiers, as shown in Fig. 38, to form a self-saturating magnetic amplifier with ac output. Have wiring approved.
2. Repeat steps 2 through 6 in Part A.
3. Write a statement comparing operation of the two circuits.

Basic Ramey Magnetic-Amplifier Circuit

Purpose: To study operation of a basic Ramey magnetic-amplifier circuit.
Devices and Equipment: Isolation transformer, 120/120 V, 150 VA; two rectifiers, silicon, 1 A, 200 V PVR; fixed 120 V ac supply; variable (0-120 V ac) supply; lamp, 60-75 W.

Procedure:
1. Wire circuit as shown in Fig. 39. Have wiring approved.
2. Connect VTVM across load.
3. Apply fixed 120 V ac to load circuit. Record lamp condition and load voltage.
4. Apply variable ac to control circuit, increasing from zero to 120 V. Record effects on lamp and load voltage.
5. Interchange line connections to either control or load circuit (not both).

254

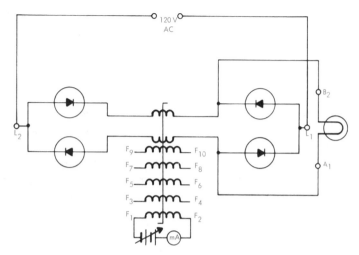

Fig. 40. *Industrial magnetic amplifier in a self-saturating, full-wave-bridge configuration.*

6. Repeat step 4, recording effects on lamp and load voltage.
7. Write a statement explaining operation of this circuit.

Industrial Magnetic Amplifier

Purpose: To study operation of an industrial magnetic amplifier in a self-saturating, full-wave-bridge configuration.

Devices and Equipment: Magnetic amplifier, (General Electric Amplistat 9T75Y24); 2 power supplies, low-voltage dc; VTVM; milliammeter; lamp, 60 W.

Procedure:

1. Study specifications and ratings of magnetic amplifier.
2. Wire load and control circuits as indicated in Fig. 40: 120 V ac line to L_1 and L_2, lamp load to A_1 and B_2; control winding, F_1-F_2, and milliammeter in series to low-voltage dc power supply. Have wiring approved.

3. Set control voltage at zero. Apply load voltage.
4. Record lamp condition and voltage.
5. Increase control current in steps from zero. (Observe rated maximum). Record corresponding load-voltage values.
6. Reverse polarity of control voltage and repeat step 5.
7. Apply low dc bias voltage to another winding. Repeat step 5.
8. Reverse polarity of bias voltage and repeat step 5.
9. Set up optimum operating conditions and check operation of system. Record results.
10. Write statement explaining: (A) operation of magnetic amplifier in steps 5 and 6 and (B) the effects of bias in steps 7 and 8.

Magnetic Amplifier with AC Load

Purpose: To study operation of a magnetic amplifier as an ac-load control.

Devices and Equipment: Magnetic amplifier, (General Electric Amplistat 9T75Y24); 2 power supplies, low voltage dc; VTVM; milliammeter; lamp, 60 W.

Procedure:

1. Study specifications and ratings of magnetic amplifier.
2. Wire load and control circuits as indicated in Fig. 41: A_1 to B_2 to L_1 to one side of 120 V ac line; lamp load between L_2 and other side of ac line; control winding, F_1-F_2, and milliammeter in series to low-voltage dc power supply. Have wiring approved.
3. Set control voltage at zero. Apply load voltage.
4. Record lamp condition and voltage.
5. Increase control current in steps from zero. (Observe rated maximum). Record corresponding load-voltage values.

6. Reverse polarity of control voltage and repeat step 5.
7. Apply low dc bias voltage to another winding. Repeat step 5.
8. Reverse polarity of bias voltage and repeat step 5.
9. Set up optimum operating conditions and check operation of system. Record results.
10. Write a statement concerning the effectiveness of a magnetic amplifier as an ac-load control.

Magnetic-Amplifier Application: Speed Change as Control Signal

Purpose: To observe how speed changes can be utilized by a magnetic amplifier to produce desired changes in load operation.
Devices and Equipment: Magnetic amplifier, (General Electric Amplistat 9T75Y24);

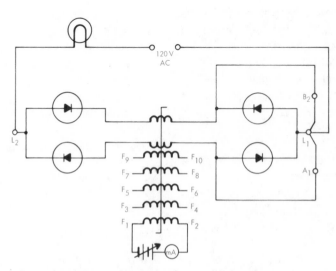

Fig. 41. *Test circuit to study magnetic amplifier as an ac-load control.*

tachometer generator, dc (Servo-Tek Products Co. type SA-740A-7); VTVM; 2 power supplies, low-voltage dc; lamp, 60 W.

Procedure:

1. Study specifications and ratings of magnetic amplifier and tachometer generator.
2. Wire magnetic amplifier in a self-saturating full-wave bridge configuration with a lamp load. (See experiment on Industrial Magnetic Amplifier.) Connect tachometer generator to a control winding. Have wiring approved.
3. Apply load voltage. Record lamp condition and voltage.
4. Apply rotational force to tachometer generator shaft (power drill, rotating wheel, etc.). Monitor generator output voltage—observe rated output.
5. Vary shaft speed and record effects on lamp condition and voltage.
6. Interchange generator leads and repeat step 5.
7. Apply low dc bias voltage to a winding and test operation of system. Record results.
8. Write a statement comparing the effects of speed changes on magnetic amplifier output with and without bias.

Try writing out the answer
to each question before look-
ing up the answer.

Review Questions

1. What is a magnetic amplifier?
2. What is the basis of saturable reactor operation?
3. Explain magnetic saturation.
4. What does the hysteresis loop of a magnetic material show?
5. Why is coil reactance minimum during saturation?
6. Why is the load coil of a saturable reactor connected in series with the load?
7. Why is the load current in Fig. 5 minimum when the control current is minimum?
8. What is a disadvantage of the circuit in Fig. 5?
9. Explain how unwanted voltages are eliminated from the control coils in Fig. 6.
10. What is an advantage of parallel-connected saturable-reactor load coils?
11. In Fig. 12, why is the load-coil voltage maximum when the control current is minimum?
12. Explain self-saturation.
13. What is an important advantage of self-saturation?
14. What purposes can be served by additional control-leg coils?
15. How does bias current set the operating point of a magnetic amplifier?
16. Why is a bridge circuit superior to the full-wave circuit of Fig. 20 when the load is inductive?
17. In Fig. 24, what causes the characteristic curves to start leveling off as the ampere-turns increase?
18. Why is good power transfer usually achieved in low-power magnetic-amplifier circuits?
19. What are two advantages of the push-pull magnetic amplifier over the single-ended form?
20. In Fig. 26 what occurs if R_A is not equal to R_B?
21. Explain how the steeper slope of the composite characteristic in Fig. 27 indicates greater amplification than is indicated by the slopes of the single characteristics.
22. Define two forms of feedback.
23. Differentiate between the time constant and the response time of a magnetic amplifier.
24. What control-circuit factors affect the response delay of a magnetic amplifier?
25. List some features of saturable reactors and magnetic amplifiers which make them suitable for a variety of industrial applications.

Answers to
Review Questions

Answers to Review Questions

1. A magnetic amplifier is a control unit consisting of a saturable reactor and additional components, principally rectifiers.

2. Saturable-reactor operation is based on the principle that a changing current in a coil produces an electromagnetic field which creates opposition to the changing current.

3. Magnetic saturation is a term which denotes complete magnetization of a piece of magnetic material. Any further increase in magnetizing force cannot increase the flux density.

4. The hysteresis loop of a magnetic material shows magnetization of the material as a function of magnetizing force for one cycle of alternating current.

5. Coil reactance is minimum during saturation because, during this time, the rate of change of flux, which determines the reactance, is minimum.

6. The load coil of a saturable reactor is connected in series with the load so that, as its reactance is varied, the load current and the load voltage vary inversely with the reactance.

7. The load current in Fig. 5 is minimum when the control current is minimum because, at this time, the load-coil reactance is maximum.

8. A disadvantage of the circuit in Fig. 5 is that the secondary-coil flux can generate undesirable voltages in the control coil.

9. Unwanted voltages are eliminated from the control coils in Fig. 6 by winding the load and control coils so that voltages induced in the control coils by the ac fluxes are of opposing polarities and thereby cancel.

10. Parallel-connected saturable-reactor load coils can control greater current than the same coils connected in series.

11. When the control current in Fig. 12 is minimum the core is unsaturated, allowing the load coil to develop maximum impedance. When the impedance of the load coil is maximum the voltage across it is maximum and that across the load is minimum (series circuit action).

12. Self-saturation occurs when the magnetism produced in a saturable-reactor core by one half-cycle of load current is not "reset" during the alternate half-cycle. The growth of magnetism over a number of cycles results in "self-saturation."

13. Self-saturation utilizes the load current to produce core saturation, allowing the control-current flux to vary the degree of magnetization.

14. Additional control-leg coils can be utilized to carry load-circuit feedback, bias currents and multiple control currents.

15. Bias current opposes the self-saturating effect of the load-coil current, thereby setting the magnetic-amplifier operating point below saturation on the B-H curve.

16. When the load is inductive a bridge rectifier is superior to the full-wave circuit of Fig. 20 because it eliminates instability of operation caused by the "inductive kick" of the load.

17. In Fig. 24 the characteristic curves

level off as the ampere-turns increase because the core saturates, causing the load-circuit impedance to become constant. This results in leveling off of the load current.

18. In low-power magnetic-amplifier circuits the source and load impedances can usually be closely matched, thereby achieving good power transfer.

19. Two advantages of the push-pull magnetic amplifier over the single-ended form are: reversible output polarity and zero output-current capability.

20. If R_A and R_B in Fig. 26 are not equal, zero output cannot be achieved under normal operating conditions.

21. Greater amplification is indicated by the composite characteristic in Fig. 27 because its steeper slope shows a greater change in load current for equal changes in control current than the slopes of the single characteristics.

22. Two forms of feedback are: (1) the self-saturating effect of the load current, known as *internal feedback*, and (2) feedback produced by passing the load current through a feedback coil, called *external feedback*.

23. The time constant of a magnetic amplifier is the time (seconds) required for the output to reach 63.2% of its final value; the response time is the time (seconds) required for the output to reach a selected percentage, such as 95%, of its final value; both parameters in response to an instantaneous control-current change.

24. The response delay of a magnetic amplifier is affected by the inductance and resistance of the control circuit. It is directly proportional to the inductance and inversely proportional to the resistance.

25. Features of saturable reactors and magnetic amplifiers which make them suitable for a variety of industrial applications are: low power dissipation, high reliability, good overload capacity, long life and resistance to shock and vibration.

UNIT 5

Thermoelectrics

Unit 5

Contents

263

Unit 5

List of Tables

List of Illustrations

Unit 5

Unit 5

section 1 Introduction

Thermoelectrics is an important area of industrial electronics. Considered broadly, the term "thermoelectric" applies to everything which involves both heat and electricity. However, this book is not concerned with electrical heating as it is found in toasters, irons, hotplates, etc. Rather, it deals with fundamental principles of thermoelectricity and their applications in such devices as thermocouples, thermistors, resistance thermometers and Peltier-effect equipment.

The field of thermoelectricity has benefitted greatly from the enormous expansion of semiconductor technology which has occurred since World War II. The use of semiconductor materials has made possible the development of various forms of thermoelectric devices: heaters, coolers and combination units which can be converted from heater to cooler and vice-versa with the flip of a switch.

At the present time thermoelectric cooling units are small-scale devices used in various laboratory and industrial applications. Some consumer units are available, such as a baby-bottle heater/cooler and a

5

food-service cart in which separate compartments keep some items hot and others cold.

Because of their high cost and low efficiency, home-size thermoelectric refrigerators are not yet available, although some demonstration models have been produced —including smaller units for trailers, boats and room air-conditioners.

The utilization of small-scale thermoelectric devices is expected to expand greatly in the years to come. The production and use of larger units (home heaters, coolers, freezers, etc.) will become practical as research in solid-state technology makes available materials which are less expensive and more efficient than those now available.

Most of the thermal data in this book are expressed in degrees Fahrenheit (°F)— part of the U.S. Customary System—because this system is the one in general use by American manufacturers of thermoelectric devices. Some temperatures, however, are given in degrees Celsius (°C), following usual metric practice. For conversion, purposes, these formulas may be used:

$$°F = \frac{9}{5}\left(°C\right) + 32° \qquad °C = \frac{5}{9}\left(°F - 32°\right)$$

or   *or*

$$°F = 1.8\left(°C\right) + 32° \qquad °C = \frac{°F - 32°}{1.8}$$

Neither Celsius nor Fahrenheit temperatures can be used for calculations involving temperature changes based on *proportions*, however. For such purposes the Kelvin (absolute temperature) scale must be used. In this scale, using the Kelvin as the recognized S.I. metric unit of thermodynamic temperature, 0° K is the point of zero molecular heat energy, and is equivalent to 273.16° C, so the freezing point of water, 0° C = 273.16° K.

Therefore:

$$°K = °C + 273.16 \text{ or } °C = °K - 273.16$$

To convert from Kelvin to Fahrenheit or vice-versa, a good method is to first make the conversion in terms of °C.

Since °0 K is absolute zero (by definition), no minus Kelvin temperatures are possible.

Unit 5

section 2 Thermocouples

One of the pioneers in the study of thermoelectricity was Thomas J. Seebeck. In 1821 he found that when the ends of two dissimilar metals were fused together and one junction heated, a current flowed in the circuit formed by the wires. This phenomenon became known as the "Seebeck effect." Modern forms of dissimilar-metal combinations which develop potentials when heated are known as *thermocouples*.

Fig. 1 shows a thermocouple formed of copper and iron wires. At the heated junction, T-1, electron flow is from the copper to the iron. If the circuit is broken a potential appears across the open terminals. Thermocouple potential can be shown by heating the fused junction while the other ends of the wires form the "cold" junction at a millivoltmeter, as in Fig. 2.

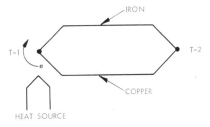

Fig. 1. *Basic thermocouple operation.*

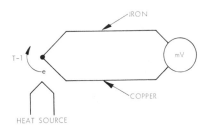

Fig. 2. *Measuring thermocouple potential.*

269

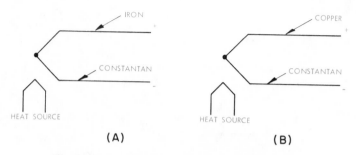

Fig. 3. *Polarities of thermocouple potentials.*

The polarity of the potential developed across the leads from a fused junction depends on the kinds of metal used to form the junction. When a junction of iron and constantan is heated the leads become polarized as at (A) in Fig. 3. A thermocouple of copper and constantan produces the potential shown at (B).

Thermocouples are used extensively as industrial temperature-sensing devices, especially in applications where there is need for high accuracy, wide range of measurement, quick response to temperature changes or good reliability.

Thermocouple Construction: Circuitry

Technically, a thermocouple consists of a loop containing two junctions of dissimilar metals. However, a typical commercial "thermocouple" consists of a fused junction of two dissimilar metals, or alloys, mounted in a metal sheath from which it is insulated, as shown in Fig. 4. Ceramic or mineral material is commonly used for insulation. The unit is completed with the addition of terminals or connecting leads. There are various features in addition to these for specific applications. Examples are the industrial spring-loaded thermocouple shown in Fig. 5 and the self-contained oil-

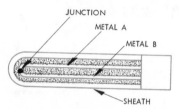

Fig. 4. *Measuring-junction detail.*

seal thermocouple shown in Fig. 6. Other available forms are illustrated in Fig. 7.

The assembly in Fig. 5 consists of a ceramic-insulated probe encased in a metal sheath, called a *thermowell*, and a standard connection head. This is a general-purpose unit which has many applications. Required temperature range determines the type of probe and environment determines the sheath and head materials. The unit in Fig. 6 has an unsheathed probe and an oil seal. It is designed for applications requiring such a seal and fast response in environments which do not require a sheath.

The units in Fig. 7 represent thermocouple forms which are very versatile. The probes can be inserted into small openings, the sheath sections of many models can be bent by hand and the standard plugs

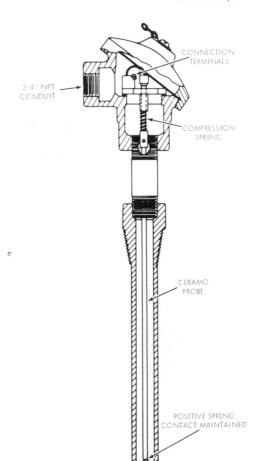

CONNECTION
TERMINALS

3/4" NPT
CONDUIT

COMPRESSION
SPRING

CERAMO
PROBE

POSITIVE SPRING
CONTACT MAINTAINED

Fig. 5. *Industrial spring-loaded thermo-couple. (Courtesy of Thermo Electric.)*

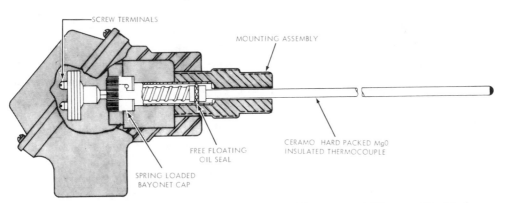

SCREW TERMINALS

MOUNTING ASSEMBLY

FREE FLOATING
OIL SEAL

SPRING LOADED
BAYONET CAP

CERAMO HARD PACKED MgO
INSULATED THERMOCOUPLE

Fig. 6. *Self-contained oil-seal thermocouple. (Courtesy of Thermo Electric.)*

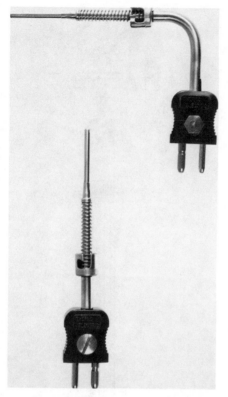

Fig. 7. *Forms of thermocouples. (Courtesy of Thermo Electric.)*

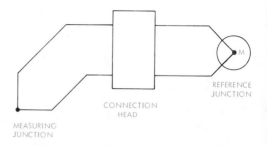

Fig. 8. *Temperature-measuring circuit.*

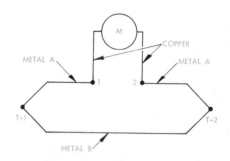

Fig. 9. *Thermocouple circuit with copper extension leads.*

allow for easy interchangeability. These units meet the needs of a large variety of temperature-sensing applications.

The second junction of a thermocouple, which completes the "couple," is formed where the unit is connected to other circuit components. When a commercial thermocouple is used for temperature measurement it is connected to an instrument which provides a reading. This is shown in Fig. 8, where the fused junction is the "hot" or "measuring" junction and the "cold" or "reference" junction is in the meter.

A third kind of conductor may be used

in a thermocouple circuit without affecting its operation if the two junctions formed with the third material are kept at the same temperature. In Fig. 9 copper extension leads are used to connect the thermocouple to an indicating meter. Junctions 1 and 2 must be kept at the same temperature to ensure that the voltage applied to the meter is due only to the difference in temperature between the hot and cold junctions. Fig. 10 shows an iron-constantan thermocouple circuit in which the reference junction is connected between the measuring junction and the meter. In this arrangement it is important that the lead connections in the junction box be at the same temperature.

The output meter may be calibrated to

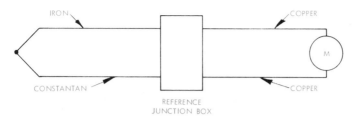

Fig. 10. *Thermocouple circuit with reference-junction box.*

TABLE 1 OUTPUT OF IRON–CONSTANTAN THERMOCOUPLE AT VARIOUS TEMPERATURES

TEMPERATURE °F	OUTPUT mV	TEMPERATURE °F	OUTPUT mV
600	18.07	650	19.61
610	18.38	660	19.92
620	18.68	670	20.23
630	19.00	680	20.53
640	19.30	690	20.84

indicate temperature directly from the generated voltage or a millivoltmeter may be used and the voltage readings converted to degrees of temperature by means of standard data tables. Table 1 gives the outputs for an iron-constantan (type J) thermocouple which generates 0.031 millivolt with each one-degree rise in temperature (Fahrenheit).

The figures in Table 1 indicate that the output of an iron-constantan (IC) thermocouple is rather low. Fig. 11 compares the voltages generated by several different thermocouples. As indicated by the graph, most other commercially-available thermocouples generate less voltage than the IC type. For this reason the output of a thermocouple is often amplified for use in control and indicating instruments.

Multiple-Thermocouple Circuits

An increased thermocouple output can be obtained by wiring two or more thermocouples in series, forming a *thermopile*. The output of the thermopile is the sum of the voltages generated by the individual thermocouples. This enables the detection of a very small temperature change, wherein the output of a single thermocouple would be minimum. Fig. 12 shows a thermopile connected to an indicating meter.

Thermocouples may also be connected in parallel. The output of parallel-connected thermocouples gives an indication of the average temperature of the measuring junctions. This circuit arrangement is illustrated in Fig. 13, where the meter reading is the average temperature of junctions 1, 2 and 3.

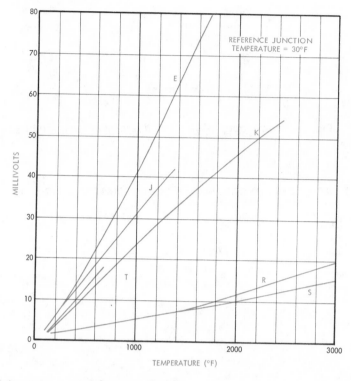

Fig. 11. *Voltage-temperature characteristics of several types of thermocouples.*

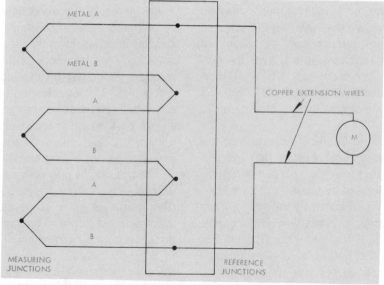

Fig. 12. *Thermopile: several series-connected thermocouples.*

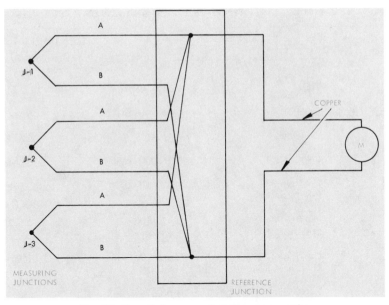

Fig. 13. *Parallel-connected thermocouples.*

Thermocouple Materials

There are many combinations of materials which produce thermoelectric effects but do not qualify for use in thermocouples. In addition to producing thermoelectric effects, thermocouple materials must have reasonable resistance to corrosion, oxidation and other deteriorating effects. The voltage-temperature relation should be linear; that is, equal changes of temperature should produce equal changes of voltage. Also, thermocouples should be made of materials which can be produced uniformly and at reasonable cost.

To meet the above-listed requirements and cover the ranges of temperature and accuracy called for in industrial, medical and other areas of application, a number of thermocouple-metal combinations have come into common use. Several have been adopted as standard, four consisting of "base" metals and alloys (types J,T,K and E) and three consisting of "noble" metals and alloys (types S,R and B). These are listed in Table 2.

The term "base" refers to the common metals used in thermocouples: copper, iron, aluminum, chromium and nickel. "Noble" metal thermocouples are made of platinum and rhodium. To measure temperatures beyond the ranges of these metals, tungsten and rhenium are used.

The four standard base-metal thermocouples are: Iron-Constantan (type J); Copper-Constantan (type T); Chromel-Alumel (type K); Chromel-Constantan (type E). Standard noble-metal thermocouples are: Platinum 100%-Platinum 87%, Rhodium 13% (type R); Platinum 100%-Platinum 90%, Rhodium 10% (type S); Platinum 94%, Rhodium 6%; Platinum 70@, Rhodium 30% (type B).

275

TABLE 2 THERMOCOUPLE TYPES, MATERIALS, AND TEMPERATURE RANGES

TYPE	CONDUCTORS		TEMPERATURE RANGE °F
	+	−	
J	IRON	CONSTANTAN	32 – 1600
T	COPPER	CONSTANTAN	–300 – 700
K	CHROMEL	ALUMEL	32 – 2300
E	CHROMEL	CONSTANTAN	32 – 1600
S	PLATINUM 90% RHODIUM 10%	PLATINUM	32 – 2700
R	PLATINUM 87% RHODIUM 13%	PLATINUM	32 – 2700
B	PLATINUM 70% RHODIUM 30%	PLATINUM 94% RHODIUM 6%	1000 – 3000
WR	TUNGSTEN 74% RHENIUM 26%	TUNGSTEN	2500 – 5000
WRR	TUNGSTEN 74% RHENIUM 26%	TUNGSTEN 95% RHENIUM 5%	2500 – 5000

Constantan is an alloy of copper and nickel, ranging from 50% copper and 50% nickel to 65% copper and 35% nickel. Chromel is an alloy of 90% nickel and 10% chromium. Alumel is an alloy used with Chromel. It consists of 94% nickel, 3% manganese, 2% aluminum and 1% silicon. Chromel and Alumel are trade names used by the Hoskins Co. Corresponding alloys made by the W.B. Driver Co. are Tophel and Nial; those made by the Kanthal Corp. are Thermokanthal KP and Thermokanthal KN. Constantan is produced by the Driver-Harris Co. under the trade name of Advance T and by W.B. Driver Co. as Cupron.

Iron-Constantan (type J) thermocouples have iron for the positive wire and constantan for the negative. Due to their good output and relatively low cost they are used extensively throughout industry. Their range is from about 0°F to 1600°F for the largest wire size, with correspondingly lower maximums for smaller wire sizes.

Copper-Constantan (type T) thermocouples have copper for the positive wire and constantan for the negative. This thermocouple has a lower minimum operating temperature than other types, extending from +700°F down to −300°F. Its good resistance to corrosion caused by moisture condensation permits it to work well at sub-zero temperatures.

Chromel-Alumel (type K) thermocouples consist of two alloys: nickel-chromium as the positive wire and nickel-aluminum as the negative wire. They can be used up to 2300°F in clean, oxidizing atmospheres.

Chromel-Constantan (type E) thermocouples have a Chromel positive wire and a constantan negative wire. They produce a high and stable output up to 1600°F, the highest output of common thermocouples. They are recommended for use in vacuums and mildly-reactive atmospheres.

Platinum-Platinum Rhodium (type S) thermocouples have a negative wire of pure platinum and a positive wire of 90% platinum and 10% rhodium. They have excellent chemical and mechanical properties, low electrical resistance and are very stable. Their operating range is from 32°F to 2700°F. Because of their reliability they are used in calibrating base-metal thermocouples and have been adopted as the standard for the International Temperature Scale between 1167°F and 1945°F.

Platinum-Platinum Rhodium (type R) thermocouples have a negative wire of pure platinum and a positive wire of 87% platinum and 13% rhodium. Like type S thermocouples, they have excellent chemical and mechanical properties and operate in temperatures up to 2700°F. Their output in the upper part of the range is slightly higher than that of type S.

Platinum, Rhodium-Platinum, Rhodium (type B) thermocouples consist of two alloys: 94% platinum and 6% rhodium as the negative wire, 70% platinum and 30% rhodium as the positive wire. They have a higher range than types S and R (up to 3000°F) but have a low output and are not recommended for temperatures below 1000°F. Because of their high cost and low output, noble-metal thermocouples are generally used where precision is required, where the temperature is beyond the range of base-metal types, and for calibration standards.

Tungsten and rhenium are used to form thermocouples for the measurement of temperatures above 3000°F. Tungsten melts at 6170°F and rhenium at 5730°F, much higher than the melting points of other metals used in thermocouples. The following combinations measure temperatures in the 2500°F-5000°F range: (a) 100% tungsten-74% tungsten, 26% rhenium; (b) 95% tungsten, 5% rhenium-74% tungsten, 26% rhenium; (c) 97% tungsten, 3% rhenium-75% tungsten, 25% rhenium. A tungsten-rhenium thermocouple oxidizes rapidly if used in an atmosphere containing oxygen. However, it can be used in a hydrogen or inert-gas atmosphere, or in a vacuum.

Thermocouple Extension Wires

In most thermocouple installations reference junctions and indicating instruments are located some distance from the measuring junctions. Connecting wires add junctions which can cause errors in the output. Provisions must be made to eliminate or minimize these errors.

One method of error reduction calls for the use of extension wires made of the same metals as the thermocouple. They are available as single leads or matched pairs. While this method is acceptable for base-metal thermocouple connections it is very expensive for platinum thermocouple installations. However, a copper-nickel alloy wire has been developed for use with a copper wire in matching platinum thermocouples. This alloy is known as "platinum-compensated lead wire." The W.B. Driver Co. markets it under the trade name "PCLW." Paired-copper PCLW wires can be used as extension leads for types R and S platinum thermocouples. Copper and 30-6 PCLW leads are recommended for use with type B thermocouples. (See Table 3.)

TABLE 3 THERMOCOUPLE EXTENSION WIRES

THERMOCOUPLE TYPE	EXTENSION TYPE	EXTENSION MATERIALS	RANGE °F
E	EX	CHROMEL–CONSTANTAN	0 – 400
J	JX	IRON–CONSTANTAN	0 – 400
T	TX	COPPER–CONSTANTAN	–75 – 200
K	KK	CHROMEL–ALUMEL	0 – 400
R	RX	COPPER–PCLW	75 – 400
S	SX	COPPER–PCLW	75 – 400
B	BX	COPPER–COPPER	32 – 250
B	BX	COPPER–PCLW (30–6)	32 – 400

Reference Junctions

Variations in the temperature of the reference junction in a thermocouple circuit can affect the output voltage, resulting in an incorrect indication of the measuring junction temperature. For accuracy, the reference junction should be kept at a constant temperature. Devices used for this purpose are: (1) ice bath, (2) refrigerated cell, (3) oven, and (4) bridge circuit.

In the ice-bath method the reference junction is immersed in a container of ice and water, as illustrated in Fig. 14. For proper operation frequent stirring is necessary. Also, water must be drawn off at the bottom and ice added at the top. In addition, correct immersion depth must be maintained. Because this method is rather inconvenient and suitable mainly for laboratory work, other methods are generally utilized in practical industrial applications.

One form of the refrigerated cell method is shown in Fig. 15. Here a thermoelectric cooling unit keeps a sealed container of water at "ice-point." (32°F). When the water freezes, pressure of the expanding ice causes a bellows to operate a microswitch, deenergizing the cooling unit. When the ice starts to melt, pressure on the bellows decreases and the switch reactivates the cooling unit. This cycle repeats continuously, maintaining the immersed reference junction at 32°F. Due to its automatic operation, the refrigerated cell does not require attention as does the simple ice bath.

The oven method of reference-junction temperature control uses either a single- or double-oven arrangement. A typical oven consists of an electrically-heated block accommodating one or more junctions which it maintains at a precisely-controlled temperature. A single-oven unit is illustrated in Fig. 16. Some ovens are made in the form of thermal blocks which can accommodate 100 or more junctions. Since all reference junctions in the block are at the same temperature, highly-accurate multiple mea-

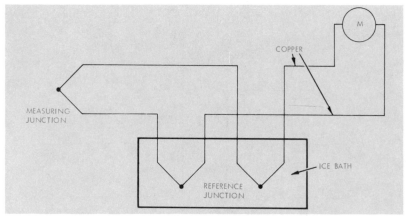

Fig. 14. *Ice bath maintains constant reference-junction temperature.*

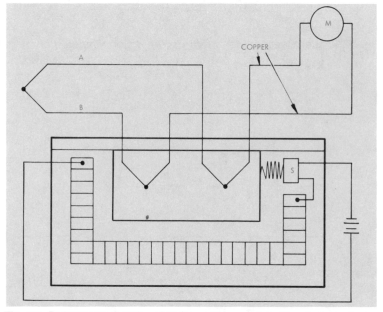

Fig. 15. *Refrigerated cell maintains reference-junction temperature.*

surements can be made. For proper operation the temperature of the single-oven unit must be at least 25°F above the ambient temperature.

A double-oven unit is shown in Fig. 17. In this arrangement the two ovens are heated to different temperatures. When these temperatures are applied to a certain

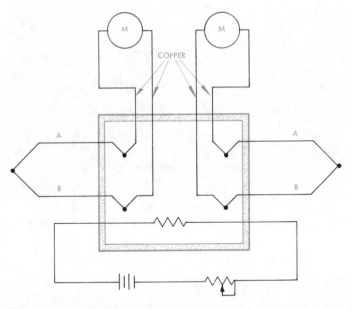

Fig. 16. *Single-oven method of reference-junction temperature control.*

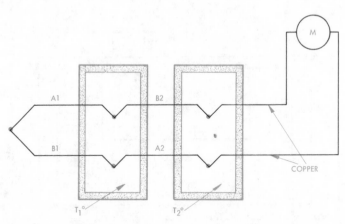

Fig. 17. *Double-oven method of producing ice-point reference temperature (32° F).*

combination of thermocouple-wire junctions (chosen to match a measuring junction) the result is the electrical equivalent of a reference temperature which is lower than either oven temperature.

In Fig. 17 leads A-1 and A-2 are of the same alloy, such as Alumel. B-1 and B-2 are also alike, but of a different alloy, such as Chromel. In oven A a certain "error" voltage is produced across leads A-1,B-1 at temperature T-1. In oven B an "error" voltage is produced across leads B-2, A-2 at temperature T-2. This voltage is equal and opposite to the A-1,B-1 voltage; hence they cancel leaving zero error volts at the output. This is equivalent to a reference temperature of 32°F. In operation, the difference between this equivalent reference temperature and the measuring junction temperature generates the output to the readout device.

The foregoing methods of reference-junction temperature control (ice bath, refrigerated cell and oven) are useful in the laboratory and in some industrial applications. However, there are many situations in industry which require the capabilities of the thermocouple but for which these methods of reference-junction temperature control are unsuitable. This is also true of aircraft and missile applications. The requirements of these applications are met by a compact, rugged device containing a bridge circuit which automatically compensates for changes in the cold-junction temperature. Because it can be made very small (less than 1″ x ¾″ x ½″) and lightweight (5 grams), it uses little space and can be placed close to the measuring junction, eliminating inaccuracy due to long leads. Its compactness and convenience has led to its use in a great variety of applica-

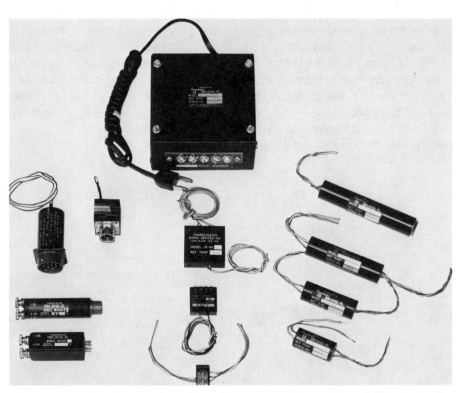

Fig. 18. *Thermocouple reference junctions. (Courtesy of Consolidated Ohmic Devices, Inc.)*

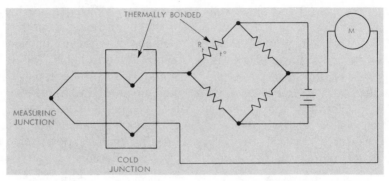

Fig. 19. *Bridge-circuit method of temperature compensation.*

tions. Commercially, units which contain the bridge circuit, cold junction, terminals, switch, and sometimes a battery, are known as *thermocouple reference junctions.* Fig. 18 shows a number of such units.

A temperature-measuring system which utilizes bridge-circuit compensation is illustrated in Fig. 19. One leg of the bridge, R_t, is a temperature-sensitive resistance which is thermally bonded to the cold junction. (Thermal bonding is joining the metals with a special thermally-conductive epoxy.) If the temperature of the junction varies, error voltages are produced which could affect the accuracy of the output. However, since R_t is bonded to the junction, its resistance will change with any change in junction temperature. The change in R_t unbalances the bridge, producing a voltage in series with error voltage. These voltages are equal and opposite. They cancel, reducing the error voltage to zero. In this manner changes in the temperature of the cold junction are automatically compensated for by operation of the bridge circuit.

Unit 5

section 3

Peltier Effect, Devices and Applications

In 1834, thirteen years after Seebeck's discovery, Jean Peltier produced the effect which bears his name. He found that when he passed a current through a junction of two dissimilar metals, the junction became either hot or cold depending on the direction of the current. Further investigation showed that when electrons move through a junction in the same direction as through the hot junction in the Seebeck effect, they pass from a lower to a higher energy level. (Electrons in different metals exist at different energy levels. When an electron passes from one metal to another its energy level changes to the energy level of the electrons in the metal to which it passes.) The increase in energy of electrons moving through a junction is achieved through the absorption of the thermal energy—which causes the junction to cool. When electrons move through a junction in the same direction as through the cold junction in the Seebeck effect they go from a higher to a lower energy level. The excess energy is given off as heat, thereby increasing the junction temperature.

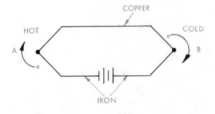

Fig. 20. *Peltier effect.*

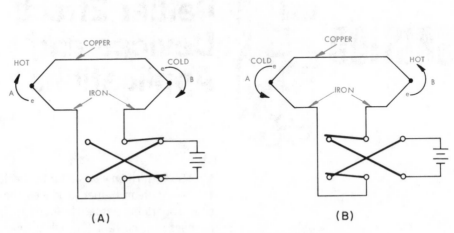

(A)   (B)

Fig. 21. *Junction temperatures may be interchanged.*

The Peltier effect is illustrated in Fig. 20. In this circuit electrons pass through junction A from the higher energy level of iron to the lower energy level of copper. The excess energy heats the junction. At junction B electrons move from a lower to a higher energy level. The additional energy is supplied from the thermal energy of the junction. As a result this junction cools.

Reversing the direction of the current causes opposite effects at the junctions. This is shown in Fig. 21. With the switch in the position shown at (A), electron flow through junction A from iron to copper creates a hot junction. At junction B, electron flow from copper to iron creates a cold junction. If the switch is thrown to its alternate position, as shown at (B), electron flow

through the junctions is reversed. Thus, at junction A current from copper to iron decreases the junction temperature and at junction B current from iron to copper increases the junction temperatur

Peltier Effect in Semiconductors

Greater thermoelectric effects can be achieved in semiconductors than in metals. Rather effective junctions are formed by combining metals with both P and N materials. Semiconductors fabricated for thermoelectric applications are much more highly doped than those formulated for transistors. However, unlike transistor action, thermoelectric effects in semiconductors do not involve minority carriers or recombination of injected *carriers*. (Carriers are energy transporters. In N-type semiconductors electrons are the *majority* carriers and holes are the *minority* carriers. In P-type materials holes are the majority carriers and electrons are the minority carriers.)

When heat is produced by the Peltier effect it is in addition to any *joule heating* (heating due to normal current flow). An index of the heating or cooling capacity of a junction is the Peltier coefficient (Π) which expresses the number of joules of heat liberated or absorbed at a junction per coulomb of charges through the junction. This figure varies according to the materials used in forming the junctions. It is much higher for semiconductor-to-metal junctions than for metal-to-metal junctions.

One of the most effective thermoelectric semiconductor materials is bismuth telluride (Bi_2Te_3). It has the property of greatly impeding the flow of conventional (joule) heat from hot to cold areas, yet is a good conductor of thermoelectric carriers. Another feature of this semiconductor is a supply of intrinsic carriers which have good heat-transport capacity.

Heating and Cooling. Whether a semiconductor-metal junction is heated or cooled by a current through it depends, as in metal-to-metal junctions, on the direction of the current. A junction formed of N-type material and metal is illustrated in Fig. 22. Here electrons going from the semiconductor to the metal have greater energy than electrons in the metal. The moving electrons give up some of their energy and drop to the energy level of the metal electrons. The excess energy heats the junction area.

If the current direction is reversed, electron movement is from metal to semiconductor. However, only the more energetic electrons pass through the junction. These electrons require additional energy to raise

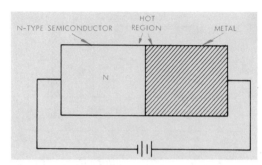

Fig. 22. *Thermoelectrically-heated semiconductor-metal junction.*

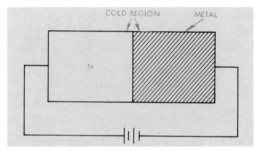

Fig. 23. *Thermoelectrically-cooled semiconductor-metal junction.*

them to the level of semiconductor electrons. This energy is absorbed from the thermal energy of the region, resulting in a cooling effect at the junction. This action is illustrated in Fig. 23.

The heating and cooling of semiconductor-metal junctions can be combined to produce practical thermoelectric configurations known as *Peltier-effect devices*. An elementary form is illustrated in Fig. 24. Here a piece of N-type semiconductor is mounted between two pieces of metal. As electrons move from the lower energy state of metal A to the higher level of the semiconductor they absorb heat energy from the

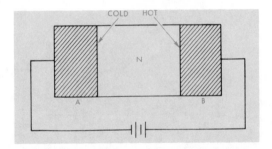

Fig. 24. *Elementary Peltier-effect device.*

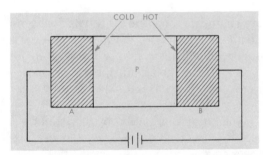

Fig. 26. *Peltier-effect device formed with P-type semiconductor.*

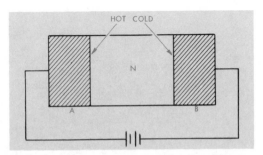

Fig. 25. *Current-reversal interchanges hot and cold junctions.*

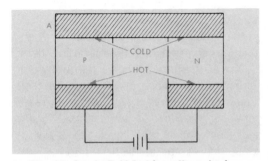

Fig. 27. *Basic P-N Peltier-effect device.*

junction region, cooling it. As electrons pass from the semiconductor to the lower energy level of metal B their excess energy heats the junction area.

If the polarity of the potential applied in Fig. 24 is reversed, the junction at metal A is heated and that at metal B is cooled. This effect is shown in Fig. 25. In each case thermal flow through the semiconductor is in the direction of the energy carriers (electrons).

Fig. 26 shows an elementary Peltier-effect device containing P-type material. When the current is in the same direction as in the N-type device the thermal effects are opposite. When potential is applied as in Fig. 26, electrons move from metal B to the semiconductor and from the semiconductor to metal A. Holes (heat carriers in P-type materials) move in the opposite direction through the semiconductor. Heat is liberated where electrons pass into the semiconductor, increasing the temperature of this junction. Where electrons pass from the semiconductor to the metal heat is absorbed and this junction cools. Reversal of current direction produces opposite effects at the junctions.

Both P- and N-type semiconductor-metal junctions can be combined to form Peltier-effect devices which are more efficient than devices containing only one type of semi-conductor. Fig. 27 illustrates a simple P-N configuration. This unit incorporates the effects produced in Figs. 25 and 26. At the junctions where electrons go from metal to P and N to metal the temperature increases. Where electrons go from P to metal and metal to N the junction temperature decreases.

Change in polarity of the applied voltage interchanges the hot and cold junctions. Thus, by means of a reversing switch (as in Fig. 21) metal A can function as a cooling element or as a heating element.

Applications of Semiconductor-Metal Junctions. The cooling effect of current flow through semiconductor-metal junctions is utilized in a number of commercially-available refrigeration units. Some contain a few P-N pairs, others contain several dozen.

Fig. 28 shows the basic components of this type of device. In addition to the junctions, the unit incorporates "interfaces" and a heat sink. The interfaces are composed of ceramics and metals. Electrically they are good insulators but thermally they are good conductors. Shown also is a "workpiece"—an item to be cooled.

In operation, as electrons move through the unit in the direction of P to N, thermo-electric action absorbs heat from the work piece and transfers it to the heat sink. Unless the heat sink is comparatively large some means must be provided for cooling it. One common method utilizes fins and a blower.

Fig. 29 shows a cooling unit consisting of a number of P-N pairs. They are connected electrically in series and thermally in parallel. The rate at which heat is absorbed and transferred to the heat sink depends on the number of P-N pairs, the amount of current and the type of semi-conductor material. For efficient operation of the unit, the semiconductor must have a good supply of carriers for thermoelectric heat transfer and minimum conventional heat conduction. As stated previously, bismuth telluride is a material which meets these requirements.

The unit in Fig. 29 is known as a single-stage module. Present state-of-the-art limits the possible temperature difference be-

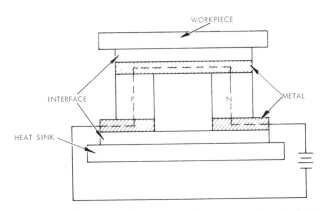

Fig. 28. *Basic thermoelectric cooling unit and workpiece.*

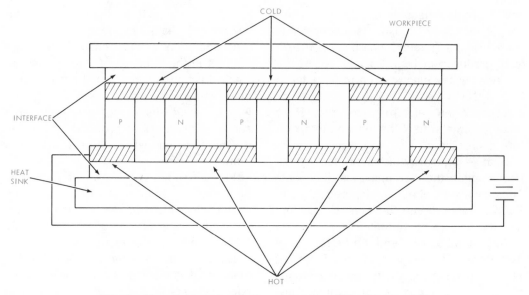

Fig. 29. *Thermoelectric cooling unit with multiple P-N pairs.*

between the hot and cold junctions of such a unit to about 70°C (158°F). To achieve greater temperature differentials, units may be "cascaded." Cascading is the stacking of units (or stages) so that they are series-connected thermally. In such a configuration each stage acts as a heat sink for the one above it.

To serve adequately as a heat sink each stage must be larger than the one it is serving. Consequently, stages are successively smaller from bottom to top. A design which meets this requirement is illustrated in Fig. 30. As the stages diminish in size, the temperature difference across each one decreases. At the present time the practical limit is five or six stages with an overall temperature difference of about 125°C, or 257°F.

Commercially-available single-stage and

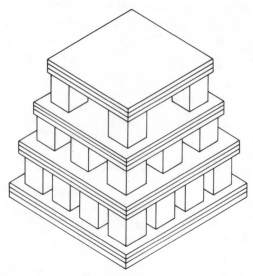

Fig. 30. *Multiple-junction stages series-connected thermally to form cooling unit.*

Fig. 31. *Cascaded thermoelectric cooling unit. (Courtesy of Borg-Warner Corp.)*

Fig. 32. *Thermoelectric heat pump. (Courtesy of Borg-Warner Corp.)*

multi-stage cooling units are shown in Figs. 31 and 32.

The unit in Fig. 32 is known as a *heat pump.* Instead of a metal heat sink it has cooling fins and a fan. Air forced over the fins by the fan acts as the heat sink. This form of heat pump is used for loads up to about 200 watts, with temperature differentials up to about 30°C (86°F).

Thermoelectric cooling devices have several features which make them appropriate for many applications. They are very reliable, have no moving parts, no liquids, no gases, and no compressor. The size of an installation can be increased or decreased by adding or subtracting P-N modules—thus cooling units can be matched closely to load requirements. Only the unit and heat sink are required where the cooling is done; the power supply and control equipment can be at a remote location. Temperatures can be maintained accurately with electronic control of the operating current.

Thermoelectric coolers are found in a variety of industrial, commercial, medical, and laboratory applications. They serve as constant-temperature chambers, circuit-testing chambers, aircraft water coolers, chemical coolers, blood coagulators, mobile drug coolers and in many other applications having requirements which can be met more efficiently by the thermoelectric method than by other methods of cooling.

The thermoelectric method of cooling seems at first glance so attractive compared to conventional electromechanical methods that these appear obsolete. However, in the present state of the art, thermoelectric cooling is inefficient for larger than "small scale" applications. Not more than 5 percent of applied energy is converted because of present limitations of material properties. The efficiency of electromechanical coolers *increases* with size, but in small sizes the electromechanical coolers decrease in efficiency. Presently thermoelectric coolers are economically competitive only in small sizes.

Unit 5

section 4

Resistance Temperature Detectors

The resistance of most electrical conductors varies directly with temperature. Increases of temperature cause corresponding changes in resistance. Such materials are said to have a positive *temperature coefficient of resistance* (alpha). (Temperature coefficient of resistance is the percent change in resistance per degree Celsius change in temperature.) This principle is utilized in a type of temperature sensor known as a resistance temperature detector (RTD).

The change in resistance of an RTD due to a temperature change can be used to indicate the amount of temperature change. The resistance of an RTD can also be used to indicate the absolute value of an ambient temperature. If an RTD is wired into a circuit, as in Fig. 33, and its temperature increases, the resulting increase in resistance will cause a decrease in current. If the meter is calibrated in degrees the temperature change can be read directly. Resistance temperature detectors are used

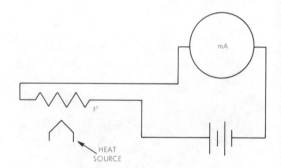

Fig. 33. *RTD circuit. RTD resistance increases with increased temperature.*

to measure temperatures ranging from −400°F to +1700°F.

RTDs have certain advantages over other types of temperature sensors. Their response is more linear (over a particular operating range, equal changes of temperature produce equal changes of resistance). This eliminates the need for non-linearity correction. There is no cold-junction compensation, and copper leads can be used to connect RTDs to readout devices. RTDs remain very stable indefinitely, making frequent recalibration unnecessary.

RTD Materials

Resistance temperature detectors are made with fine wires of platinum, nickel, copper, tungsten and nickel-iron alloys. The most common are made of nickel and platinum. Generally, nickel is used to measure temperatures from about $-200°F$ to $+600°F$ with an accuracy of $0.6°F$. Platinum is used over a greater range: $-450°F$ to $+1700°F$. Accuracy of $0.1°F$ or better is possible with platinum. While copper can be used from $-300°F$ to $+250°F$, its linear range is from $+32°F$ to $+212°F$. Sensors of nickel-iron alloy can measure temperatures from $-150°F$ to $+1100°F$ and those made of tungsten from $-350°F$ to $+500°F$.

Nickel is the most sensitive RTD material, having the greatest change in resistance for a unit change in temperature (alpha). This is shown in Table 4, which lists the alpha coefficients of several common sensor materials.

Although nickel is the most sensitive material (alpha $= 0.0067$) the overall performance of the platinum RTD exceeds that of all others. It is used as a standard in defining the International Temperature Scale and is widely used for laboratory standards, calibration of other temperature instruments and precise measurements.

Forms of RTDs

The most common form of RTD is the probe, as shown in Fig. 34. The heart of a

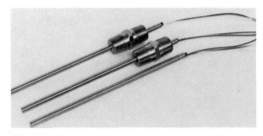

Fig. 34. *General-purpose capsule and spring-loaded RTD probes. (Courtesy of Rosemount, Inc.)*

TABLE 4 ALPHA COEFFICIENTS OF RTD MATERIALS

MATERIAL	ALPHA (%/°C)
PLATINUM	0.0039
NICKEL	0.0067
COPPER	0.0038
TUNGSTEN	0.0045
NICKEL-IRON	0.0045

typical probe is the sensing element, a length of fine wire (platinum, nickel, etc.) wound on a ceramic core. This assembly is mounted in a sheath, usually stainless steel. Some elements are mounted in glass or other material which insulates them from the sheath while providing good thermal transfer from the sheath to the sensor. The construction of an RTD probe is illustrated in Fig. 35. Listed in Table 5 are the materials, resistance values and ranges of some representative industrial RTD probes.

Another form of RTD is a flat, flexible

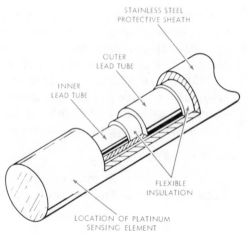

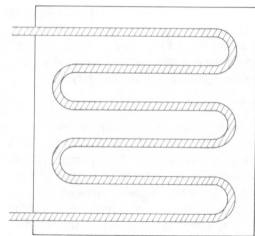

Fig. 35. *Sensor detail of RTD probes shown in Fig. 34. (Courtesy of Rosemount, Inc.)*

Fig. 36. *Flat, flexible RTD unit suitable for surface mounting.*

TABLE 5 INDUSTRIAL RTD PROBES

TYPE	MATERIAL	RESISTANCE (OHMS)	RANGE (°F)
A	NICKEL	110	−160 – 500
B	PLATINUM	100	−320 – 1000
C	PLATINUM	100	−435 – 1700
D	NICKEL-IRON	100	−100 – 800
E	NICKEL	50	−100 – 500
F	PLATINUM	50	−320 – 1500
G	PLATINUM	100	−300 – 1500
H	PLATINUM	100	−60 – 1500
I	NICKEL	200	−100 – 600
J	NICKEL-IRON	200	−50 – 700

unit for use on plane or curved surfaces. The sensing element is formed as shown in Fig. 36 and placed between two layers of insulating material. Some flat RTDs have pressure-sensitive backing to facilitate mounting.

International Temperature-Resistance Characteristic

A number of the larger industrial nations have adopted a set of standard resistance values for RTDs at certain temperatures. These are listed in Table 6 and shown graphically in Fig. 37. According to Fig. 37, the relationship between the temperature and resistance values is approximately linear (equal changes of resistance from equal changes of temperature).

The advantage of an international temperature-resistance characteristic is that RTDs from different manufacturers are interchangeable and may be used as replacements without recalibration of equipment.

RTD Circuits

In Fig. 33 the RTD is a series resistance which varies the current through the meter as the temperature of the RTD changes. Increases in temperature cause increases in resistance which result in decreases in current. A more sensitive system is one in which the RTD is placed in one leg of a bridge circuit, as in Fig. 38. In this circuit changes in the resistance of an RTD can have a greater effect than in a simple series circuit. Small variations in the resistance of an RTD which would not change the meter reading in Fig. 33 could unbalance a bridge circuit (as in Fig. 38) and produce a reading.

Fig. 38 is the simplest RTD bridge con-

TABLE 6 INTERNATIONAL STANDARD RTD TEMPERATURE-RESISTANCE VALUES

TEMPERATURE (°F)	RESISTANCE (OHMS)	TEMPERATURE (°C)	RESISTANCE (OHMS)
-100	70.96	-100	60.20
0	93.01	-50	80.25
32	100.00	0	100.00
100	114.68	50	119.40
200	135.97	100	138.50
300	156.90	150	157.32
400	177.47	200	175.84
500	197.70	250	194.08
600	217.56	300	212.03
700	237.06	350	229.69
800	256.21	400	247.06
900	274.99	450	264.14
932	280.93	500	280.93

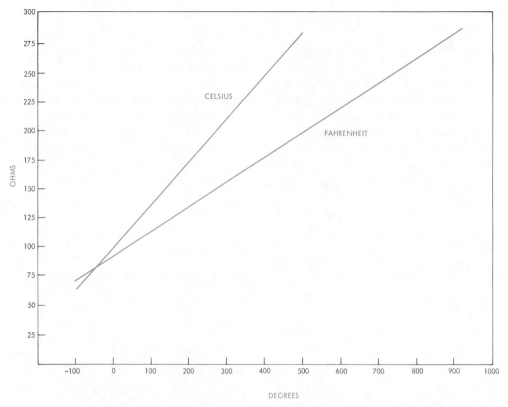

Fig. 37. *Standard international RTD temperature-resistance characteristics.*

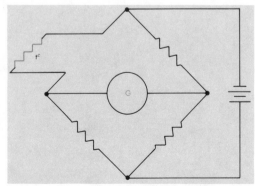

Fig. 38. *Bridge circuit converts small RTD resistance changes to observable output.*

figuration. It is used when the resistance of the lead wires is included as part of the sensing leg and where there is little or no change in lead resistance due to ambient temperature changes.

A more common RTD bridge circuit is shown in Fig. 39. In this temperature-sensing system three leads connect the RTD to the other legs of the bridge. The resistance of lead A is part of leg 1 and the resistance of lead B is part of leg 2. Since leads A and B run together, any change in ambient temperature produces the same re-

294

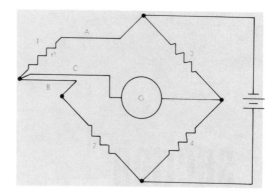

Fig. 39. *RTD bridge circuit with compensation for lead-resistance changes.*

sistance change in both leads. Such resistance changes do not affect the bridge balance because they appear as equal changes in legs 1 and 2. Thus, lead temperature changes contribute no error. The third lead,

C, is part of the readout branch, and, as such, does not contribute to the bridge ratio. Therefore changes in the resistance of this lead do not affect the bridge balance.

Unit 5

section 5 Thermistors

About the time that Peltier was experimenting with thermoelectric effects (1834), Michael Faraday noted that the resistance of certain semiconductors decreased with an increase in temperature. However, progress with these temperature-sensitive materials was very slow until about the time of World War II, when extensive research and development began. Since that time the work has progressed rapidly.

As a result, thermally-sensitive resistors, now known as *thermistors*, are found in countless industrial, military and commercial applications. Their range of operation is from about $-450°F$ to $+1200°F$. When combined with sensitive circuitry, thermistors can indicate temperature changes as small as $0.001°F$.

Most thermistors are made of oxides of nickel, manganese, and cobalt. Some consist of all three oxides. The oxides of iron, copper, titanium and uranium have also been used. Selection of oxides and proportions depends on the desired characteristics of the thermistor. Resistance values from a fraction of an ohm to many megohms are possible with these oxides.

Thermistor Forms

Modern thermistors are constructed by forming paste-like oxide mixtures into certain shapes such as discs, beads, and small rods, as shown in Fig. 40. These thermistors are then sintered at high temperatures. (Sintering is a process whereby powdered materials are fused together by the application of heat.)

Bead Type. A bead-type thermistor is formed when a small amount of oxide mix-

ture is set on two platinum wires and heated. This type is generally very small, from about 0.006″ to 0.10″ in diameter. The electrical characteristics of a bead are determined primarily by the composition of the oxide mixture, the spacing of the wires, and the heat treatment of the bead.

Probe-type temperature sensors are formed by sealing thermistor beads in glass rods. These units retain the characteristics of the bead and have the added advantages of the glass probe. They are more rugged, easier to use in certain applications than other types, and work well in liquids.

Bead-type thermistors operate in tem-

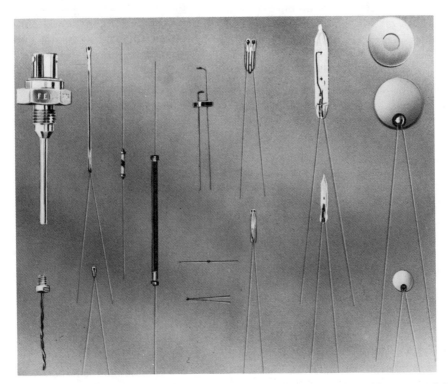

Fig. 40. *Group of thermistors, showing bead, disc, and washer forms. (Courtesy of Fenwall Electronics, Inc.)*

peratures up to 600°F with precision and good stability. They are available in resistance values from 100 ohms to 10 megohms. Because they can be made very small, they are useful where temperature sensing must be done in very limited spaces. Beads can be used for surface-temperature measurement by mounting them on metal discs cemented to the surface. They can also be inserted into machine screws and hollow rivets.

Disc and Washer Types. To meet certain industrial requirements, thermistors are manufactured as discs and washers. Thin discs of large diameter (up to one inch) have low resistance, medium power dissipation, and short response times. Thicker and smaller-diameter units have higher resistance and longer response times. Some manufacturers produce disc-type thermistors with diameters as small as 0.05 inch. Thickness ranges from 0.02 to 0.5 inch and resistance from 0.2 to 10,000 ohms. Disc-type thermistors are used widely for surface-temperature measurements, since good surface contact can be achieved between a disc and a surface.

Washer-type thermistors are designed for assembly with such hardware as terminal lugs, insulators, and compression washers. Often they are bolted directly to the material being sensed for temperature. They can be arranged in series to obtain higher resistance and longer response time and in parallel to form low-resistance units. To obtain increased capacity, series-parallel connections can be utilized. Washer-type thermistors are used to advantage where relatively-high power dissipation is a primary consideration.

Rod Type. Thermistors of high resistance and relatively long response time are produced by forming metal oxides into thin, round rods. Depending on the manufac-

turer, they vary in length from about 0.25 to 2.0 inches and in diameter from about 0.05 to about 0.27 inch. This form of thermistor has moderate power-dissipation capacity. In addition to being utilized where high resistance is required, rod-type thermistors can also be used as time-delay devices or as compensators for temperature changes in electronic equipment.

Thermistor Operation

Thermistors can be operated in three modes: self-heated, externally-heated, and a combination of self- and externally-heated.

Self Heating. Self-heated operation is illustrated in Fig. 41. Here the current can be regulated so that the power dissipated in the thermistor will raise its temperature above the ambient temperature. This temperature increase can also be produced by a small heater coil mounted close to the thermistor. Changes in heater current create changes in thermistor temperature which result in variations in its resistance.

Units which contain both thermistor and heater are known as *indirectly-heated thermistors*. A typical model is shown in Fig. 42. This form of sensor can be utilized in applications where it is desirable to have

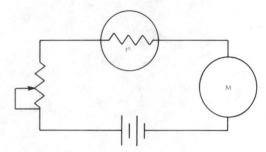

Fig. 41. *Self heating decreases thermistor resistance, allowing circuit current to increase.*

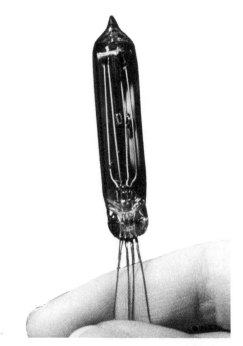

Fig. 42. *Indirectly-heated thermistor. (Courtesy of Fenwall Electronics, Inc.)*

changes in a control circuit produce changes in a load circuit without wired connections between the two circuits. This application is illustrated in Fig. 43.

Temperature increases decrease the resistance of a thermistor. Decreases in temperature increase its resistance. Materials in which this inverse action occurs are said to have a *negative temperature coefficient of resistance.* During normal operation the temperature of a self-heated thermistor can increase 350°F—decreasing its resistance to one-thousandth of its low-current value.

When a thermistor is heated there is a time lag between the start of current flow or current change and the final temperature. The amount of lag depends on the size and construction of the thermistor. In cases where a heater is used, its size is also a factor. Different time lags can be achieved by using various sizes of thermistors, from a fraction of a second for small beads to several minutes for larger thermistors. This resistance-time characteristic can be utilized in such applications as power-supply regulation, overload protection, time delays, and amplifier gain controls.

External Heating. The operation of an externally-heated thermistor is illustrated in Fig. 44. In this type of application current

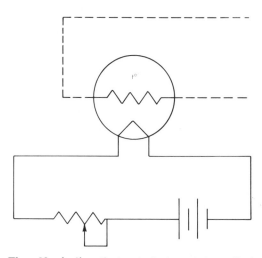

Fig. 43. *Indirectly-heated thermistor eliminates wired connections between controlled and control circuits.*

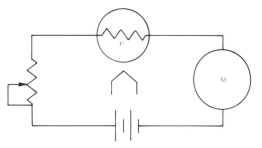

Fig. 44. *Externally-heated thermistor. Current is low to minimize internal heating.*

through the thermistor is kept at a low value to prevent heating the thermistor enough to change its resistance. The function of the thermistor is to react to changes in the temperature of an external source of heat (contact or ambient), its resistance varying inversely to the temperature changes it senses. In this manner the thermistor can convert change in the temperature of a surface or medium to circuit-current changes. If the meter is calibrated in de- grees the external temperature can be read directly.

Self and External Heating. The effects of self heating and ambient temperature on a thermistor can be combined into a method of sensing changes in the thermistor's environment. In this method a certain amount of self heating and the ambient temperature determine the operating temperature and resistance of the thermistor. Changes in the environment affect its tem-

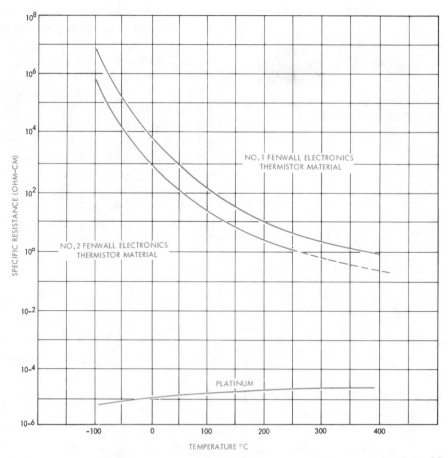

Fig. 45. *Temperature-resistance characteristics of two typical thermistor materials. (Courtesy of Fenwall Electronics, Inc.)*

perature which, in turn, changes the temperature and resistance of the thermistor. In this way changes in thermistor resistance can be used to indicate environmental changes such as flow rates of liquids and gases, liquid levels, and changes in pressure.

Thermistor Characteristics

Thermistors have three characteristics which make them useful in a great variety of temperature-sensing applications: (A)

temperature-resistance, (B) voltage-current, and (C) current-time.

Temperature-Resistance Characteristic. The changes in resistance of two typical thermistor materials resulting from change in temperature are given in Fig. 45. Shown for comparison is the change in the resistance of platinum over the same temperature range.

The thermistor curves indicate a change in resistance of ten million times for a temperature change of 500°C: from −100°C

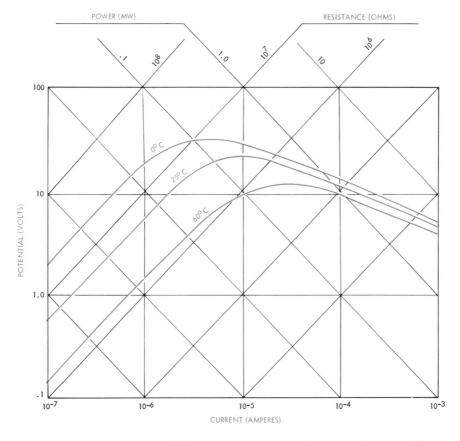

Fig. 46. *Voltage-current characteristic of a typical thermistor at various ambient temperatures. (Courtesy of Fenwall Electronics, Inc.)*

to $+400°C$. The change in platinum resistance over the same range is less than ten times. The curves of most thermistors show a temperature coefficient of resistance (alpha) of 3 percent to 5.8 percent. Platinum has an alpha of about 0.39 percent. (Temperature coefficient of resistance is the percent change in resistance per degree Celsius change in temperature.)

Voltage-Current Characteristic. Generally, when a very low value of current is flowing in a thermistor its temperature is not raised above the ambient. However, increasing the applied voltage increases the current, and the power dissipated begins heating the thermistor, raising its temperature and lowering its resistance. This decrease in resistance allows a greater current flow than if the resistance remained constant. The decrease in resistance also decreases the potential across the thermistor.

The voltage-current characteristic curves given in Fig. 46 show that the thermistor voltage and current increase together until, at a peak value of voltage, the increasing power dissipation causes a rapid decrease in thermistor resistance. From that point on, the thermistor voltage decreases as the current increases. This portion of the curve shows the effect of the negative temperature-resistance coefficient.

Current-Time Characteristic. If the initial flow of current in the circuit of Fig. 41 is sufficient to produce self heating of the thermistor, its resistance will decrease and the current will increase. This will produce a further decrease in resistance and increase in current. This process will continue until the thermistor reaches a certain

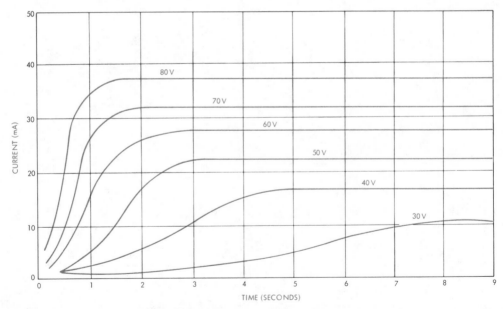

Fig. 47. *Current-time characteristic of a typical thermistor at several applied potentials. (Courtesy of Fenwall Electronics, Inc.)*

maximum temperature, determined by the applied potential and the circuit components. The time required for the thermistor to reach this temperature depends on the size and type of thermistor, the voltage, and the ohmic value of the series resistance.

The fact that a thermistor in a particular circuit requires a certain amount of time to reach a selected operating point makes it a valuable device in current-surge protection and time-delay applications. With proper selection of thermistor and circuitry, time delays from fractions of a second to many minutes are possible. Fig. 47 shows the current-time characteristic of a typical thermistor at several potentials.

Thermistor Applications

Thermistors are used extensively in industrial, commercial, medical, and household applications wherein temperature and temperature changes are measured or utilized in control devices and equipment. The following applications illustrate the versatility of these important thermoelectric components.

Temperature Measurement. Since thermistor resistance changes with temperature, it is an excellent means of temperature measurement. Because the changes in resistance are relatively large, simple indicating methods may be used where precision is not required. Fig. 48 shows a simple series circuit in which the current varies with changes in thermistor temperature and resistance. If the meter is calibrated in degrees, the temperature sensed by the thermistor can be read directly. The variable resistance is used to make adjustments in the circuit current and compensate for battery aging.

If the thermistor resistance is high (over 100,000 ohms), long copper leads may be used for connections to a remotely-located

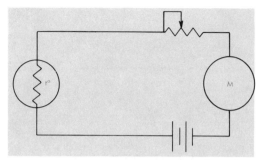

Fig. 48. *Simple temperature-sensing thermistor circuit.*

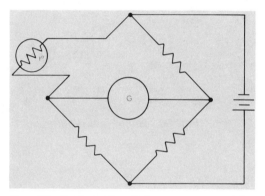

Fig. 49. *Bridge circuit increases precision of thermistor response.*

meter. Any change in lead resistance due to an ambient temperature change does not affect accuracy of measurement since the effect on circuit resistance and current is minimum, not enough to change the meter reading.

More precise measurement is possible if the thermistor is connected as one leg of a bridge circuit, as in Fig. 49. If the meter is a sensitive galvanometer this circuit can indicate temperature changes of a fraction of a degree.

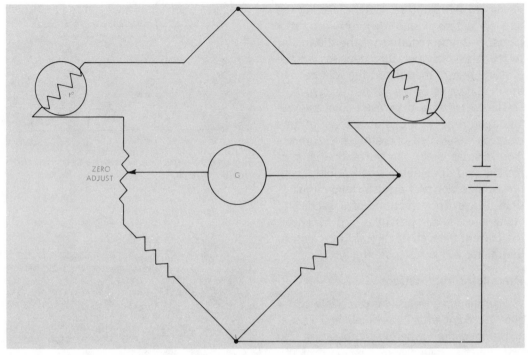

Fig. 50. *Temperature-differential measurement using two thermistors.*

The circuit of Fig. 50 is used to measure the difference between two temperatures. When the system is put in operation the thermistors are placed in desired locations and the bridge is balanced. Any subsequent difference in the thermistor temperatures will change the resistance ratios, unbalancing the bridge. This imbalance creates a current in the meter, which is usually calibrated in degrees. If high-resistance thermistors are used, the leads do not affect the measurement.

Temperature Compensation. Metals such as copper have positive temperature coefficients of resistance: an increase in temperature produces an increase in resis-

tance. Such changes in resistance can affect the operation of sensitive devices which contain copper coils, such as meters, gyroscopes, etc. To offset these temperature-resistance changes, the negative temperature coefficient of resistance of the thermistor can be utilized.

In Fig. 51 the thermistor-resistor combination provides compensation for temperature-resistance changes in the copper meter coil. The thermistor and shunt resistor are selected to provide a negative coefficient equal to the positive coefficient of the copper over a wide temperature range. Fig. 52 shows the temperature-resistance curves of the various circuit compo-

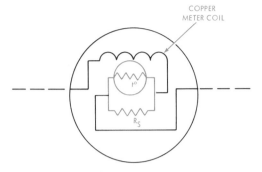

Fig. 51. *Thermistor-resistor temperature compensation of copper meter coil.*

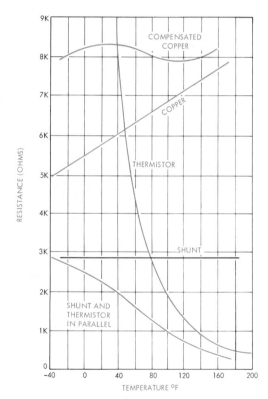

Fig. 52. *T-R characteristics of components in compensated meter-coil circuit. (Courtesy of Fenwall Electronics, Inc.)*

nents and how they combine to compensate for any temperature-created changes in the resistance of the copper coil.

According to the data in Fig. 52, as the temperature increases, the coil resistance increases in a linear manner. At the same time, the decreasing thermistor resistance combines with the constant shunt resistance to provide the resultant parallel value. This decreasing resistance in series with the increasing coil resistance gives a final compensated-coil value which is almost constant over the full temperature range.

Thermistors are also used to provide temperature compensation in magnetic amplifier circuits, transistor circuits, and other forms of electronic equipment.

Time Delay; Surge Protection. The current-time characteristic of the thermistor makes it a useful time-delay device. This is illustrated in Fig. 53. When this circuit is energized, the initial current is determined by the setting of the variable resistance and the starting resistance of the thermistor. As the thermistor heats, its resistance decreases and the current increases.

After a time the current reaches a value sufficient to operate the relay. Adjustment of the series resistance varies the time delay. By combining various values of circuit components and applied voltages, time delays of milliseconds to minutes can be achieved.

Surge protection for series-connected vacuum-tube heaters can be provided by a thermistor. This is illustrated in Fig. 54. Without the thermistor the initial current through the cold heaters would be much greater than the normal operating value. However, when potential is applied with the thermistor in the circuit, the high starting resistance of the thermistor limits the current to a safe value. As current flows

305

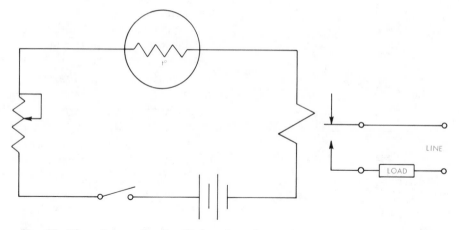

Fig. 53. *Time-delay circuit utilizing thermistor current-time characteristic.*

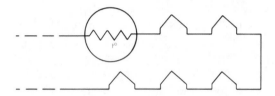

Fig. 54. *Vacuum-tube heater circuit with thermistor added to protect against initial high-current surges.*

through the thermistor and heaters, the thermistor temperature increases and its resistance decreases. At the same time, the temperature and resistance of the heaters increase to normal operating values.

Liquid-Level Measurement. Liquids generally have greater thermal conductivity than air. Consequently, a thermistor operates at lower temperature (and higher resistance) in liquid than in air of the same temperature. This relationship makes possible the use of thermistors in many liquid-measuring applications.

In Fig. 55 a thermistor is mounted in a tank and connected to a level or volume indicator such as a milliammeter calibrated

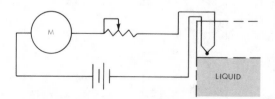

Fig. 55. *Thermistor as liquid-level measurement device.*

in linear or volumetric units. When the liquid reaches the level of the thermistor the temperature of the thermistor decreases and its resistance increases. The circuit current decreases and the meter reading

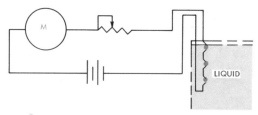

Fig. 56. *Thermistors indicating several liquid levels.*

changes, indicating a level or volume measurement.

The system in Fig. 55 can be expanded to provide additional measurements. This is illustrated in Fig. 56. If the tank is full, the thermistors are at their maximum operating resistances and the circuit current is minimum. This results in minimum meter deflection (marked "Full"). As the liquid level decreases, successive thermistors become exposed to the air, creating step decreases in the total circuit resistance. These decreases cause corresponding current increases, which produce successively greater meter deflections. These deflections can be marked in fractions of a full tank, such as $3/4$, $1/2$, $1/4$, etc.

Thermistors can be used to indicate the level of some hot liquids. In such applications the resistance of the sensing thermistor will be less in the hot liquid than in the air above it.

When the metering circuit is wired as in Fig. 55, the decrease in thermistor resistance (which occurs on contact with the liquid) causes an increase in meter current, giving an indication of liquid-level or volume. Multiple levels may be indicated as shown in Fig. 56.

Other Thermistor Applications. In addition to the preceding applications, other

physical phenomena which involve changes in the thermal conductivity of various media can be sensed and measured by thermistors. Such applications are possible because of the ability of a thermistor to: (1) operate in a self-heat mode and (2) respond to small changes in its own temperature.

Most industrial thermal-conductivity devices contain two thermistors in a Wheatstone-bridge circuit, as illustrated in Fig. 57. In most cases the circuit is designed so that the current through the thermistors is sufficient to heat them to a temperature above the ambient temperature.

In a typical application of this device one thermistor is placed in the medium to be sensed and the other in a static area. Any variation in the thermal conductivity of the medium changes the rate at which heat from the sensing thermistor is dissipated by the medium. This changes the temperature, and consequently, the resistance of this thermistor. The change in thermistor resistance unbalances the bridge and an output to a readout device appears across the 5 kΩ resistor.

The circuit in Fig. 57 can be used as a gas analyzer—to measure the carbon-dioxide content of air. In this application the two thermistors are mounted in separate cavities in a metal block. The bridge is balanced with air in both cavities. Then the air in one cavity is replaced with CO_2. (The thermistor in this cavity becomes the sensing thermistor).

Because the thermal conductivity of CO_2 is less than that of air, the temperature of the sensing thermistor increases and its resistance decreases. This change in thermistor resistance unbalances the bridge, providing an output to a meter. Under these conditions the meter is calibrated to indicate 100% CO_2. A mixture of 50% CO_2

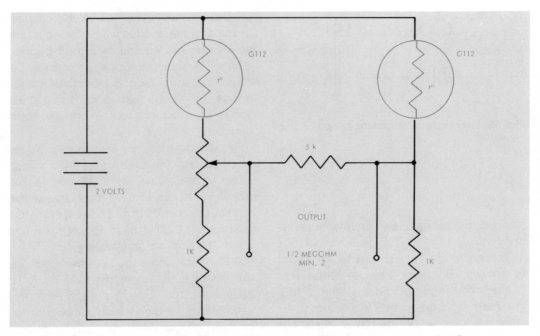

Fig. 57. *Typical thermistor thermal-conductivity measurement circuit. (Courtesy of Fenwall Electronics, Inc.)*

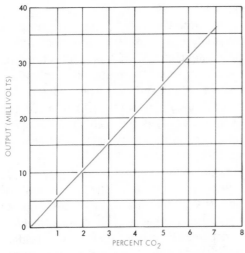

Fig. 58. *Analyzer-circuit output as a function of CO_2 content. (Courtesy of Fenwall Electronics, Inc.)*

and 50% air causes a half-scale deflection. Thus the percentage of CO_2 can be read on a linear scale. This linearity is indicated in Fig. 58, which gives meter readings for a low range of CO_2-content values. Other mixtures of two gases can be analyzed in this same manner.

The thermal conductivity of a moving medium, such as a gas or a liquid, varies with the rate of movement of the medium. Consequently, thermistors operate cooler in a particular medium when it is moving. As a result, circuits similar to that in Fig. 57 can be used in flowmeters, measuring flow rates as low as 0.001 cubic centimeter per minute. Some units have good response over a flow-rate range as great as 100,000 to 1.

Characteristics of thermistors which permit their use in the above applications also make possible the utilization of thermistors in bridge-circuit configurations in such devices as vacuum gages, anemometers and radio-frequency power meters.

Unit 5

section 6

Laboratory Procedures

The laboratory procedures outlined in this Section assume that the student has access to the devices and equipment listed for each experiment, is familiar with basic circuits and circuit diagrams, and performs the work under the supervision of an instructor.

Some of the devices and circuits require 120 V ac. Adequate precautions should be observed.

Thermocouples

Purpose: To determine and study the output responses of various thermocouples.

Devices and Equipment:

Thermocouple: Iron-Constantan (type J) (Omega IRCO, Thermo Electric type C (J), Nanmac 30FF(J) or 36FF(J).)

Thermocouple: Copper-Constantan (type T) (Omega COCO, Thermo Electric type C (T), Nanmac 30FF(T) or 36FF(T).)

Thermocouple: Chromel-Constantan (type E) (Omega CHCO), Nanmac 30FF(E) or 36FF(E).)

Thermocouple: Chromel-Alumel (tye (K) (Omega CHAL, Thermo Electric type C (K), Nanmac 30FF(K) or 36FF(K).)

Millivoltmeter; heat source—iron, torch, etc.

Procedure:

1. Connect thermocouple to millivoltmeter.
2. Apply heat (torch, hot iron, lighted match, etc.) to junction. Record speed of response and output voltage.
3. Repeat testing procedure using other types of thermocouples.
4. Connect two or three thermocouples series-aiding. Heat junctions. Measure and record output.
5. Write a statement comparing (A) outputs, and (B) speeds of response of tested thermocouples.

Thermistor: Basic Operation

Purpose: To study (A) resistive response of thermistor to ambient temperature changes, and (B) recovery time of thermistor.

Devices and Equipment: Thermistor, rod-type, (Veco 51R6, Carborundum 0325F-124, Keystone 15-110K-404S1, or equivalent); ohmmeter; heat source—soldering iron, lamp, etc.

Procedure:
1. Study specifications and ratings of selected thermistor.
2. Measure and record thermistor resistance.
3. Heat thermistor with hand. Record resistance change and heating time.
4. Hold thermistor near heat source. Record resistance change and heating time. Remove from heat and record recovery time.
5. Write a statement describing the effects of temperature changes on thermistor resistance.

Thermistor Operation: Self-Heating Mode

Purpose: To study the operational changes produced in a thermistor by self heating.
Devices and Equipment: Thermistor, bead-type (Veco 31D7, Keystone L0504-550-71-M2 or equivalent); power supply, 0-10 V ac or dc; milliammeter, 0-100 mA; VTVM; lamp, No. 49.

Procedure:
1. Study specifications and ratings of selected thermistor.
2. Measure and record thermistor resistance.
3. Connect lamp and milliammeter to power supply.
4. Increase supply voltage slowly and record voltage and current at which lamp begins to glow.
5. Increase voltage to two volts (rated lamp voltage) and record current.

6. Connect thermistor in series with lamp and milliammeter. Increase supply voltage slowly until meter reads 65 mA.
7. Touch thermistor and note its thermal condition. Measure voltage across thermistor. Calculate thermistor resistance.
8. Compare calculated resistance with value measured in step 2.
9. Write a statement describing self-heat operation.

Thermistor T-R Characteristic

Purpose: To determine and study thermistor resistance as a function of temperature.
Devices and Equipment: Thermistor, glass-probe type (Veco 51A37, Fenwall GA51P8, Fenwall GA52P48 or equivalent); ohmmeter; thermometer, $0°$-$110°C$; heater; container of water.

Procedure:
1. Study specifications and ratings of selected thermistor.
2. Tape thermistor to thermometer. Place assembly in water at room temperature.
3. Connect thermistor to ohmmeter and record thermistor resistance.
4. Heat water and record thermistor resistance at a number of temperatures.
5. Plot data, showing resistance as a function of temperature.
6. Write a statement explaining non-linearity of T-R characteristic.

Thermistor Operation at Low Temperature

Purpose: To study operation of glass-probe thermistor at ice-water temperature.
Devices and Equipment: Thermistor, glass-probe type (Veco 51A37, Fenwall GA51P8, Fenwall GA52P48 or equivalent); ohmmeter; container of ice and water.

Procedure:

1. Study specifications and ratings of selected thermistor.
2. Measure and record resistance of thermistor at room temperature.
3. Hold thermistor above surface of ice water and record resistance.
4. Immerse thermistor bead just below surface of water. Record resistance.
5. Immerse thermistor assembly almost completely. Do not immerse leads. Record resistance.
6. Immerse thermistor assembly and partially immerse leads. Record resistance.
7. Write a statement describing low-temperature operation of a glass-bead thermistor. Account for any difference between resistance readings in steps 5 and 6.

Washer-Type Thermistor: Basic Operation

Purpose: To study operation of washer-type thermistor under conditions of ambient and contact heating.

Devices and Equipment: Thermistor, washer-type (Veco 21W12, Keystone 7605-W28-58.2-97-S1, or equivalent); power supply, low voltage, ac or dc; lamp, No. 49; milliammeter; soldering iron; VTVM.

Procedure:

1. Study specifications and ratings of selected thermistor.
2. Wire circuit as shown in Fig. 59. Have wiring approved.
3. Apply about 2.5 volts to circuit. Record current, thermistor voltage, lamp voltage and lamp condition.
4. Hold hot soldering iron near thermistor and repeat step 3.
5. Momentarily apply heat directly to thermistor and repeat step 3.
6. Remove heat and record effect.

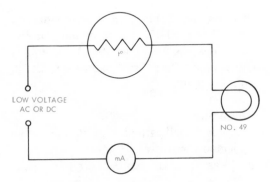

LOW VOLTAGE
AC OR DC

NO. 49

mA

Fig. 59. *Thermistor test circuit.*

7. Write a statement describing a possible application of this form of thermistor.

Operation of Low-Resistance Washer-Type Thermistor

Purpose: To study operation of low-resistance washer-type thermistor when sensing surface temperature.

Devices and Equipment: Thermistor, washer-type (Veco 12X13, Keystone 7611-W28-1965-73-S1, or equivalent); power supply, low-voltage, ac or dc; milliammeter; lamp, No. 49; sheet metal, No. 20-27 gage, 6" square; VTVM; heat source; soldering iron, etc.

Procedure:

1. Study specifications and ratings of selected thermistor.
2. Assemble thermistor to sheet metal.
3. Wire circuit as shown in Fig. 60. Have wiring approved.
4. Apply about 2.0 volts to circuit. Record current, thermistor voltage, lamp voltage and lamp condition.
5. Heat sheet metal and repeat step 4.
6. Remove heat and record effect.
7. Write a statement describing advantages of washer-type thermistors.

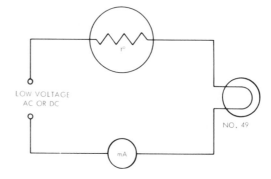

Fig. 60. *Test circuit for low-resistance washer-type thermistor.*

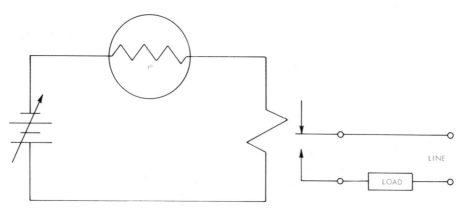

Fig. 61. *Circuit of thermistor liquid-level control.*

Thermistor Application: Liquid-Level Control

Purpose: To simulate the utilization of a thermistor as a liquid-level control.

Devices and Equipment: Thermistor, glass-probe type (Veco 51A37, Fenwall GA51P8, Fenwall GA52P48, or equivalent); power supply, 0-100 V dc; relay, dc, 2500 ohm (Potter and Brumfield LB5 or equivalent); glass container. *Option:* ac relay and ac supply.

Procedure:

1. Study specifications and ratings of selected thermistor.

2. Mount thermistor on inside wall of container.

3. Wire circuit as shown in Fig. 61. Have wiring approved.

4. Increase supply voltage until relay operates (opening filling valve). Note thermal condition of thermistor.

5. Add water to container slowly, submerging thermistor. Note effect.

6. Adjust voltage for best operation of system.

7. Write a statement explaining operation of this control circuit.

Try writing out the answer
to each question before look-
ing up the answer.

Review Questions

1. List some features of thermocouples which make them suitable for many industrial temperature-sensing applications.
2. Describe a thermopile. How is it capable of detecting minute temperature changes?
3. For what purpose might thermocouples be connected in parallel?
4. List some characteristics of a good thermocouple material.
5. Why are tungsten and rhenium used in thermocouples?
6. Why is a constant reference-junction temperature important?
7. Describe the makeup of a typical commercial "thermocouple reference junction".
8. In Fig. 19, why is R_t bonded to the reference junction?
9. In Fig. 21(B) why does electron movement from copper to iron decrease the junction temperature?
10. How does the majority-carrier count in a thermoelectric semiconductor compare with that of a transistor semiconductor?
11. Why is bismuth telluride a good thermoelectric semiconductor?
12. Explain how heat is produced at the junction in Fig. 22.
13. What would result from current-reversal in Fig. 24?
14. Name two important characteristics of a good interface material.
15. What determines the rate of heat transfer from workpiece to heat sink in Fig. 29?
16. Differentiate between positive and negative temperature-resistance coefficients.
17. What does the alpha of an RTD material indicate?
18. Describe the construction of a typical RTD probe.
19. What advantage does the RTD circuit

in Fig. 38 have over the circuit in Fig. 33?

20. Describe the temperature-resistance relationship of a thermistor.

21. When does thermistor self heating occur?

22. What circuit requirement does the indirectly-heated thermistor meet?

23. What characteristic of thermistor operation provides time-delay capability?

24. How can the time delay in Fig. 53 be increased?

25. What characteristic of thermistor operation allows for the use of thermistors in liquid-level measurement?

Answers to Review Questions

1. Thermocouples have high accuracy, good reliability, quick response to temperature changes, and a wide temperature range.

2. Two or more thermocouples connected in series form a thermopile. A thermopile can detect minute temperature changes because its output is the sum of the voltages produced by the individual thermocouples.

3. Thermocouples can be connected in parallel to provide the average temperature of the measuring junctions.

4. A good thermocouple material is one which can be produced uniformly, resists oxidation and other destructive effects, and has a linear voltage-temperature relationship.

5. Tungsten and rhenium are used in thermocouples to measure temperatures above 3000°F. Their melting points are much higher than those of other metals used in thermocouples: tungsten–6170°F., rhenium–5730°F.

6. Reference-junction temperature variations can alter the thermocouple-circuit output voltage, resulting in incor-

rect indications of measuring-junction temperature.

7. A typical commercial "thermocouple reference junction" contains a bridge circuit, cold junction, terminals and switch. Some units also include batteries.

8. In Fig. 19 R_t is bonded to the junction to sense changes in junction temperature.

9. In Fig. 21(B) electrons moving from the lower energy level of copper to the higher energy level of iron absorb thermal energy, causing the junction to cool.

10. The majority-carrier count in a thermoelectric semiconductor is much higher than that of a transistor semiconductor.

11. Bismuth telluride is a good thermoelectric semiconductor because it is a good conductor of thermal carriers but presents high impedance to the flow of conventional heat.

12. As electrons pass through the junction in Fig. 22 from the semiconductor to the metal they give up some energy as

they drop to the lower energy level of the metal electrons. The excess energy produces a heating effect.

13. Reversal of the current in Fig. 24 would cause the temperature of the junction at metal A to increase to a heated state and that at metal B to decrease to a cooled state.

14. Two important characteristics of a good interface material are good thermal conductivity and good electrical insulation.

15. The rate of heat transfer in Fig. 29 is determined by the number of P-N pairs, the kind of semiconductor material, and the amount of current.

16. The resistance of a material with a positive temperature coefficient of resistance increases as its temperature increases; the resistance of a material with a negative coefficient decreases as its temperature increases.

17. The alpha of an RTD material is the percent change in resistance per degree (C) change in temperature.

18. A typical RTD probe consists of a metal (nickel, platinum, etc.) sensing element wound on a ceramic core and encased in a sheath, from which it is electrically insulated by material which provides good thermal transfer.

19. The circuit in Fig. 38 can detect smaller changes in RTD resistance than the circuit in Fig. 33.

20. As the temperature of a thermistor increases, its resistance decreases nonlinearly.

21. Self heating occurs in a thermistor when the current is sufficient to raise the thermistor temperature above the ambient temperature.

22. The indirectly-heated thermistor can be used in various temperature-sensing applications requiring electrical isolation of control circuit from load circuit.

23. The time-delay capability of a thermistor is due to the lapse of time between the start of current flow or current change and the final temperature.

24. The time delay in Fig. 53 can be increased by increasing the series resistance.

25. Thermistors can be used in liquid-level measurement because the operating temperature of a self-heated thermistor is lower in liquid than in air.

UNIT 6

Photoelectrics

Unit 6

Contents

Unit 6

List of Illustrations

Unit 6

Unit 6

Unit 6

Unit 6

section 1 Introduction

Utilization of radiant energy in producing electrical effects is the basis of several forms of photoelectric devices that perform detection and control functions in a great variety of industrial, military, commercial, and household applications. These photoelectric devices can detect almost anything the human eye can see and many operate beyond the limits of human vision—in the invisible ultraviolet and infrared spectral regions.

Photoelectric effects were observed almost a hundred and forty years ago, in 1839. At that time the scientist and experimenter Alexander Becquerel noted that some batteries he was developing generated increased voltage when they were illuminated. Thirty-four years later, in 1873, Willoughby Smith found that the electrical resistance of selenium was decreased by illumination. During this time other experimenters, such as Adam, Day, and Fritts, were also working with the photoelectric properties of selenium. Still later in the nineteenth century (1887-1888) Henrich Hertz and William Hallwachs found that ultraviolet radiation produced photoelectric effects in a number of other metals.

6

Work in photoelectricity was largely experimental until the 1930's, when the selenium photovoltaic cell was produced commercially for use in light meters and photographic exposure meters. Another early development was the phototube—the so-called "electric eye" used in familiar door-opening applications.

Since World War II new forms of photoelectric devices have been developed and

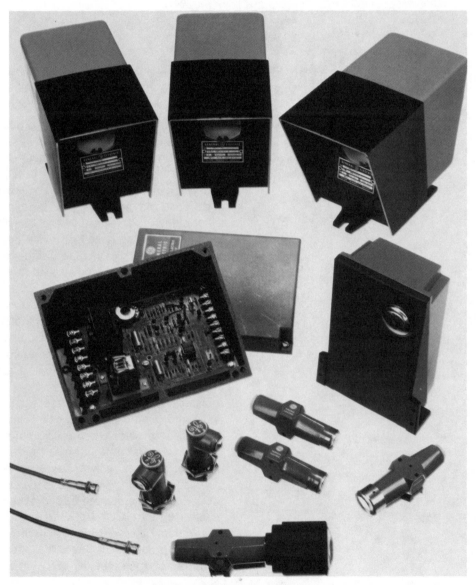

Fig. 1. *Group of industrial photoelectric devices. (Courtesy of General Electric Co.)*

their use has become widespread. Industrial applications are almost unlimited. Photoelectric devices are now used for turning equipment on and off, sensing defective materials, counting moving objects, checking colors, etc. In the home a photoelectric device can turn lights on at dusk and off at dawn or check the flame in a furnace to ensure proper combustion. Energized by invisible infrared rays, a photoelectric device can trigger a burglar alarm. Other applications include counting traffic, reading punched cards in data-processing equipment, and converting solar energy into electrical energy for use in man-made satellites. The variety of these devices continues to increase. A group of industrial photoelectric units is shown in Fig. 1.

Photoelectric systems have certain advantages over other forms of detection equipment which make them more appropriate in a variety of applications. One advantage is that the radiant beam applies no force to objects being sensed. This is important when the objects are small, delicate, or affected by physical contact. Irregularly-shaped, rough, or fast-moving objects are more easily detected by a radiant beam than by mechanical means. Detection of objects can be accomplished over short or long distances. Photoelectric devices can be made to respond to colors, identifying marks or other indicators which can only be detected optically. Photoelectric devices can be used for security reasons when operated in an invisible portion of the optical spectrum (infrared or ultraviolet). Also, be-

cause photoelectric devices utilize radiant beams, they can be installed in non-critical locations at various distances from sensing areas. Whether photoelectric systems utilizing radiant energy can be developed which will be capable of replacing more conventional energy sources is a matter of much speculation and intensive research.

Devices which produce electric effects from the application of radiant energy or, conversely, which produce radiation directly from the application of electricity, are mainly of four types:

1. *Photoemissive,* in which radiant energy striking a sensitive material causes the emission of electrons.
2. *Electroluminescent,* in which electrical energy applied to a sensitive material causes the emission of radiant energy.
3. *Photovoltaic,* in which radiant energy creates a voltage.
4. *Photoconductive,* in which radiant energy causes a change in electrical resistance.

Each of these four types will be described and illustrated in sections to follow, which will include examples of their industrial applications.

In addition to these types, Section 7 will be devoted entirely to devices known as LASCR's (light-activated SCR's), which in most respects operate as conventional SCR's (silicon controlled rectifiers) but which can also be triggered into conduction by radiant energy.

Unit 6

section 2

Photoelectric Action and Behavior of Radiant Energy

At times photoelectric effects (produced by radiation) and thermoelectric effects (produced by heat) appear to be the same. However, there are important differences between photoelectricity and thermoelectricity. Therefore, before photoelectric action and photoelectric devices and systems are discussed in detail, it is appropriate to distinguish between photoelectric and thermoelectric phenomena.

Thermal Action

When heat is applied to conventional conductors and semiconductors some of the thermal (heat) energy is absorbed by electrons in the outer atomic orbits of the material, raising their energy levels. When the absorbed energy is sufficient to change electronic energy levels from "valence" to "conduction" — that is, to overcome the force that holds valence electrons in their normal orbits around the atomic nucleus—

electrons become dislodged from the atoms. These electrons are then free to move and can be controlled by applied voltages. They are known as *thermal electrons*. This is an instance of thermoelectricity.

Photoelectric Action

Conduction electrons can also be generated by the application of radiant energy, which travels in discrete quantities or packets called *photons*. *The frequency of the radiation, not the intensity, determines the energy of a photon.* Photons at higher frequency levels have more energy than those at lower frequencies. Electrons which absorb the radiant energy and become free are known as *photoelectrons*.

Optical Spectrum. Practical photoelectric devices operate in the optical portion of the electromagnetic spectrum. This portion is generally considered to consist of three sections: infrared (IR), visible, and ultraviolet (UV). Infrared frequencies are too low (wavelengths too long) and ultraviolet frequencies are too high (wavelengths too short) for human eye response.

The longest wavelength of radiation visible to the human eye is about 0.75 micron (1 micron = 0.000001 meter, or 10^{-6}m). This radiation contains the lowest energy photons of light and is seen as red. The highest energy photons of light are in the high-frequency range of the visible section. They have wavelengths of about 0.4 micron and correspond to violet.

The infrared, visible, and ultraviolet sections of the optical spectrum are indicated in Fig. 2, which shows the radiation re-sponse of the average human eye. The wavelengths of infrared radiation extend from about 0.76 micron to about 4,000 microns. The ultraviolet wavelengths range from about 0.005 micron to about 0.38 micron. Radiation to which the human eye responds has wavelengths from about 0.4 micron to 0.75 micron. In Fig. 2 frequency increases from right to left.

The wavelengths of radiation in the op-tical spectrum can also be given in ang-stroms. An angstrom is a much smaller unit than a micron. One micron equals 10,000 angstroms. The response of the hu-man eye ranges, in angstroms, from about 4,000 Å (violet) to about 7500 Å (red). The

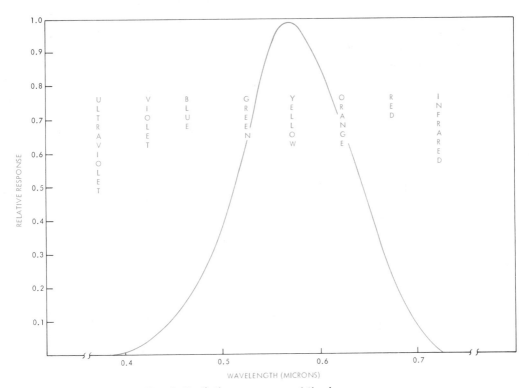

Fig. 2. *Radiation response of the human eye.*

angstrom is the unit of wavelength in Fig. 3.

Sources of Radiation

When considered in relation to emission frequencies (or wavelengths), industrial optical radiation sources can be classified as *panchromatic, heterochromatic,* and *monochromatic.* Examples of such sources are given in Fig. 3.

Radiation from a number of panchromatic sources, such as incandescent lamps, extends over a large portion of the optical spectrum. However, radiation from some panchromatic sources is limited to the visible region.

Heterochromatic emission differs from panchromatic in that it contains a number of discrete wavelengths rather than a continuous range. An example of a heterochromatic source is the mercury arc lamp.

A monochromatic source, such as a sodium–vapor lamp, radiates energy at one wavelength. Some sources such as neon lamps, which radiate at a number of wavelengths within a narrow range, are considered monochromatic.

Incandescent Lamp. Because it is readily available, reliable and consistent in operation, the tungsten incandescent lamp is the most widely-used source of radiation for industrial purposes. With a maximum output at about 10,000 A, this lamp is a good generator of invisible radiation. When used with a light-blocking filter, it can serve as a radiation source for burglar alarms and other forms of protection equipment. In applications requiring ultraviolet radiation, low-pressure mercury-vapor lamps can be used. This is shown in Fig. 3.

The most common source of visual radiation found in industry is an enclosure containing an incandescent lamp and one or more lenses which focus and direct the beam of light toward the sensor (phototube or photocell). A typical model is shown in Fig. 4. Generally, the lamps in these units operate at voltages ranging from 4 to 48 volts.

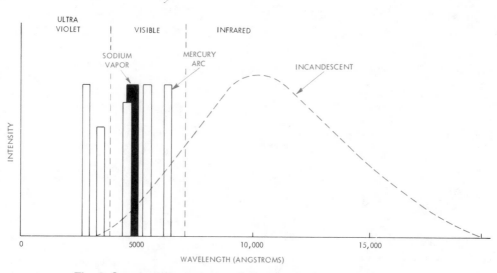

Fig. 3. *Spectral diagram of radiation from various light sources.*

Fig. 4. *Industrial incandescent light source. (Courtesy of General Electric Co.)*

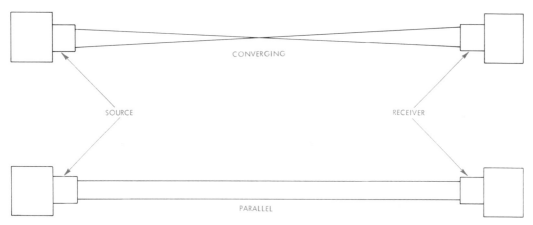

Fig. 5. *Converging and parallel light beams.*

When operated at the lowest voltage consistent with good system performance, an incandescent lamp has a maximum lifespan. This is due to the fact that any increase in lamp life beyond that at rated voltage is equal to the twelfth power of the ratio of the rated voltage to the operating voltage. Lamp life ranges from about 4500 hours to over 50,000 hours, depending on type of lamp and operating voltage.

The lens, or lens system, focuses the radiation into one of several forms of beams: converging, parallel, reflective, or modulated. Converging and parallel beams are illustrated in Fig. 5. A converging beam is used in applications where the objects to be sensed are very small. The beam produces a small, bright spot on the object and diverges toward the sensor. A parallel beam is a cylinder of light from source to sensor. It is used for large objects and long distances.

Where reflective light beams are used, the objects reflect the light toward the sensor. Three forms of reflection are found in industrial applications: *diffuse reflective, specular reflective,* and *retroreflective.* These are illustrated in Fig. 6.

As shown in the illustration, diffuse reflection is scattered. Consequently, variable amounts of radiant energy are reflected to the sensor. This is the type of reflection produced by a matte surface.

Specular reflection forms a beam of light which resembles the incident beam. This kind of reflection is produced by a shiny

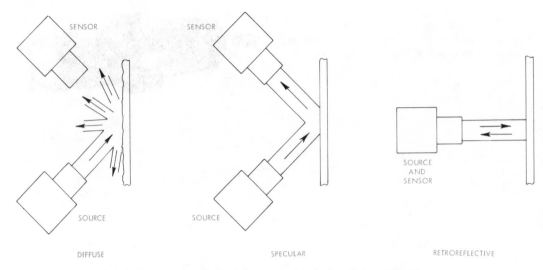

Fig. 6. *Forms of reflected light used in industrial applications.*

surface which reflects most of the radiant energy to the sensor.

In a retroreflective system the light source and sensor are housed in the same enclosure. A commercial model is shown in Fig. 7. The component parts and operation of a typical unit are illustrated in Fig. 8.

A modulated light beam is one that is interrupted or pulsed at a rate which can range from 100 pulses per second (pps) to several thousand. The pulsing can be done electrically by switching the lamp circuit or mechanically with a slotted rotating disc or vibrating reed. A modulated-beam system is illustrated in Fig. 9. This system is often used where the effects of strong ambient light are objectionable.

For various applications light beams can be modified by means of optical filters. As stated previously, an infrared filter can be used to block the visible portion of incandescent radiation and pass the invisible infrared rays. However, such filtering can

Fig. 7. *Industrial retroreflective control unit housing light source, sensor, amplifier, and output relay. (Courtesy of General Electric Co.)*

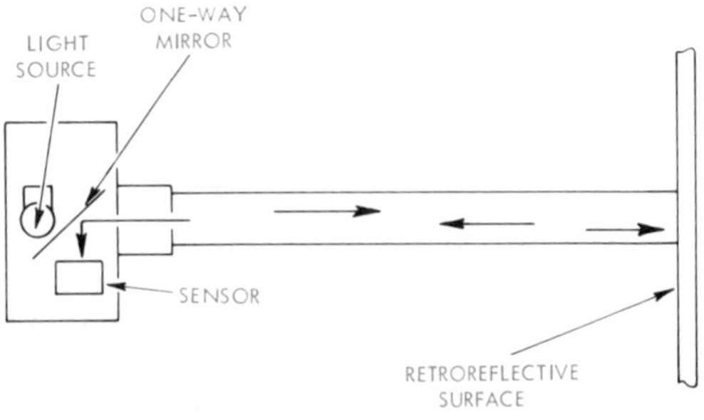

Fig. 8. *Retroreflective system.*

Fig. 9. *Light beam modulated by rotating disc.*

cause an appreciable drop in beam strength —as much as 40 percent.

The use of color filters enables photo-electric equipment to discriminate between two or more colors. These filters are selected for maximum transmission of desired color wavelengths and minimum transmission of all others. Also, masks can be used to form beams into special configurations. This technique is sometimes employed in applications involving small or oddly-shaped objects.

In applications where straight light beams cannot be used, mirrors may be utilized to reflect the beams to target areas. Good quality, clean mirrors reflect over 70 percent of the incident light. Where it is necessary to confine the light to a small area, plastic tubing with a reflective inner wall can carry the light from source to object. Optical fibers can be used also to transmit the light into intricate locations and around corners.

Unit 6

section 3

Solid-State Lamp (SSL's)

Recent advances in semiconductor technology have made possible the use of *electroluminescence* (direct conversion of electrical energy to light energy) as a source of radiation for photoelectric applications. The solid-state lamp (SSL), also known as a light-emitting diode (LED), is an electroluminescent device which emits radiation in the visible and infrared portions of the optical spectrum. Several models are shown in Fig. 10. Shown in Fig. 11 is an industrial retroreflective unit which incorporates an SSL as the radiation source. It also contains a phototransistor, SSL driver, amplifier and reflex optics.

The SSL has several features which make it suitable for a variety of applications. Due to its ruggedness and inherent long life it is highly reliable. Its response time is very short. (The rise and fall times of the General Electric SSL-65 are 0.5 microsecond. The General Electric SSL-12 has ratings of 500 nanoseconds.) SSL's are small and

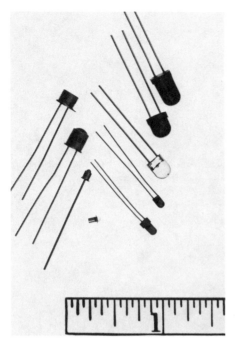

Fig. 10. *Group of solid-state lamps (SSL's). (Courtesy of General Electric Co.)*

Fig. 11. *Photoelectric control with SSL light source. (Courtesy of General Electric Co.)*

lightweight. They can be hermetically sealed, protecting them from environmental effects. They have no heaters which require warm-up time, and they dissipate little power. The radiant output of an SSL is confined to a comparatively narrow band. It is a low-impedance device, making it compatible with transistors and other solid-state circuitry.

SSL Construction and Operation

The construction of a solid-state lamp is illustrated in Fig. 12, where a PN junction is shown mounted on a metal base and enclosed in a hermetically-sealed container. The P side is connected through the metal header to the positive lead and the N side through an insulated terminal to the nega-

tive lead. To direct the emitted radiation a lens cap is fitted into the container.

PN junctions for SSL's are fabricated from intermetallic compounds such as gallium arsenide (GaAs), gallium arsenide phosphide (GaAsP) and gallium phosphide (GaP). These materials are much more efficient as optical emitters than single-element semiconductors because they are, for the most part, "direct-gap" materials. Other semiconductors are "indirect-gap" radiators.

The terms "direct-gap" and "indirect-gap" refer to the transition of electrons from the conduction level to the valence level. This transition takes place when electrons flow through a PN junction from N to P and recombine with holes in the P ma-

335

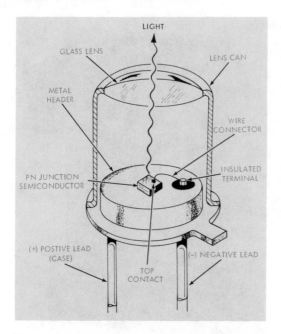

Fig. 12. *Construction of solid-state lamp (SSL). (Courtesy of General Electric Co.)*

terial. As the electrons drop from the conduction (higher) to the valence (lower) energy level, excess energy is released as photons of radiant energy.

In direct-gap materials the transition from conduction level to valence level is a relatively simple process. However, in indirect-gap materials more energy and momentum are lost during the recombination process than in direct-gap materials. This is due to the fact that electrons in an indirect-gap material can momentarily be trapped at levels in the forbidden gap, since donor and acceptor atoms in these materials exist at such levels. Differences between the recombination processes of direct-gap and indirect-gap materials are illustrated in Fig. 13. The wavy lines indicate optical emission and the straight lines thermal emission.

Direct band-to-band recombination is illustrated at (A) in Fig. 13. Temporary

entrapment followed by recombination is depicted at (B) and (C). Three-step recombination is illustrated at (D). Here an electron and hole are captured by donor and acceptor levels. They then combine and some radiation occurs. Thus it can be seen that direct-gap materials are better radiant-energy emitters than indirect-gap materials.

The wavelength of the emitted radiation depends on the band-gap energy of the material. Gallium arsenide (GaAs), with band-gap energy of 1.37 electron-volts (eV), has a peak-emission wave length of 9,000 angstroms. (One electron volt is the kinetic energy acquired by an electron in passing through a potential difference of one volt.) Gallium phosphide, with greater band-gap energy (1.8 eV), has a peak-emission wavelength of 7,000 angstroms. Thus, radiation wavelength is inversely proportional to band-gap energy.

The amount of optical emission from an

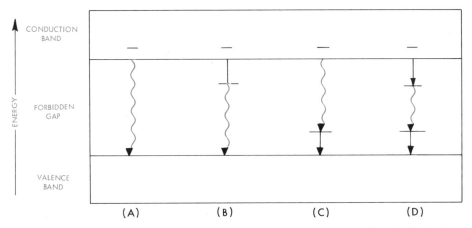

Fig. 13. *Optical-emission processes. (Courtesy of General Electric Co.)*

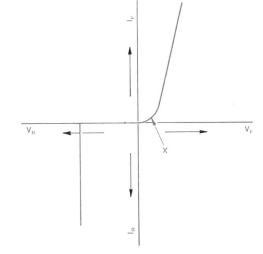

Fig. 14. *Volt-ampere characteristic of typical SSL.*

SSL varies with junction current. As shown by the volt-ampere characteristic in Fig. 14, as the forward bias V_F is increased, the current I_F increases, resulting in increased photoemission. In a typical SSL, emission begins at approximately point X. The voltage at this point is called the *threshold voltage*.

Operation with reverse bias V_R produces detrimental effects. When reverse bias is increased to the breakdown level some photoemission may occur due to ionization by collision. However, excessive heating produced by the reverse current I_R may damage the lamp.

Gallium Arsenide (GaAs) SSL. Solid-state lamps fabricated from gallium arsenide (GaAs) do not emit visible radiation. Their emission falls in the infrared range of the optical spectrum. The General Electric SSL-4 and SSL-34 are GaAs lamps, with peak emission at 9,000 Å. The spectral response of these lamps is shown by the solid curve in Fig. 15.

GaAs crystals can be doped with other materials to produce peak emission at other wavelengths. The General Electric SSL-5 and SSL-35 are examples of lamps fabricated with doped GaAs. The dashed curve in Fig. 15 shows the emission range of these lamps—peak emission occurring at 9400 Å.

Important considerations in the operation of SSL's are power dissipation and power output. Power dissipation is the product of the forward voltage drop (typically 1.25-1.35 V) and the forward current. Typi-cal forward current of the General Electric SSL-4, SSL-5, SSL-34 and SSL-35 is 100 mA. Power output of an SSL depends on its power-dissipation rating. As lamp current increases, output power increases to a maximum and then drops off as the lamp approaches its maximum power dissipation rating. Fig. 16 shows power output versus forward current for two SSL's.

Temperature is an important factor in the operation of SSL's. Increasing temperature produces additional trapping levels in the energy gap between the conduction and valence bands. The additional entrapment of electrons causes more conversion of electrical energy to thermal and less to radiant energy. As temperature decreases, opposite conditions prevail and output increases. Fig. 17 shows the variations in output of typical GaAs SSL's over a range of temperature values. For comparison purposes, output at room temperature is set at 100%.

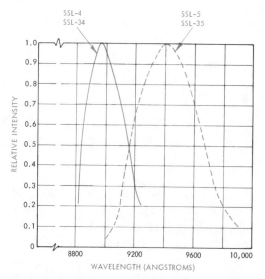

Fig. 15. *Spectral responses of representative SSL's. (Courtesy of General Electric Co.)*

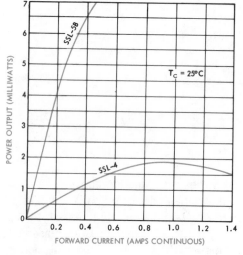

Fig. 16. *Forward current-power output characteristics of two SSL's. (Courtesy of General Electric Co.)*

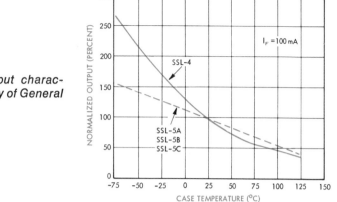

Fig. 17. *Temperature-versus-output charac-teristics of typical SSL's. (Courtesy of General Electric Co.)*

The wavelength of SSL emission is also affected by temperature. As the lamp temperature increases, the wavelength increases—2 to 3 angstroms per degree (C). Thus, as lamp temperature increases, output decreases and wavelength increases, and, as lamp temperature decreases, output increases and wavelength decreases.

Gallium Arsenide Phosphide (GaAsP) SSL. When silicon is added to gallium arsenide the peak radiation wavelength is shifted from 9,000 Å to 9,400 Å. If a phosphor is added to the GaAs-silicon combination, forming a GaAsP SSL, peak emission is again shifted—from infrared at 9,400 Å to visible at 5,400 Å. At 5,400 Å the radiation is green, the color to which the human eye is most responsive. This change in radiation wavelength allows the use of such SSL's as indicators.

The General Electric SSL-3 is a phosphor-coated unit which emits both green (5,400 Å) and infrared (9,400 Å) radiation. The spectral response of this lamp is shown in Fig. 18 and the current-power characteristics are given in Figs. 19 and 20. The solid lines show output as a function of forward current with the case temperature fixed at 25°C. The dashed curves are at a fixed ambient temperature of 25°C. GaAsP SSL's are also fabricated to emit in the red range (7,000 Å). Lamps in the General Electric SSL-22 series are examples of this type.

Gallium Phosphide (GaP) SSL. Gallium phosphide is a material which is very suitable for solid-state lamps. With band-gap energy of 1.8 eV, it emits highly-visible red radiation at 700 nanometers (7,000 Å). The spectral response of a GaP SSL, the General Electric SSL-22, is given in Fig. 21. The composition of the GaP pellet can be altered to produce green or yellow radiation. The General Electric SSL-44 is a GaP unit which emits green light, peaking at 562 nanometers (5,620 Å).

GaP is more efficient than GaAsP in converting electrical energy to light energy. GaAsP lamps are typically 0.1%-0.2% efficient while GaP lamps are typically 1.0% efficient with some units achieving 2.0%-3.0%. Because GaP pellets are transparent and GaAsP pellets emit only through the top layer, more light output is possible from GaP SSL's. In addition, operating currents

339

SSL-3
SSL-3F

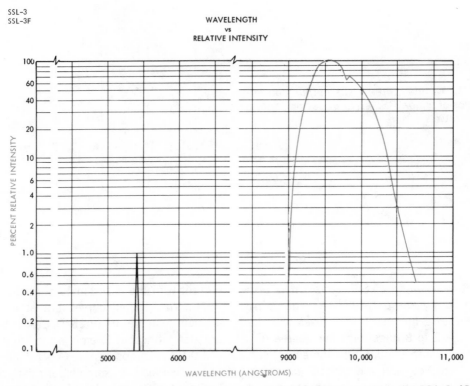

Fig. 18. *Spectral response of gallium arsenide phosphide SSL: General Electric SSL-3. (Courtesy of General Electric Co.)*

of GaP lamps are lower than those of GaAsP lamps. An example is given in Fig. 22, which shows the forward current-output characteristic of a typical GaP SSL, the General Electric SSL-12. At room temperature (25°C) the normal operating current is 5 mA.

The effects of temperature on the output of the General Electric SSL-12 are shown in Fig. 23. This is also the temperature-output characteristic of the SSL-22. As the characteristic indicates, the relationship is inversely linear—each 25°C change in temperature causing a 20% change in output.

SSL Applications

The applications of solid-state lamps are many and varied. Among them are information displays, data transmission, relay operation, detection and surveillance, edge tracking, size monitoring and card and tape reading. SSL's are used extensively in indicating and contactless-control applications.

A basic SSL circuit is shown in Fig. 24. In this application the SSL is part of a "contactless potentiometer". Variations in SSL current produce emission changes which, in turn, vary the photoconductor resistance. The series resistor limits SSL current to a

SSL-3
SSL-3F

FORWARD CURRENT
vs
NORMALIZED OUTPUT
(VISIBLE)

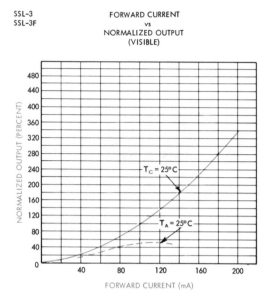

Fig. 19. Current-power output (visible) characteristic of General Electric SSL-3. (Courtesy of General Electric Co.)

SSL-22
SSL-22L

WAVELENGTH
vs
RELATIVE INTENSITY

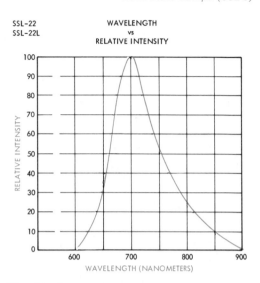

Fig. 21. Spectral response of gallium-phosphide (GaP) SSL: General Electric SSL-22. (Courtesy of General Electric Co.)

SSL-3
SSL-3F

FORWARD CURRENT
vs
NORMALIZED OUTPUT
(INFRARED)

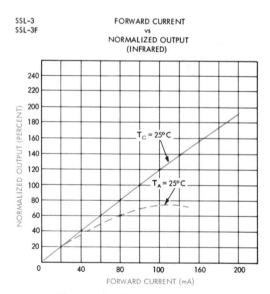

Fig. 20. Current-power output (infrared) characteristic of General Electric SSL-3. (Courtesy of General Electric Co.)

SSL-12
SSL-212

FORWARD CURRENT
vs
RELATIVE POWER OUTPUT

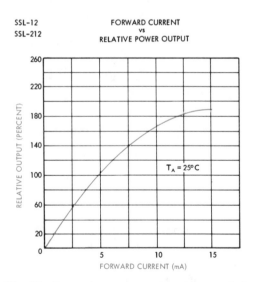

Fig. 22. Current-power output characteristic of GaP SSL: General SSL-12, 212. (Courtesy of General Electric Co.)

341

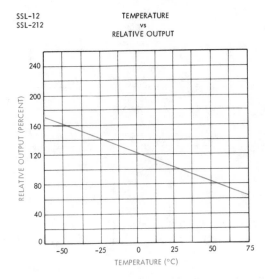

SSL–12
SSL–212

TEMPERATURE
vs
RELATIVE OUTPUT

Fig. 23. *Temperature-versus-output characteristic of General Electric SSL-12, 212. (Courtesy of General Electric Co.)*

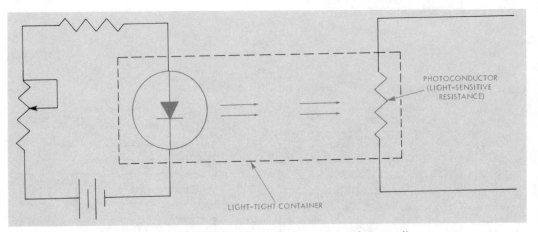

PHOTOCONDUCTOR
(LIGHT–SENSITIVE
RESISTANCE)

LIGHT-TIGHT CONTAINER

Fig. 24. *SSL as part of "contactless potentiometer."*

safe value when the variable resistance is set to a very low or zero value.

Audio modulation of a radiant beam can be achieved using an SSL as in Fig. 25. Since the SSL is part of the transistor load, any variation in collector current due to the input signal (voice, etc.) will produce similar variations in the radiant output of the SSL. In this manner intelligence, etc. may be transmitted on a radiant beam with a minimum of circuitry.

Fig. 26 illustrates an SSL operating as an

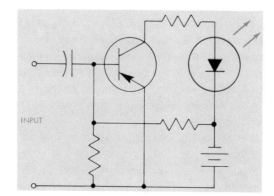

Fig. 25. *Modulation of SSL emission.*

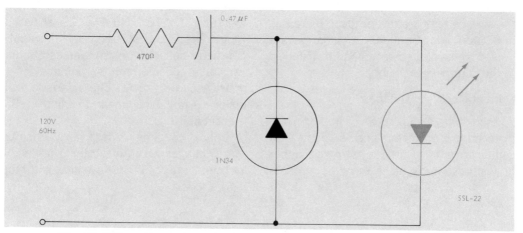

Fig. 26. *SSL as line-voltage indicator. (Courtesy of General Electric Co.)*

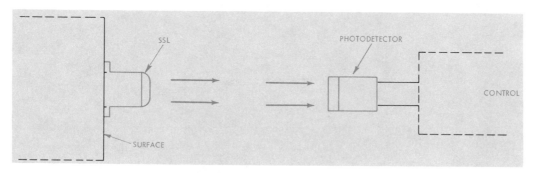

Fig. 27. *SSL as temperature sensor.*

343

ac line-voltage indicator. Since, in many applications, this unit would be required to operate continuously, inclusion of the capacitor holds power dissipation to less than 0.2 watts. The shunting diode provides a bypass during half-cycles when the SSL is non-conducting.

Because its operation is temperature-dependent, an SSL can be used in temperature-sensing applications. One can be mounted as in Fig. 27 so that its temperature varies with that of the surface being monitored. As the surface temperature increases, the SSL temperature increases and its radiant output decreases. Decreases in the surface temperature produce increases in SSL output. Variations in radiation are sensed by the photodetector and transferred to the control equipment.

Optical Coupling Devices

Solid-state lamps are combined with matched photodetectors in small, light-tight containers to form devices having a number of features which make them appropriate for many isolating and coupling applications. The packaged units are known by various names, such as: *optically-coupled isolators, optoisolators, photon couplers,* and *phototransistor coupled pairs.* Representative units are: General Electric PC 15-26 and PC 4-73, each consisting of an SSL and a phototransistor; Hewlett-Packard 5082 series, each comprising an SSL, a PN photodiode and a transistor; Monsanto MCT-2, an SSL-phototransistor pair; and the Monsanto MCD-2, an SSL-photodiode combination.

Fig. 28 illustrates the components of a typical packaged unit, such as the General Electric PC 4-73, and Fig. 29 shows an input-output characteristic of this unit—transistor collector current versus SSL current at a collector-emitter potential of 10 volts. According to the characteristic, transistor current is a linear function of SSL current above 20 mA.

Optical coupling devices have a number of advantages which make them preferable to transformers, direct switching and other

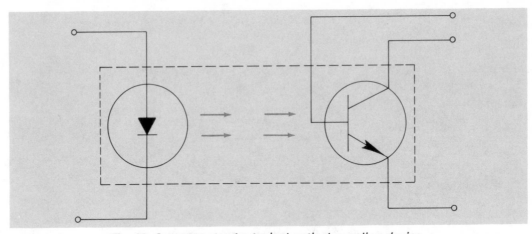

Fig. 28. *Components of a typical optical coupling device.*

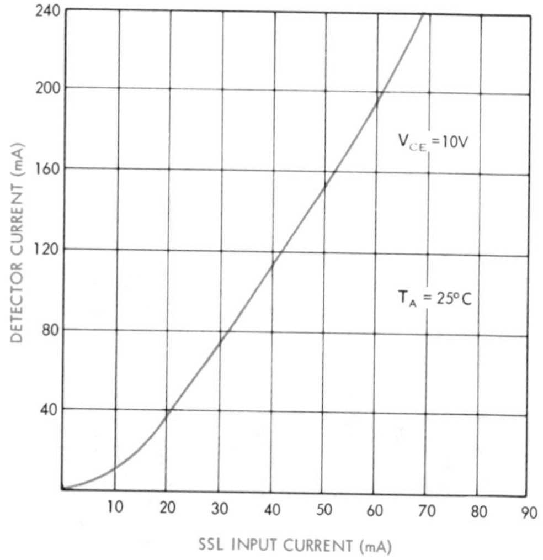

Fig. 29. *Input-output current characteristic of optical coupler: General Electric PC 4-73. (Courtesy of General Electric Co.)*

coupling methods in various applications. They are small in size and can withstand much shock and vibration. They are capable of high-speed, contactless switching, can provide simple coupling between different voltage levels, eliminate ground loops, and isolate noise.

345

Unit 6

Photoemissive Devices

Photoemissive devices, as mentioned in Section 1, are devices in which radiant energy striking a sensitive material causes the emission of electrons. These devices, called *phototubes*, are of several types: *vacuum phototubes*, *gas-filled phototubes*, and *multiplier phototubes*. Each of these types will be described in this section. The final portion of the section will give examples of phototube applications.

Vacuum Phototube

The basic vacuum phototube consists of an anode and cathode in an evacuated glass envelope, similar to a diode without a heater. A typical commercial unit is shown in Fig. 30. The construction of this tube is illustrated in Fig. 31.

As shown in Fig. 31, the anode is a rod-

Fig. 30. *Vacuum phototube. (Courtesy of RCA Corp.)*

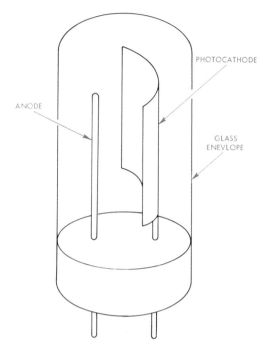

Fig. 31. *Vacuum phototube construction.*

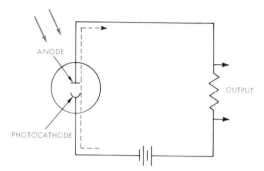

Fig. 32. *Basic vacuum phototube circuit.*

like conductor and the cathode is a half-cylinder coated on its concave side with a radiation-sensitive material. Because of their ability to emit electrons (low work functions) when exposed to optical radiation, alkali metals such as sodium, lithium, potassium, cesium, and rubidium can be used as cathode coatings.

It has been found that thin films of alkali metals on other metals can produce lower work functions (minimum energy for electron emission) than either metal alone. Cesium is the most commonly used coating. It has a low work function (1.91 eV) and its spectral response matches that of the human eye more closely than other alkali metals.

When radiation within the spectral range of the phototube strikes the cathode coat-

ing, electrons are emitted. A positive potential at the anode attracts the emitted electrons. This action is illustrated in Fig. 32.

The magnitude of the electron flow depends on the applied potential and the amount and intensity of the radiation falling on the cathode. When the cathode is illuminated, the *amount* of illumination can be expressed in terms of *lumens*. One lumen is the amount of illumination produced on one square foot of spherical surface one foot from a one-candle source. (The lumen is also defined as the amount of luminous flux emitted through a solid angle (one steradian) from a uniform point source of one candle.) The *intensity* of the cathode illumination can be expressed in footcandles. One footcandle indicates the intensity of illumination at all points on a spherical surface one foot from a one-candle source. The relationship between the two units (lumens and footcandles) is indicated by the fact that the intensity of illumination is one footcandle when the luminous flux is one lumen per square foot.

Both terms, *lumen* and *footcandle*, are used in technical literature (manufacturers' data, journals, etc.) to specify illumination values pertaining to photoelectric devices.

347

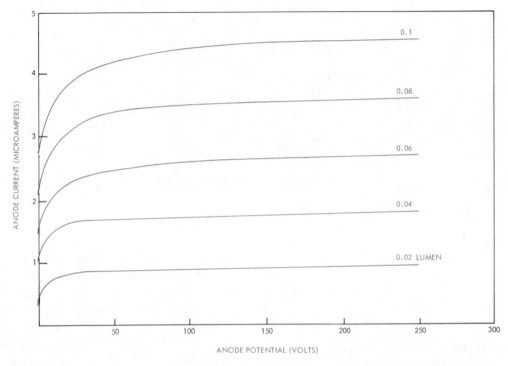

Fig. 33. *Voltage-current characteristic of a typical vacuum phototube for several levels of illumination.*

In the following sections the lumen is used in some illustrations as the illumination variable and in others the footcandle is used.

For a particular amount of cathode illumination, an anode voltage increasing from zero creates a current which increases to a saturation level. After this level is reached, further increases in anode voltage do not increase the current. This is illustrated in Fig. 33, which shows the anode voltage-current characteristic of a typical vacuum phototube. According to the data in Fig. 33, when the anode voltage is beyond a relatively low value, substantial increases in tube current can only be achieved by increasing cathode illumination.

Vacuum phototubes are normally oper-

ated in the region to the right of the knee area of the characteristic curves. Fig. 34 shows a 40-megohm load-line added to the curves of Fig. 33. Because the load is resistive the line is linear. To locate the high-current end of the line, the tube is assumed to be short-circuited. In this mode tube voltage is zero and the current is determined by the source voltage and the load resistance. The high-voltage end of the line is determined by assuming the tube is open-circuited. Current is then zero and the voltage across the tube equals the supply voltage.

According to the data in Fig. 34, the operating current of a vacuum phototube is relatively low—a few microamperes. Consequently, amplification is necessary if a

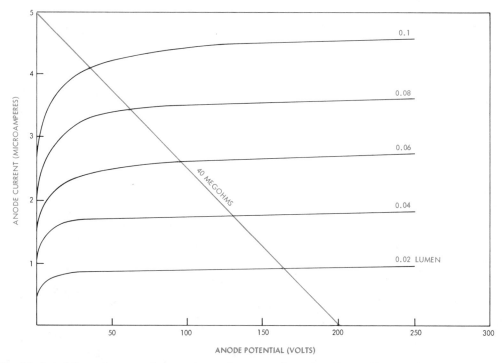

Fig. 34. *Load line shows region of phototube operation with 40 megohm load at several lighting levels.*

usable electrical signal is to result from the optical input. Although it has this limitation, the vacuum phototube has several features which make it a valuable photoelectric transducer. Its response is linear (electrical output is directly proportional to optical input). It has good dynamic response at high frequencies, it is stable, and has high red-sensitivity.

Gas-Filled Phototube

The low current limitation of the vacuum phototube can be overcome by the addition of an inert gas, such as argon, to the basic tube. This modification can result in a current two to ten times greater than that in a vacuum phototube. The increased current is due to ionization of the gas and secondary emission from the cathode. Pressure of the gas must be sufficient for ionization but too low for arcing.

The operation of a gas-filled phototube is based on an effect called the "Townsend discharge." When radiant energy strikes the cathode, emitted electrons collide with atoms of the gas, causing the release of electrons from the atoms. The free electrons bcome part of the current to the anode. Gas atoms which lose electrons in this manner become positive ions. They are attracted to the negative cathode, which they strike with enough force to cause secondary emission. These secondary-emission electrons add to the primary tube current.

349

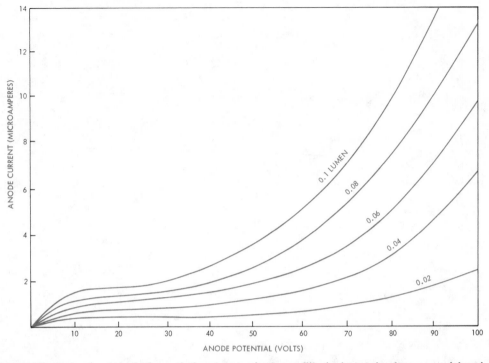

Fig. 35. *Voltage-current characteristic of a typical gas-filled phototube for several levels of illumination.*

Thus, through ionization and secondary emission, the current in a gas-filled phototube is several times greater than in a comparable vacuum phototube. Possessing both primary and secondary emission makes the gas-filled tube more sensitive than the vacuum type; for equal amounts of radiation the reaction of the gas-filled tube is much greater than that of the vacuum phototube.

With a fixed amount of illumination on the cathode of a gas-filled tube, increasing the anode voltage causes the tube current to increase. The increasing current does not reach saturation, as in the vacuum phototube. In contrast to the operation of the vacuum-type tube, the current in the gas-filled tube increases rapidly at upper anode potentials, especially at higher illumination levels. This is indicated by the characteristic curves in Fig. 35, which show the anode voltage-current values of a typical gas-filled phototube at several radiation levels.

To ensure proper operation of a gas-filled phototube the anode potential should not exceed the rated value. Excessive anode voltage can cause "gas discharge". When this occurs the tube conducts like a gas-filled rectifier and the radiation has no effect on its operation. Tube action must be limited to the Townsend-discharge region of the anode characteristic. This region begins at the ionization potential, as indicated in Fig. 36. Also shown in Fig. 36 is a rapid increase in current as operation moves from

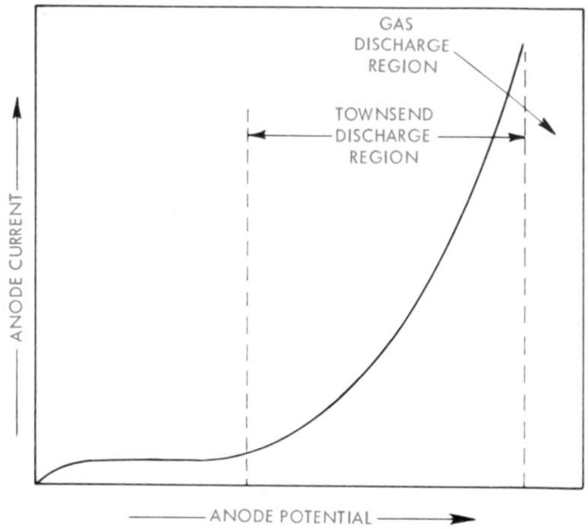

Fig. 36. *Townsend-discharge and gas-discharge regions of gas-filled phototube voltage-current characteristic.*

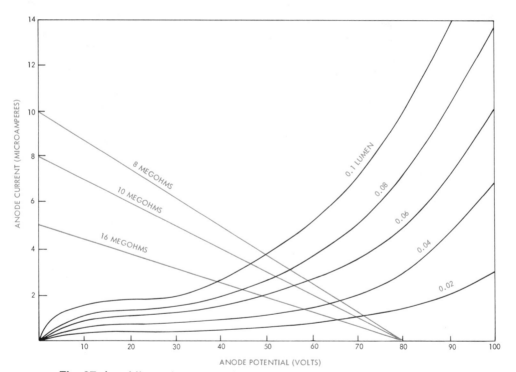

Fig. 37. *Load lines show operation of gas phototube with typical loads.*

the Townsend-discharge region to the gas discharge region, the level of operation at which conducting gases glow, as in mercury-vapor rectifiers, neon lamps, glow switches, etc.

The response of the gas-filled phototube

to cathode illumination is non-linear. This is evident in Fig. 35, which shows that, for a fixed anode voltage, equal changes in illumination do not produce equal changes in tube current.

This non-linearity is also shown in Fig. 37, which gives the operation of a gas-filled phototube with typical loads. Examination of the data in Fig. 37 reveals that, at various values of load resistance, tube output is not a linear function of radiant input. Because of its non-linearity, this type of phototube is not usually employed in the measurement of illumination. However, this characteristic of operation does not appreciably limit its use industrially since most industrial photoelectric applications involve comparison or detection, not measurement.

The dynamic response of the gas-filled phototube is not as good as that of the vacuum type, especially at higher frequencies. (Dynamic response refers to how well the tube current follows rapid changes in radiation.) This limitation is due to the relatively slow movement of the gas ions as they travel toward the cathode to produce secondary emission. At a high frequency the radiation can drop to a low level and begin a new increase before the resultant decrease in secondary emission due to the radiation drop occurs. Meanwhile, the primary emission, which can follow the radiation more closely, is experiencing a new change. Because the secondary emission is "out of phase" with the primary emission and the radiation, the gas-filled phototube

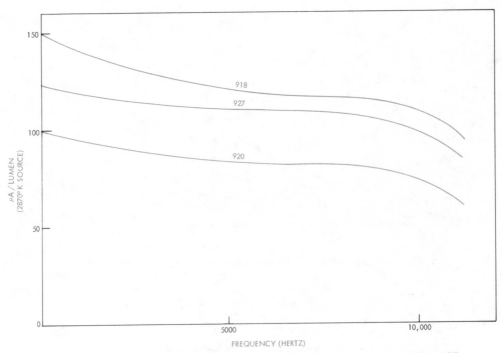

Fig. 38. *Frequency response of typical gas-filled phototubes: 918, 920, 927.*

cannot convert high-frequency changes in radiation into corresponding changes in tube current. The frequency response characteristics of typical gas-filled phototubes (918, 920, 927) are given in Fig. 38.

Multiplier Phototube

The vacuum phototube has certain limitations. In applications requiring its linearity, amplification must be provided because its output is very low. If several stages of amplification are necessary to produce a usable signal, achieving good fidelity becomes a problem. Also, because of its inherent characteristics, the vacuum phototube must operate into a high-impedance load. This precludes its use in certain modulated-radiation applications.

The vacuum-type multiplier phototube (also called "photomultiplier" or "electron multiplier") does not have these limitations. It can amplify a radiant signal as much as 1,000,000 times and works well with lower-impedance loads. A typical unit is shown in Fig. 39.

The multiplier phototube consists of a cathode, anode and several dynodes mounted in an evacuated glass envelope. Both primary and secondary emission are utilized in the operation of this tube, as illustrated in Fig. 40, which is an explanatory diagram, not an actual tube layout.

When radiant energy excites the cathode coating, primary emission occurs, as in the simpler form of vacuum phototube. The emitted electrons are attracted by dynode No. 1 which is at a positive potential. (As shown in Fig. 40, successive dynodes are at increasingly higher potentials.) Arriving at dynode No. 1, the primary-emission electrons cause secondary emission. The amount of secondary emission depends on the number of primary electrons, the work-function of the dynode coating, and the ap-

Fig. 39. *6342A multiplier phototube. (Courtesy of RCA Corp.)*

plied potential. It is usually several times the primary emission.

Dynode No. 2 is positioned so that its positive potential (which could be 100 volts higher than that of dynode No. 1) has optimum effect in attracting electrons emitted from the first dynode. Electrons arriving at the second dynode have higher velocity due to the greater positive potential at this dynode. The increased number and velocity of these electrons cause greatly increased emission from dynode No. 2. This action continues with increasingly larger emission from each succeeding dynode until emission from the last dynode is attracted to the anode.

Theoretically, amplification by means of secondary emission could be increased indefinitely by addition of more electrodes.

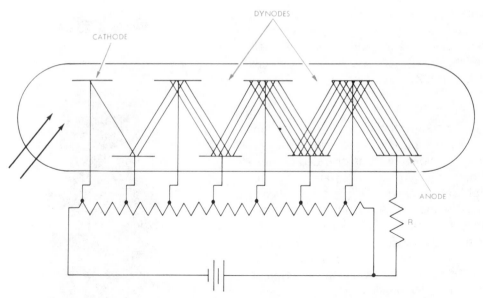

Fig. 40. *Operational diagram of multiplier phototube and power supply.*

However, there is a practical maximum of nine or ten. This is due to space-charge effects around the dynodes and the considerable heating and power dissipation of the last few dynodes.

A commercial multiplier phototube, the 931A, is shown in Fig. 41. The electrode layout for this tube is given in Fig. 42. In this form of construction a mica shield is used to separate input and output electrodes.

In operation, radiation passing through the light shield to the cathode starts the emission process. This continues through nine stages to the anode. When the potential of each dynode is at least 100 volts greater than that of the previous one, this tube is capable of amplifying signals over 800,000 times.

When used as recommended, the 931A has an output which is a linear function of the radiant input. It has good frequency response up to about 100 megahertz. (MHz.).

Fig. 41. *931A multiplier phototube. (Courtesy of RCA Corp.)*

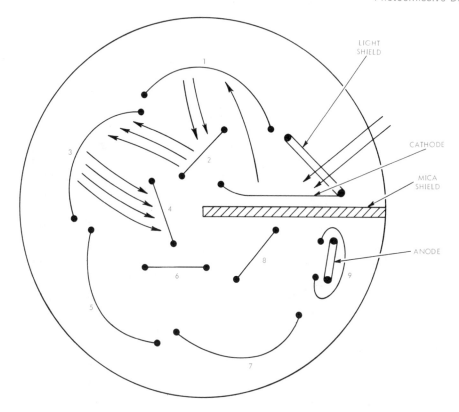

Fig. 42. *Electrode arrangement in 931A multiplier phototube.*

Beyond this frequency electron transit time is too long for proper operation. The 931A is sensitive to optical radiation extending from 3,000 Å. to 6,200 Å. with maximum response at 4,000 Å. Thus, it is highly sensitive in the blue-violet region and insensitive in the infrared and most of the ultraviolet. When exposed to incandescent radiation its response depends on the color-temperature of the source.

The multiplier phototube has a number of features which make it a useful photoelectric device: small size (the 931A has a diameter of 1⅛"), rugged construction, high sensitivity, good linearity, and rela-

tively low output impedance. It is used in X-ray controls, light-flux meters, scintillators (radiation detectors) and in many other applications involving low radiation levels, especially where the use of vacuum phototubes and amplifiers would not be feasible.

Phototube Applications

A basic phototube circuit was given in Fig. 32. The output of a phototube in this simple arrangement is very small and must be amplified to control a work function. In virtually all applications amplifiers are part of the photoelectric units.

The circuit in Fig. 43 is an experimental

355

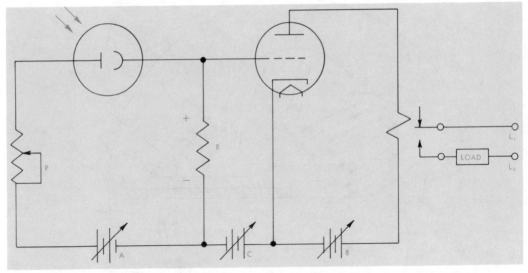

Fig. 43. *"Forward" phototube circuit: increased illumination increases output.*

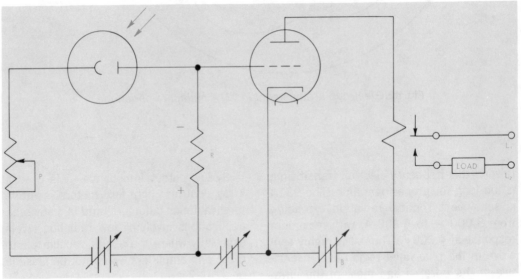

Fig. 44. *"Reverse" phototube circuit: increased illumination decreases output.*

one which includes amplification and variable potentials. This is a "forward" light-amplifier circuit—one in which increases in illumination produce increases in output.

When the phototube is "dark" the grid-bias voltage from battery C keeps the triode tube current off or at a low value. Illumination of the photocathode cause the phototube circuit to conduct and a voltage is developed across resistor R. This potential overcomes some of the bias, allowing an increase in triode current. At a certain value of illumination this current is sufficient to operate the relay. The sensitivity of the circuit is adjusted by potentiometer P.

A "reverse" circuit can be arranged by connecting the phototube and its power supply as in Fig. 44. When sufficient light strikes the photocathode and the tube conducts, the voltage developed across resistor R adds to the grid bias. This decreases the tube-relay current to a value below that required to operate the relay. Thus, in this case, increased illumination deenergizes the relay.

A more practical circuit is shown in Fig. 45. Here the phototube and amplifier have a common power supply. This is a forward circuit. Illumination of the phototube causes it to conduct, completing the grid-control circuit. The potential developed across the grid resistor overcomes some of the bias and current through the amplifier tube increases, operating the relay.

If the phototube and grid resistor are interchanged, as shown in Fig. 46, a reverse circuit is produced. When the phototube is illuminated its resistance is low. Potentials are adjusted so that the voltage across the phototube (positive at the grid) combines with the cathode voltage to yield a bias sufficient to hold the tube current to a value

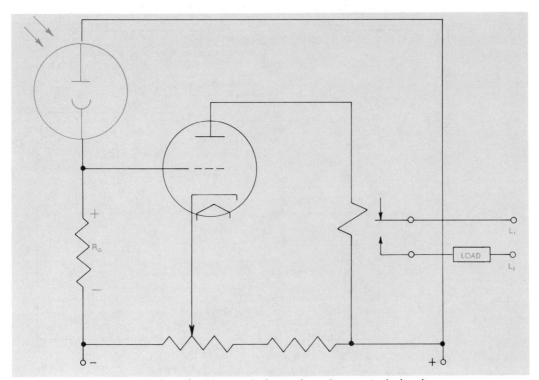

Fig. 45. *Practical forward phototube-relay control circuit.*

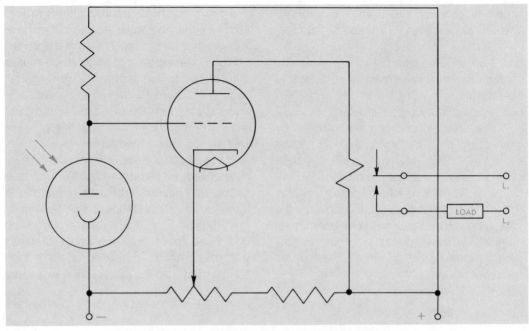

Fig. 46. *Reverse phototube-relay control circuit.*

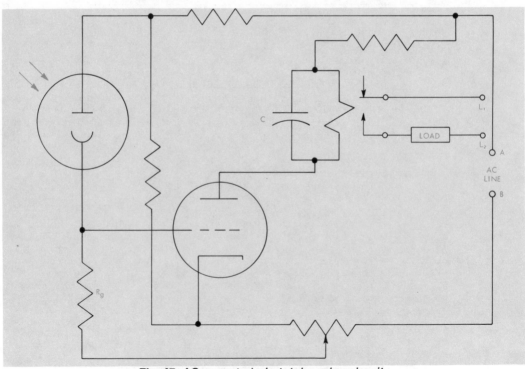

Fig. 47. *AC-operated phototube-relay circuit.*

too low to operate the relay. Interruption of the illumination greatly increases the resistance of the phototube. Consequently, the voltage across it increases, yielding a low value of bias which allows tube current to increase, operating the relay.

An ac-operated phototube-relay circuit is given in Fig. 47. During the half-cycle when line A is positive: with minimum light to the photocathode (nonconducting), the triode grid is highly negative and the tube-relay current is minimum or zero. With an increase in light the phototube conducts, the voltage developed across R_g decreases the bias and an increased current flows through the relay coil. At a certain value of illumination the current will be sufficient to operate the relay. While this current is

flowing, capacitor C charges. On the next half-cycle, when line A is negative, the triode cannot conduct, but capacitor C discharges through the relay coil, maintaining operation. The potentiometer adjusts the bias and light level required for actuation of the relay.

Phototube control of a thyratron-relay circuit is illustrated in Fig. 48. The thyratron can conduct only when its plate is positive. However, during this half-cycle the grid is negative since it is connected to the opposite end of the transformer secondary. Thus, the tube is cut off and no current flows through the relay coil. When illuminated, the phototube completes the circuit through resistor R. Point X becomes less negative, reducing the grid bias. This trig-

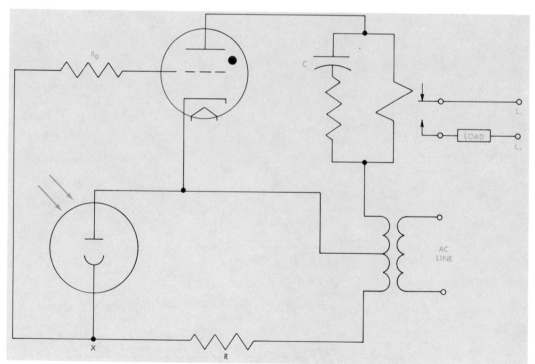

Fig. 48. *Phototube control of thyratron-relay circuit.*

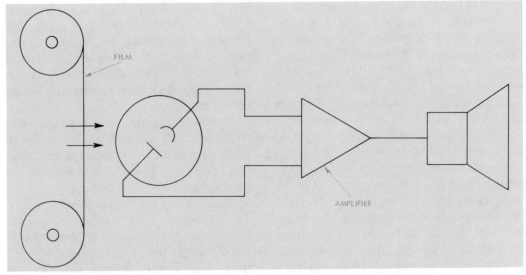

Fig. 49. *Phototube application: sound production from movie-film sound track.*

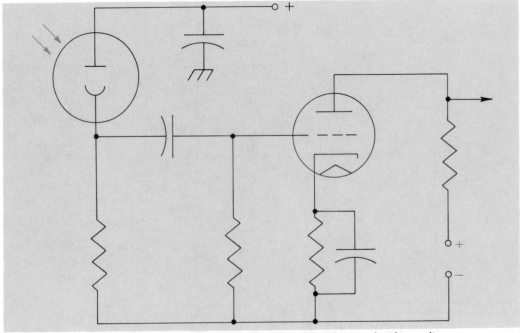

Fig. 50. *Photo-amplifier circuit of film-sound reproduction unit.*

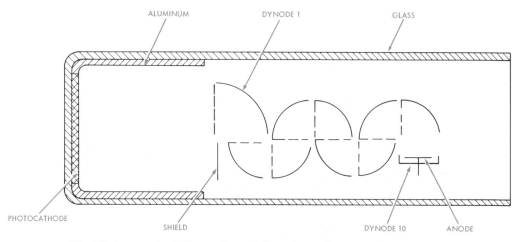

ALUMINUM   DYNODE 1   GLASS

PHOTOCATHODE

SHIELD   DYNODE 10   ANODE

Fig. 51. *Box-and grid form of multiplier phototube used in scintillator.*

gers the thyratron into conduction and the relay operates. Interruption of the light beam turns off the thyratron. Capacitor C serves to maintain current through the relay coil on non-conducting half-cycles. If the capacitor is large, its high charging current could damage the tube if the series resistor were not included to limit this current to a safe value.

In Fig. 49 a photoemissive tube is part of a system for sound reproduction from a movie-film sound track. Light shines from a source through the film sound track to the phototube. Variations in the track (density of dark area) produce similar changes in the beam of light arriving at the photo-cathode. The resulting phototube output is amplified and converted into a sound at the loudspeaker. The circuit diagram of a sound-reproduction unit is given in Fig. 50.

A multiplier phototube is widely used as an amplifier in a form of radiation detector called a *scintillator.* Fig. 51 illustrates the type of tube utilized in many commercial units. This form of dynode construction is known as the *box and grid system.* Radiation strikes a photocathode mounted in one end of the tube. The dynodes are quarter-cylinders arranged as shown to provide for emission multiplication. Amplified output is applied to a counting device for conversion to readable indications of radiation levels.

Unit 6

Photovoltaic Devices

The work of early experimenters—Becquerel, Adam, Day and others — showed that illumination produced a potential between electrodes immersed in a solution or in direct contact. Modern devices which operate on this principle are known as photovoltaic cells. An early form of photovoltaic cell having copper and copper-oxide electrodes is illustrated in Fig. 52. Radiation striking the copper oxide caused ionization. Some of the electrons freed by ionization acquired enough energy to move into the copper section. Continuation of this process created a potential between the copper and the ring connected to the copper oxide, negative at the copper. Electron flow through a load is shown in the illustration.

Two forms of construction have been used in photovoltaic-cell fabrication: back-effect and front-effect (also known as back-

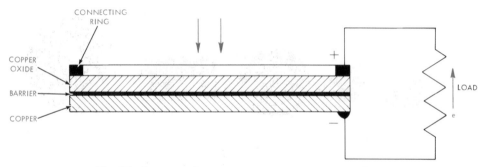

Fig. 52. *Construction of back-effect photovoltaic cell.*

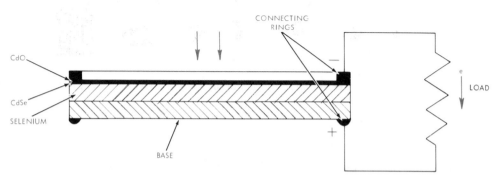

Fig. 53. *Construction of selenium photovoltaic cell (front-effect type).*

plate and front-plate). The main difference between the two forms is the location of the barrier layer. The cell in Fig. 52 is a back-effect type. Here the barrier layer is so situated that the light must pass through the copper oxide to reach it. Consequently, some of the radiant energy is absorbed by the copper oxide. Front-effect construction does not have this limitation. In a cell of this type the barrier layer is placed closer to the surface which receives the radiation. In addition, a thin film of transparent metal (gold, etc.) is formed over the barrier layer. This arrangement yields a more sensitive and more efficient device. Front-effect construction is used in the manufacture of modern photovoltaic cells, such as the selenium cell illustrated in Fig. 53.

Selenium Photovoltaic Cell

The selenium cell is a device fabricated to convert radiant energy directly into an electrical output which is proportional to the radiant input. It is this property of the selenium cell which makes it a valuable device for measuring light intensity.

Construction of Selenium Cell. The construction of a typical standard unit is illustrated in Fig. 53. This type of cell is formed by first depositing a layer of se-

363

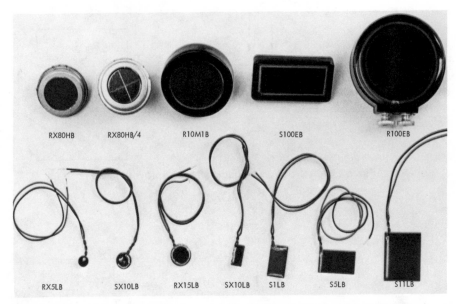

Fig. 54. *Various forms of selenium photovoltaic cells. (Courtesy of Vactec Inc.)*

lenium, about 75 microns thick, on a metal plate. Then a coating of cadmium is placed over the selenium and the junction is grown. The growth process produces a gradient layer of cadmium selenide (CdSe) and cadmium oxide (CdO). A line or ring of highly conductive alloy is deposited on the cadmium-oxide layer and also on the metal base to provide lead connections.

In a variation of the standard cell, a transparent layer of gold is deposited over the junction, forming a connecting electrode. The gold acts as a filter, transmitting better at shorter wavelengths. This property gives this form of selenium cell a higher blue-to-red response ratio. Because the gold film reduces radiation transmission, this unit is somewhat less efficient than the standard selenium cell. Typical cells are shown in Fig. 54.

Operation of Selenium Cell. The selenium photovoltaic cell operates as a PN junction, which is N on P, the active-surface electrode being negative with respect to the base electrode. In the unit in Fig. 53 the cadmium selenide is N-type (containing an excess of electrons) and the selenium is P-type (excess holes).

When the junction is formed, the normal diffusion process which occurs at a semiconductor PN junction produces a potential across the junction. With this condition existing, radiant energy striking the selenium releases valence electrons which become conduction electrons. They move through the junction creating holes in the selenium which move in the opposite direction. As this occurs, electrons pass from the metallic baseplate into the selenium. Thus a potential is developed across the cell, negative at the active electrode and positive at the base. In the external circuit electron flow is from the active electrode through the circuit and back to the base.

To produce conduction electrons, photons of radiation must have enough energy to raise the energy level of a selenium valence electron to the conduction level. Since radiant energy is a function of wavelength, the spectral response of a semiconductor is determined by its valence-to-conduction bandgap. Consequently, carriers are produced in selenium only by photons with energy equivalent to, or greater than, the bandgap of selenium. Each photon creates one carrier. Shorter–wavelength photons possess more energy than longer ones but still produce only one carrier.

The spectral response of selenium is given in Fig. 55, where it is compared to that of the human eye. Shown also is the response of silicon, another semiconductor widely used in photovoltaic cells. According to Fig. 55, the peak response of selenium is at 5800 Å. This is shorter than the peak-response wavelength of silicon, which is at 8200 Å. Consequently, more energy is required to produce peak response in selenium than in silicon.

Generally, selenium cells have an efficiency of less than one percent when converting input radiation to output voltage. Silicon cells are 8 to 12% efficient. For this reason, silicon rather than selenium is used in solar-energy converters. However, when the radiant energy is confined to the visible range and the load resistance is high, the output of a selenium cell is equivalent to

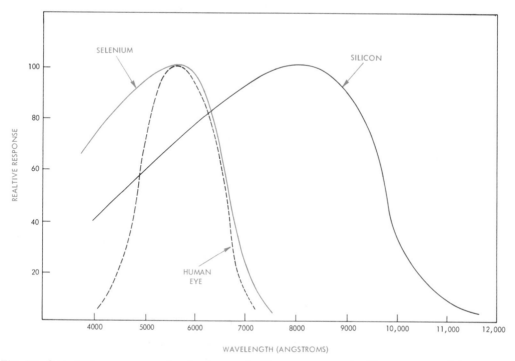

Fig. 55. *Spectral responses of selenium and silicon compared with response of human eye.*

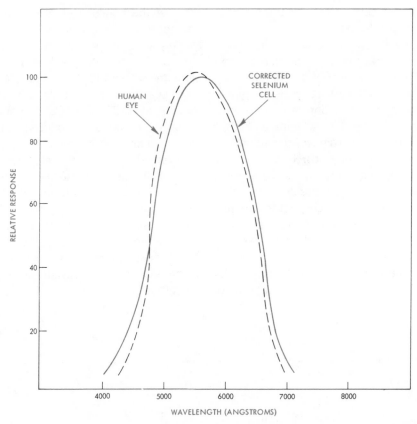

Fig. 56. *Response of corrected selenium cell compared with response of human eye.*

that of a comparable silicon cell. Fig. 56 shows the response of a selenium cell filter-corrected to match the response of the human eye.

The open-circuit voltage of a selenium photovoltaic cell increases linearly with increasing illumination at low lighting levels. However, above one footcandle the relationship is logarithmic, as indicated by the data in Fig. 57, where the output voltage of a selenium cell is shown as a function of illumination.

Fig. 58 shows the circuit current produced by a typical selenium photovoltaic cell through a number of load resistances as illumination is increased over a range. According to the data, linearity is achieved only when the output is short-circuited. Also, as load resistance increases, changes in illumination have a decreasing effect on load current. Therefore, the selenium cell and load resistance should be matched to ensure that changes in illumination over a desired range will produce significant changes in electrical output.

Silicon Photovoltaic Cell

A silicon photovoltaic cell is essentially

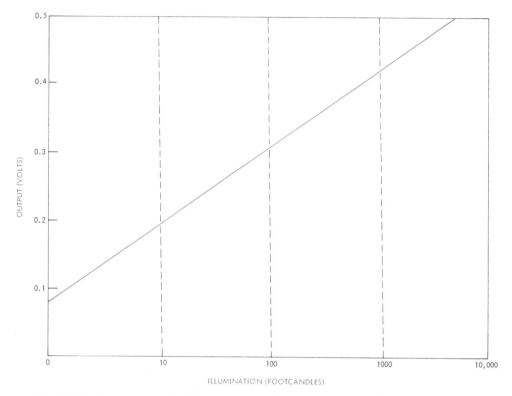

Fig. 57. *Output voltage of selenium photovoltaic cell as a function of illumination.*

a PN diode which develops a potential when exposed to ultraviolet, visible, or infrared radiation. (The spectral response of silicon is shown in Fig. 55.) Without radiation it operates in about the same manner as a regular PN diode, passing current when forward-biased and blocking it when reverse-biased.

Construction of Silicon Cell. The construction of a typical unit is illustrated in Fig. 59. Here a thin wafer of N-type silicon forms the negative member of the junction. Boron, or another suitable "impurity" material, is fused into one surface of the silicon, forming the P layer. The opposite surface of the silicon is plated, providing a good electrical contact. This is the negative terminal of the cell. The positive terminal is a metal ring in contact with the P layer. The P layer is covered with a translucent window which allows radiation to reach the junction. A number of typical silicon cells are shown in Fig. 60.

Operation of Silicon Cell. As in the selenium photovoltaic cell, the normal diffusion process at the PN junction of the silicon cell produces a potential across the junction. When the cell is illuminated, radiant energy produces electron-hole pairs in the junction region. These carriers move

367

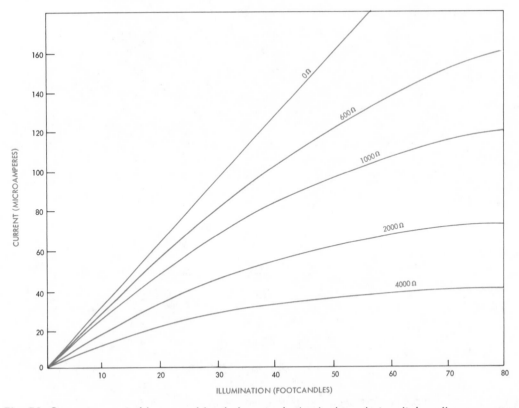

Fig. 58. *Currents created in several loads by a typical selenium photovoltaic cell over a range of illumination.*

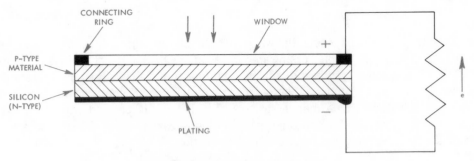

Fig. 59. *Silicon photovoltaic cell.*

under the influence of the constant potential—electrons from P to N, and holes from N to P. In this manner a potential is developed across the cell—positive at the P-layer connecting ring and negative at the plated surface.

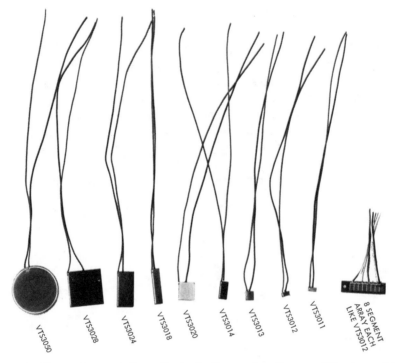

Fig. 60. *Forms of silicon photovoltaic cells, including an 8-cell array. (Courtesy of Vactec Inc.)*

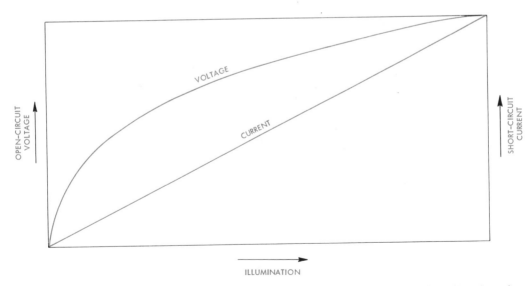

Fig. 61. *Open-circuit voltage and short-circuit current of silicon photovoltaic cell as functions of illumination.*

369

The voltage developed across a photovoltaic silicon cell increases with illumination, as shown in Fig. 61. As the curve indicates, this is a non-linear relationship, increasing rapidly at lower illumination levels and tending to level off at higher values. Also shown is the growth of short-circuit current with increasing radiation. As in the selenium cell, this is a linear relationship.

Modes of Operation. Silicon photovoltaic cells may be operated in four modes:

short-circuit, open-circuit, reverse-bias, and power-conversion. These modes are indicated in Figs. 62 and 63. In Fig. 62 the dark volt-ampere characteristic is given for a typical cell. Forward-bias operation is shown in the first quadrant and reverse-bias operation in the third quadrant.

The dashed curve shows operation when the PN junction is illuminated. When operating in the fourth quadrant the cell is a generator, converting radiant energy to

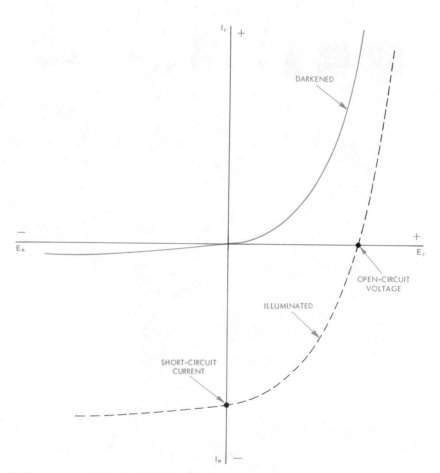

Fig. 62. *Volt-ampere characteristic of darkened and illuminated silicon photovoltaic cell (solar type).*

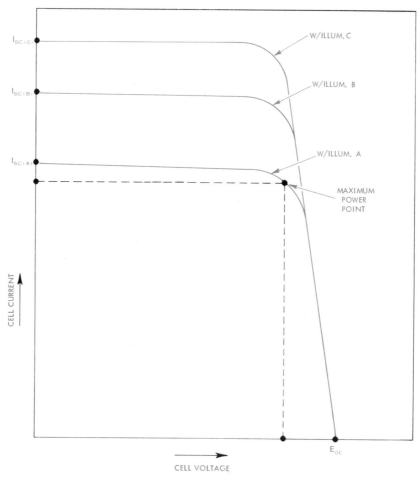

Fig. 63. *Volt-ampere characteristic of silicon photovoltaic cell (solar type) for three values of illumination.*

electrical output. Open-circuit voltage and short-circuit current occur at the limits of the curve in this quadrant. Reverse-bias operation occurs in the third quadrant. In Fig. 63, volt-ampere curves (fourth–quadrant data) are plotted for three values of illumination. Three values of short-circuit current and one maximum-power-transfer point are indicated.

Short-circuit operation is that condition existing when the load voltage is 20%, or less, of the open-circuit voltage under equal lighting levels. When a silicon photovoltaic cell is operated in the short-circuit mode, the electrical output is a linear function of the light input. It has a low positive temperature coefficient, about +0.25%/°C. Also, it responds quickly to changes in illumination.

Open-circuit operation is accomplished

by using a very high load impedance. This mode produces an open-circuit voltage which varies logarithmically with linear changes in radiant input. It has a negative temperature coefficient of about 2.0 mV/°C. The response time of this mode of operation is relatively long. This is due to the long RC time constant of the shunt capacitance of the cell and the high value of load resistance. It takes the cell capacitance much longer to discharge through the high-impedance load than through the low-impedance load of the short-circuit mode.

In the reverse-bias mode (third quadrant) a silicon photovoltaic cell acts like a photoconductor, resistance varying inversely with illumination. Without illumination it has very high resistance, the value of which depends on the reverse-bias voltage and the reverse-leakage current. When the cell is illuminated, the generation of carriers increases the cell current at a rate which is almost linear.

The power-conversion mode of operation is best achieved when the load impedance is that which produces maximum transfer of power at a particular illumination level. The point on a characteristic curve at which this occurs is indicated in Fig. 63. For any characteristic curve the maximum power point is the point at which the largest-area rectangle which can be fitted under the curve touches the curve. Power rectangles vary with lighting levels; power output increases as the shape of the volt-ampere curve approaches a square.

Applications of Operational Modes. Because of its linearity, short-circuit operation is generally used in light-measurement applications. Where precision is required, compensation of the positive temperature coefficient can be accomplished by increasing the load resistance. This shifts operation toward the power-conversion mode,

which has a negative temperature coefficient. At some point between the two modes (on the horizontal section of the curves in Fig. 63) the temperature coefficient is zero. The range of compensated operation is limited because, if the load remains fixed and the illumination increased appreciably, operation would be in the power-conversion mode where it would be neither linear nor compensated.

Open-circuit operation of a silicon photovoltaic cell provides logarithmic variations in voltage output when the cell is activated by linear changes in radiant input. Due to its non-linearity this mode of operation is not feasible for measurement applications. However, because the changes in output are logarithmic, open-circuit operation is quite suitable for switching applications which require good response to the presence of radiation.

The reverse-bias mode of operation is used in punch-card and tape-reading equipment and in switching applications. As a switching element, a reverse-biased silicon photovoltaic cell can trigger a transistor. This application is illustrated in Fig. 64. When the cell in this circuit is deactivated it acts as a high impedance in parallel with the base-emitter-ground section. The applied potential forward-biases the base-emitter junction turning on the transistor. Activation of the silicon cell lowers its impedance. This low value of impedance shunting the base-emitter junction turns off the transistor. In some instances, depending on components and amount of radiation, the photovoltaic potential of the silicon cell actually reverse-biases the base-emitter junction.

The power-conversion mode of operation is generally used in solar applications, wherein sunlight is converted to electrical energy. In some applications the silicon

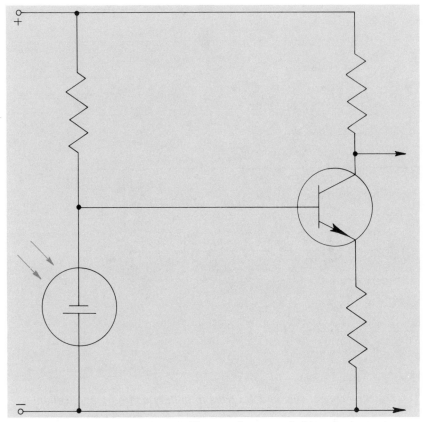

Fig. 64. *Reverse-biased silicon cell as a switching device.*

"solar-cell" provides power directly to a load; in others it serves as a battery-charging device. Panel arrays consisting of hundreds of cells are used as power generators for space satellites. They are also used as energy converters for telephone repeater stations and for environmental and geophysical equipment in remote locations.

In these applications the silicon photovoltaic cells are usually connected in a series-parallel configuration—in series for additive voltage, in parallel to meet current requirements. Fig. 65 shows the circuit of a series-parallel array maintaining the charge on a battery-bank. The charging diode, D, prevents loss of charge from the bank when the cells are dark. Without the blocking action of the diode the darkened cells would act as a resistive load on the bank, creating a current drain.

The capacity of a satellite solar-panel is usually greater than that required for the application. (A voltage regulator is used to adjust the output automatically to the desired value.) The extra capacity is necessary because solar cells are subject to radiation damage caused by high-energy particles. Cells which consist of an N-type layer

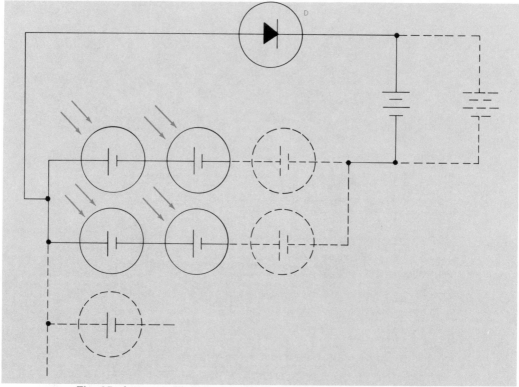

Fig. 65. *Array of silicon solar cells in battery-charging application.*

on a P-type base withstand harmful radiation more than P-on-N cells. Consequently, panel arrays for space applications are made up of NP silicon photovoltaic cells.

Circuits with Photovoltaic Cells

In many applications of photovoltaic cells the circuitry is very simple. Fig. 66 shows a circuit for measuring light intensity. The potential generated by the cell creates a current through the meter proportional to the illumination. The familiar foot-candle meter is an example of such simplified circuitry.

A circuit more sensitive than that in Fig. 66 is given in Fig. 67. Here the signal gen-

Fig. 66. *Photovoltaic cell sensing light intensity.*

erated by the photovoltaic cell provides the base-emitter bias of the transistor. An increase in illumination causes an increase in the forward bias resulting in greater transistor current. As the transistor current

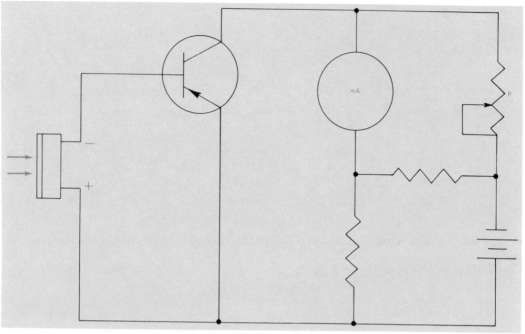

Fig. 67. *Amplifier multiplies low output of photocell.*

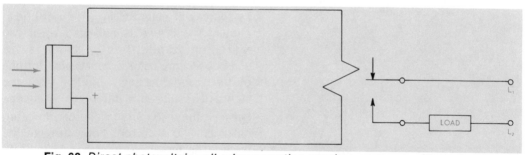

Fig. 68. *Direct photovoltaic cell-relay operation requires a very sensitive relay.*

increases the meter current increases, indicating the change in illumination. Potentiometer P is used to zero the meter when the cell is dark.

Fig. 68 shows a photovoltaic cell energizing a sensitive relay. If a transistor is added for amplification, as in Fig. 69, a less-sensitive and less-expensive relay may be used when small changes in illumination are being sensed.

Photovoltaic cells are used in various forms of comparators. Fig. 70 illustrates how two matched cells can be used to compare color samples. The two cells are wired

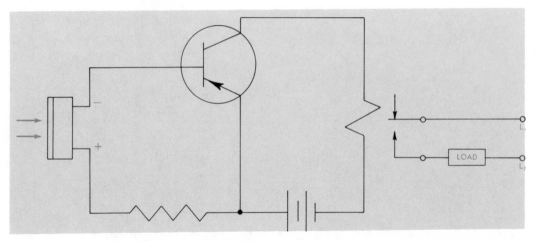

Fig. 69. *Transistor amplifies photocell output for operation of medium-sensitivity relay.*

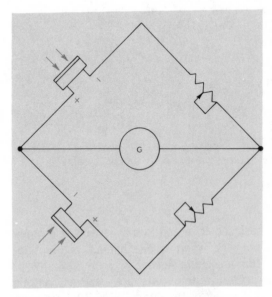

Fig. 70. *Matched photovoltaic cells are sources of potential in color-comparator circuit.*

as sources of potential in a form of bridge circuit. The bridge is balanced when two matching standard color samples are sensed. When a color is substituted for one of the standards any variation from the standard results in a difference in voltage between the cells. The bridge becomes unbalanced and a current flows through the meter. The meter is calibrated to indicate the extent to which the tested color differs from the standard.

Photovoltaic circuits have many uses. In addition to reading lighting levels directly, they are used in cameras to automatically determine correct film exposure, in checking the density of smoke and liquids and the translucency and reflectance of materials, in blood studies and chemical analysis, and in many other scientific and industrial applications.

Unit 6

section 6 Photoconductive Devices

An important photoelectric effect is the change in resistance that optical radiation produces in certain semiconductors. Materials which respond in this manner are known as *photoconductors*. The most-commonly used photoconductive materials are cadmium sulfide (CdS) and cadmium selenide (CdSe). Lead sulfide (PbS) is used in some applications.

Varieties of photoconductive devices described and illustrated in this section include: *photoconductive cells, photodiodes,* and *phototransistors*. Construction, operation, and applications of each type of device are also described and illustrated.

Photoconductive Cell

Photoconductive cells have replaced photoemissive tubes in some forms of lighting control and in other applications. They have also replaced photovoltaic cells in some photographic exposure meters, providing 1,000 times as much sensitivity as selenium photovoltaic cells. Some photoconductive cells are a million times more sensitive than photoemissive devices, equalling the sensitivity of the multiplier phototube while operating from a much simpler, lower-voltage supply. Generally, when photoconductive devices replace photoemissive ones they can operate relays without the amplification which is required with photoemissive tubes. They are also utilized in a variety of applications because of their wide range of spectral response, stability, ruggedness, simplicity of installation and good temperature characteristics. Fig. 71 shows a number of typical photoconductive cells, including a 20-unit array.

Construction of Photoconductive Cell. The construction of a photoconductive wafer is illustrated in Fig. 72. A thin layer of semiconductor material is deposited on a base (substrate) of ceramic or similar in-

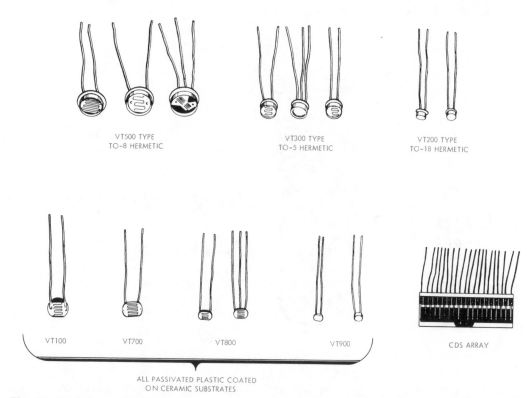

VT500 TYPE
TO-8 HERMETIC

VT300 TYPE
TO-5 HERMETIC

VT200 TYPE
TO-18 HERMETIC

VT100 VT700 VT800 VT900

CDS ARRAY

ALL PASSIVATED PLASTIC COATED
ON CERAMIC SUBSTRATES

Fig. 71. *Cadmium sulfide and cadmium selenide photoconductive cells, including a 20-unit array. (Courtesy of Vactec Inc.)*

sulating material. Connecting electrodes are plated onto the semiconductor in a pattern which provides maximum contact. Tin is a commonly-used electrode material because of its chemical stability and low work function.

The wafer, consisting of substrate, semiconductor and electrodes is mounted in a glass, steel-glass, ceramic-glass or plastic enclosure. The enclosure contains a window which allows radiation to reach the semiconductor. Clear plastic enclosures are used in the construction of less-expensive units for low-initial-cost applications. However, since humidity is a primary cause of

photoconductive-cell failure, where reliability is important the all-glass or glass combination enclosure is required to provide a dependable hermetic seal. Although they are more expensive, all-glass units can withstand extensive temperature changes, impact shocks of several hundred g and extensive fatigue testing. The construction of a glass-steel unit is shown in Fig. 73.

Operation of Photoconductive Cell. Cadmium sulfide and cadmium selenide function effectively as photoconductive materials. When photons of radiant energy strike these materials, valence electrons are freed from orbit. These electrons become

378

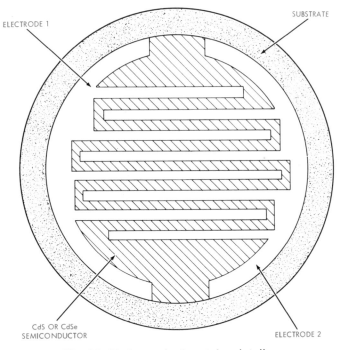

ELECTRODE 1

SUBSTRATE

CdS OR CdSe
SEMICONDUCTOR

ELECTRODE 2

Fig. 72. *Photoconductor wafer detail.*

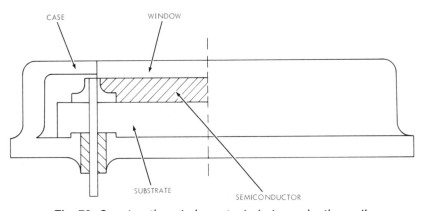

CASE

WINDOW

SUBSTRATE

SEMICONDUCTOR

Fig. 73. *Construction of glass-steel photoconductive cell.*

conduction electrons, effectively lowering the resistance of the material. Increases in radiation increase the number of free elec- trons, further lowering the resistance. If the radiation decreases, recombination occurs and the effective resistance of the material

379

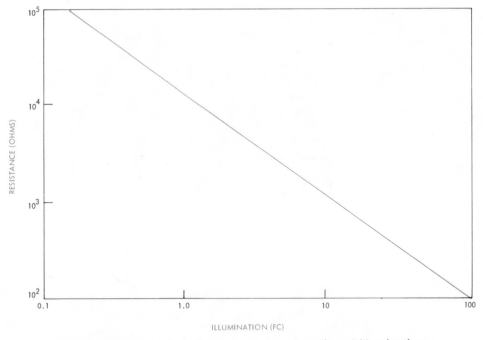

Fig. 74. *Resistance of photoconductor as a function of illumination.*

increases. Thus, the resistance of the semiconductor follows inversely the amount of radiation.

In total darkness the resistance of a photoconductor may be several megohms, and less than 100 ohms when well-illuminated. Fig. 74 shows the decrease in resistance of a typical photoconductor with increase in illumination.

Since photoconductor dark resistance approaches infinity its use as a specification is limited. Instead, manufacturers specify a minimum dark resistance, taken a number of seconds (5,10,etc.) after removal from a two f.c. source of illumination, or a minimum ratio of this dark resistance to that at two f.c. Typical values might range from 100:1 to 10,000:1.

Typical spectral-response curves of cad-

mium-sulfide and cadmium-selenide photoconductive materials are given in Fig. 75, where they are compared with the response of the human eye. Since the cadmium-sulfide response closely resembles that of the eye, cells of this semiconductor are used in white-light and photographic equipment. Because cadmium selenide responds well in the infrared region it is used in surveillance applications requiring invisible radiation.

Because of the time required to change the resistance of a photoconductor, its response to variations in radiation is relatively slow. The response times of a selection of typical cadmium sulfide cells might range from a few thousandths of a second at 100 f.c. to hundredths at one f.c. and tenths of a second at 0.1 f.c. This range of

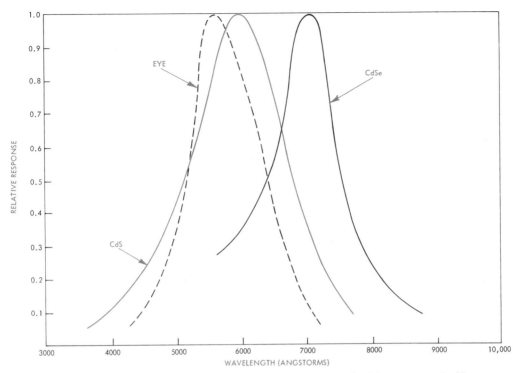

Fig. 75. *Spectral responses of cadmium sulfide and cadmium selenide compared with response of the human eye.*

response is shown in Fig. 76. According to Fig. 76, cadmium selenide has a much shorter response time at lower lighting levels than cadmium sulfide. Because of their response-time limitations, photoconductive cells are not used in such applications as movie-film sound pickups or code-modulated devices where the response must be at audio-frequency rates.

Photoconductor Circuits. A simple photoconductor light-measuring circuit is given in Fig. 77. The indicating meter is calibrated in lighting units, such as foot-candles. At low levels of illumination the cell has high resistance. This limits the circuit current, resulting in a low meter reading.

With increased illumination, reduced cell resistance results in greater current flow and an increased reading. Various ranges of illumination may be measured by proper selection of voltage, photoconductor, meter, and shunt.

A more elaborate photometer circuit is shown in Fig. 78. This device is capable of measuring illumination over five different ranges. Provision is also made for calibration of the unit.

In Fig. 79 a relay is controlled by a photoconductor. At low radiation levels the high resistance of the cell maintains the relay current below the "pull-in" value. If the radiation is increased sufficiently, the

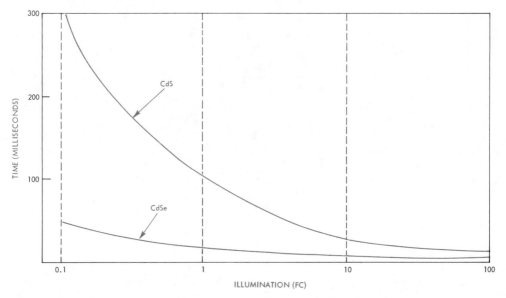

Fig. 76. *One-time-constant response times of CdS and CdSe over a range of illumination.*

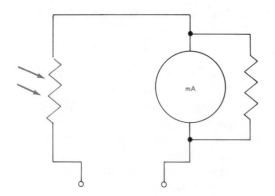

Fig. 77. *Photoconductor light-measurement circuit.*

decreased cell resistance allows enough current flow to operate the relay. The variable resistance adjusts the radiation-level operating point of the relay.

Figs. 77 through 79 show the photoconductor as a series-connected device. In Fig.

80 it is a shunt control, operating in a manner opposite to the series control. When the radiation level is low and the resistance of the photocell is high the voltage across the cell and relay coil is relatively high. This makes the relay current sufficient to oper-

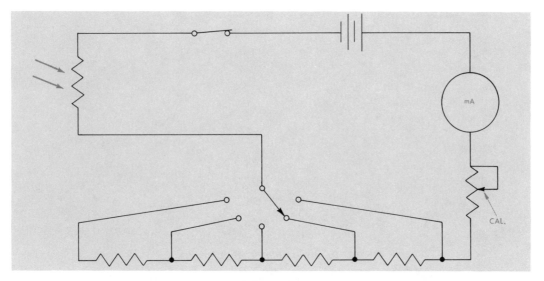

Fig. 78. *Photometer circuit with photoconductor as light sensor.*

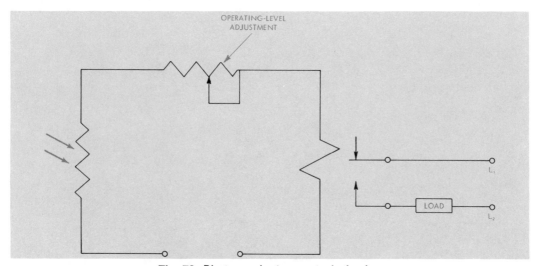

Fig. 79. *Photoconductor control of relay.*

ate it. Increased radiation reduces the resistance of the parallel combination, causing a decrease in voltage across the relay coil. The resultant decrease in relay cur-

rent may be enough to cause the relay to "drop out."

Fig. 81 shows two matched photoconductors connected as legs in a bridge circuit.

383

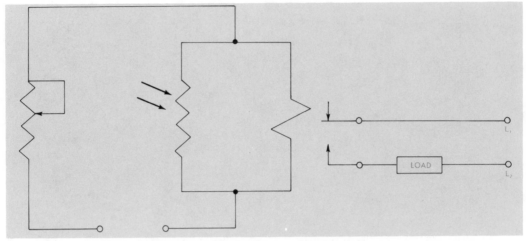

Fig. 80. *Photoconductor shunt control.*

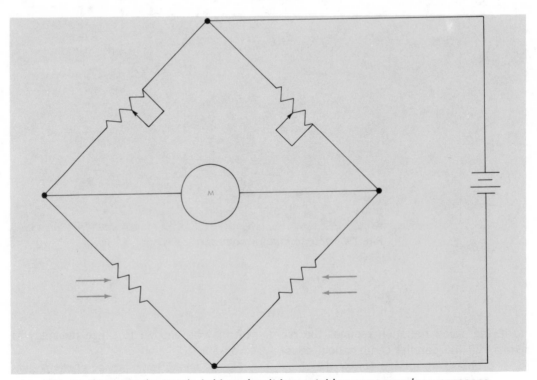

Fig. 81. *Photoconductors in bridge circuit for matching or comparison purposes.*

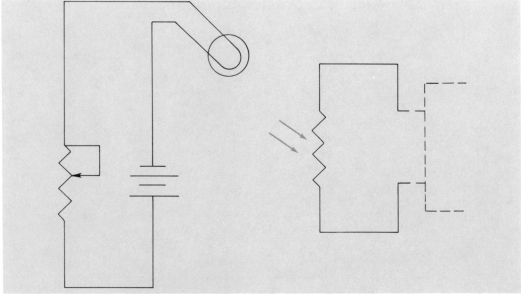

Fig. 82. *Contactless control using photoconductor.*

This circuit can be used to match two light sources or compare their outputs. To match two sources the bridge is balanced (meter at zero) and the cells are exposed to the sources. If imbalance occurs the sources are adjusted until the meter reads zero. A zero reading indicates equal cell resistances, resulting from equal illumination from equal sources. When used to compare two light sources, the bridge is balanced and the cells are exposed to the sources. Any difference in illumination creates a difference in resistance between the cells which unbalances the bridge. The direction of the resulting meter deflection indicates which light source is stronger and the amount of deflection indicates how much.

In Fig. 82 a control circuit is connected optically to the circuit it is controlling. This arrangement provides a remote, contactless type of control. Adjustment of the rheostat varies the radiation, which varies the photoconductor resistance. In this manner the photocell is operated as a variable resistance in the circuit to be controlled.

Photoconductor "turn-on" of a silicon controlled rectifier (SCR) is illustrated in Fig. 83. Here the photocell is in series with a sensitivity control across a dc supply. When radiation lowers the resistance of the photoconductor the voltage across the sensitivity control increases, making the SCR gate more positive. This fires the SCR, completing the load circuit. The load could be a motor, heater or other electrical equipment. Removal of radiation does not cause "turn-off" since the gate loses control when the SCR fires. It is accomplished by opening the line switch.

The circuit in Fig. 84 can be used to turn a street light on at dusk and off at dawn. In this control a bridge rectifier provides

385

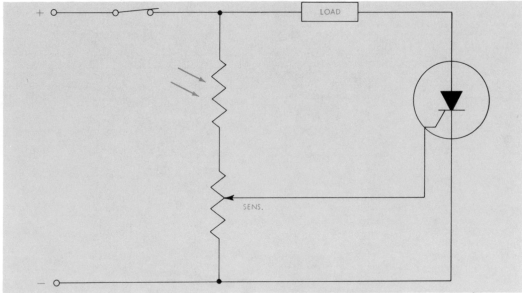

Fig. 83. *Photoconductor turn-on of SCR.*

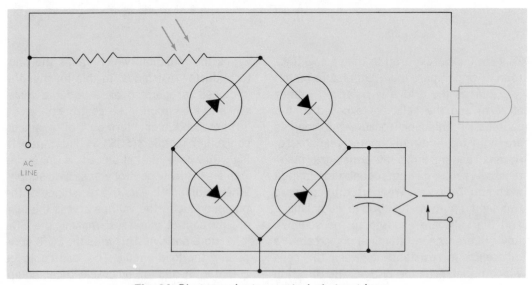

Fig. 84. *Photoconductor control of street lamp.*

direct current to the relay coil. During daylight hours the cadmium-sulfide cell has low resistance, allowing sufficient current-flow to operate the relay. This holds the load contacts open and no current flows through the lamp. At dusk the resistance of the photocell increases, the coil current decreases and the relay cannot hold the load contacts open. The contacts close, completing the lamp circuit.

The control circuit in Fig. 84 is a "fail-safe" arrangement. If some part of the circuit (cell, relay coil, etc.) fails, causing the coil to become deenergized, the load contacts close. The lamp lights and remains lighted night and day, indicating trouble in the control.

Photodiode

A previous section included a type of diode designed to produce a photovoltaic effect. Diodes are also fabricated to act as photoconductive devices. Such units, commonly called photodiodes, are available in both silicon and germanium. Typical models are shown in Fig. 85.

Construction of Photodiode. A photodiode is made much like the conventional semiconductor diode, with the addition of a lens for focusing radiation on the contact or junction area. A point-contact type of photodiode is illustrated in Fig. 86. Here a whisker makes contact with the semicon-

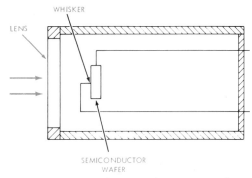

Fig. 86. *Construction of point-contact photodiode.*

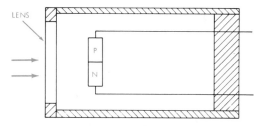

Fig. 87. *PN-junction photodiode.*

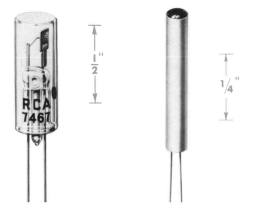

Fig. 85. *Photodiodes. (Courtesy of RCA Corp.)*

ductor wafer to form the diode and the lens focuses radiation on the area around the contact. A PN-junction form of photodiode is illustrated in Fig. 87. In this unit the lens focuses the radiation on the junction between the N- and P-type materials.

The spectral responses of silicon and germanium make them suitable for use as photodiode semiconductors. Fig. 88 shows that, although the response curves of these materials peak in the infrared region, they are also compatible with the human eye. Fig. 88 also indicates that silicon and germanium respond to incandescent radiation. This allows the use of readily-available incandescent lamps as radiation sources in photodiode applications.

387

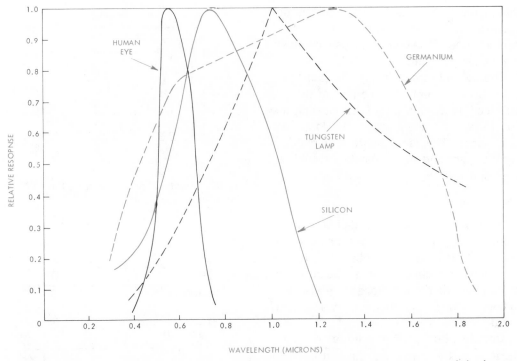

Fig. 88. *Spectral responses of silicon and germanium compared with response of the human eye and output of tungsten lamp.*

Operation of Photodiode. A photodiode is normally operated in a reverse-bias mode, as in Fig. 89. Here the diode is in a light-tight box. Unilluminated, it has very high inverse resistance. A small leakage current may flow, known as "dark current." This current, which may be only a few microamperes, is due to thermal generation of carriers which diffuse across the junction. It increases with an increase in temperature.

When the diode is illuminated, as in Fig. 90, radiant energy releases valence electrons in the semiconductor. This action causes electron movement across the PN junction in the normally-nonconducting direction. This, in effect, is a lowering of the high inverse resistance of the back-biased

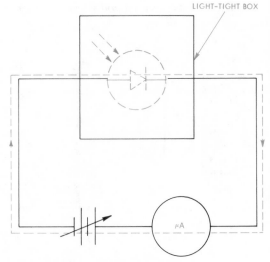

Fig. 89. *Dark current (leakage) flows through photodiode in light-tight box.*

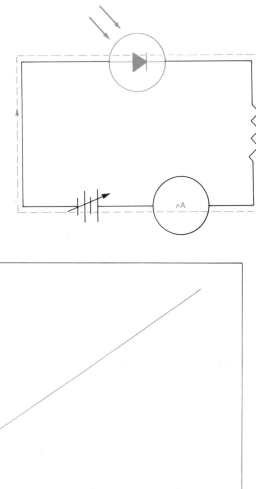

Fig. 90. *Photodiode conducts in reverse-bias mode when illuminated.*

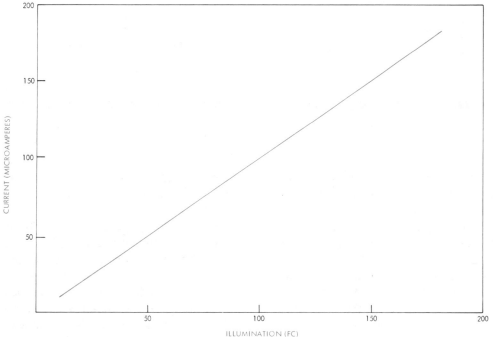

Fig. 91. *Photodiode current as a function of illumination.*

diode. Increased illumination produces a further reduction in effective resistance and increase in circuit current.

Increases in current with changing illumination are shown by the characteristic curve of a typical photodiode, given in Fig.

389

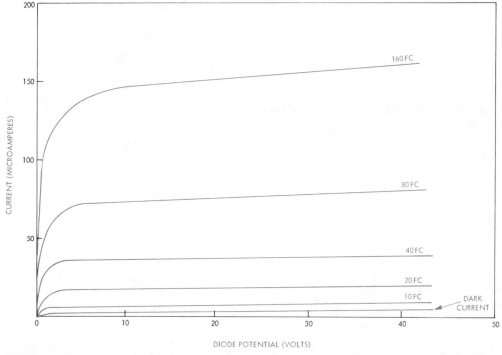

Fig. 92. *Volt-ampere characteristic of a typical photodiode at several illumination levels.*

91. Operation of such a diode at various illumination levels is also shown by the volt-ampere curves in Fig. 92. These curves indicate that, for a particular light level, once the bias voltage reaches a certain value, any further increase in bias does not increase the current. Such current saturation occurs because most of the potential across the diode appears across the junction while the radiation-produced carriers move toward the junction through a section not affected by the potential. Any increase in current requires additional illumination.

Photodiode Applications. Photodiodes have features which make them very suitable for a number of optical-sensing applications. They use little power and perform at high efficiency. They can operate at rela-tively low voltages in simple circuitry. They are small and rugged, have good optical sensitivity and long life.

Photodiodes respond more quickly than photoconductive cells to changes in radiation intensity. Consequently, they can be utilized in applications where the radiation varies at audio-frequency rates, such as in the movie-film sound-pickup equipment illustrated in Fig. 93. In this application the photodiode also provides the linear response required for good sound reproduction. Because of their small size and good response, photodiodes can also be used in punched-tape and punched-card readers.

The output of a photodiode is compara-tively low. In most applications it must be amplified, as illustrated in Fig. 94. Here the

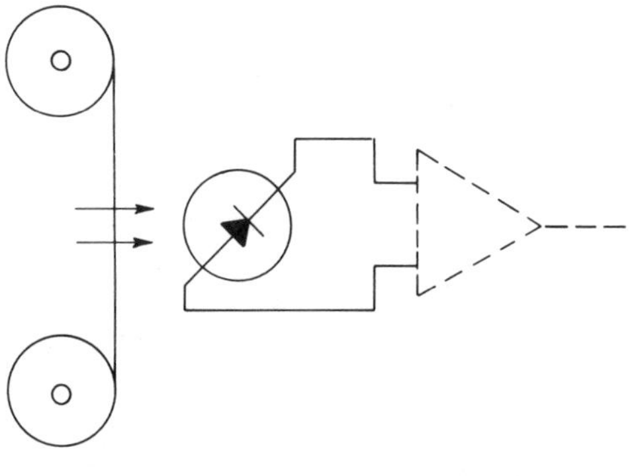

Fig. 93. *Fast response of photodiode is utilized in movie-film sound-track conversion.*

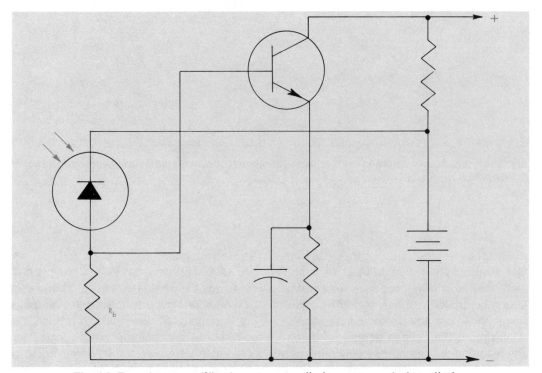

Fig. 94. *Transistor amplifier boosts normally-low output of photodiode.*

response of a photodiode to radiation is multiplied by a transistor amplifier. Changes in radiation vary the photodiode resistance, which, in turn, varies the voltage across resistor R_b. The changing voltage across R_b varies the base-emitter bias. The changing bias creates an output which is an amplified reproduction of the varying radiation at the photodiode.

Fig. 95 shows a photodiode providing the

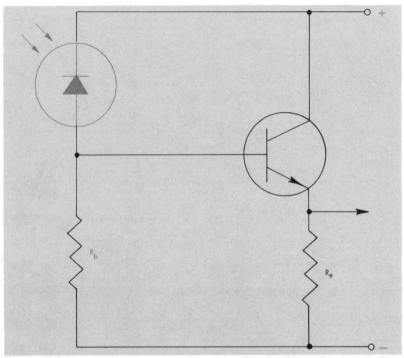

Fig. 95. *Photodiode combined with emitter-follower to provide radiation-controlled signal to low-impedance device.*

input to an emitter-follower transistor circuit. This configuration is used to supply an output to a low-impedance load: relay, silicon controlled rectifier, etc. When radiation is minimum and photodiode resistance is maximum the voltage across R_b is low. The resulting low bias allows only minimum current flow, and voltage across R_e, which is the output, is minimum. With increased radiation, photodiode resistance decreases and the voltage across R_b increases, providing increased forward bias to the base-emitter junction. Transistor conduction increases and the resulting increased voltage across R_e (output) is perhaps sufficient to operate a relay or trigger a silicon controlled rectifier.

Phototransistor

The phototransistor is a device which combines the photo-responsive characteristics of a semiconductor with the amplifying capability of the transistor. Like the conventional transistor it can be constructed of germanium or silicon in either NPN or PNP configurations. An NPN silicon phototransistor (GE L14A502) is illustrated in Fig. 96.

Construction of Phototransistor. Practical phototransistors can be constructed in both point-contact and junction designs. Fig. 97 illustrates the structure of a point-contact model. Here a pellet of N-type semiconductor is held in place in a cartridge by a retaining ring. A depression or "dimple"

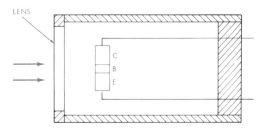

Fig. 98. *Construction of junction-type photo-transistor.*

Fig. 96. *NPN silicon phototransistor. (Courtesy of General Electric Co.)*

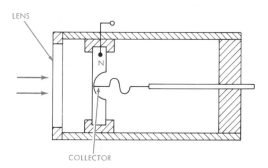

Fig. 97. *Construction of point-contact photo-transistor.*

is ground into one side of the pellet, creating a thickness of less than 0.005 in. A phosphor-bronze wire pressed against this thin section forms the collector. The semiconductor area close to the contact assumes P-type characteristics when a forming current is passed through the device.

Point-contact phototransistors are more sensitive when the available radiant energy is confined to the contact area. This is due to the fact that electron-hole pairs formed at some distance from the junction tend to recombine before they become carriers. Use of a lens to focus the radiation on the contact area overcomes this loss of radiant signal, resulting in a more efficient and more sensitive device.

Fig. 98 illustrates the construction of a junction-type phototransistor. This unit consists of a PNP or NPN germanium wafer mounted so that a lens can focus radiation in the area of the base-emitter junction. Concentration of the radiant energy at the junction is important for the same reason as in the point-contact type. A base lead is not necessary, since radiation replaces the electrical signal input. However, some phototransistors have base leads which are used in temperature stabilization and in setting the operating point.

Operation of Phototransistor. An NPN phototransistor is shown as a transducer-amplifier in Fig. 99. Without radiation a small transistor current flows. This is normal leakage. In a phototransistor it is also known as "dark" current (as in the photodiode). With radiation applied to the base-emitter area a small base current flows. This is amplified by conventional transistor action. Variations in the radiation appear in the amplifier output as variations in collector-load current.

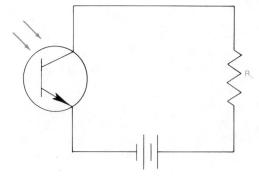

Fig. 99. *Phototransistor as transducer-amplifier.*

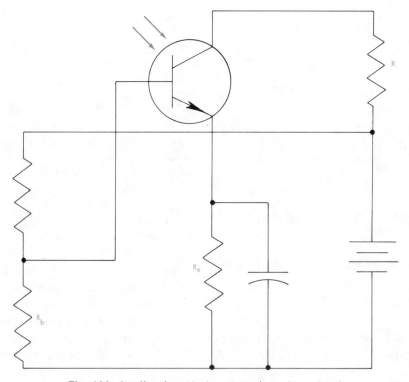

Fig. 100. *Application of phototransistor base lead.*

A phototransistor with a base lead is illustrated in Fig. 100. This lead is connected to a voltage divider which, in conjunction with resistor R_e, determines the base-emitter bias. A base lead allows for variation in the optical operating point of the phototransistor and also serves as an electrode for electrical triggering.

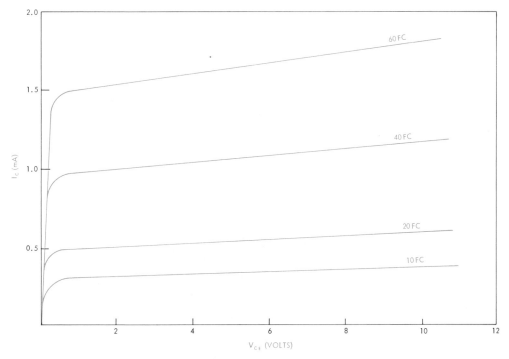

Fig. 101. *Volt-ampere characteristic of typical phototransistor for several levels of illumination.*

Circuit values in Fig. 100 are selected so that, without radiation, the phototransistor base current is below the value required for transistor turn-on. When a predetermined level of radiation is applied to the phototransistor, the carriers freed by the radiation add to the base current and increase it to a value which triggers the phototransistor. The conducting phototransistor completes the circuit between the power supply and the load.

Operation of a typical phototransistor at different levels of illumination is shown by the volt-ampere characteristic curves given in Fig. 101. The curves resemble those of a conventional transistor except that the volt-ampere curves of the conventional transistor are plotted at various values of base current.

Not all phototransistors exhibit the linearity shown in Fig. 101. Some volt-ampere curves resemble those in Fig. 102. According to Fig. 102, higher values of radiation intensity (75 to 100 f.c.) require only low values of collector voltage for maximum current flow.

Phototransistor Applications

Phototransistors are utilized in many applications in which photodiodes are used. Although their response is somewhat slower than that of photodiodes, phototransistors have the advantage of amplification. They are small, rugged, have long life, and respond well to incandescent radiation.

395

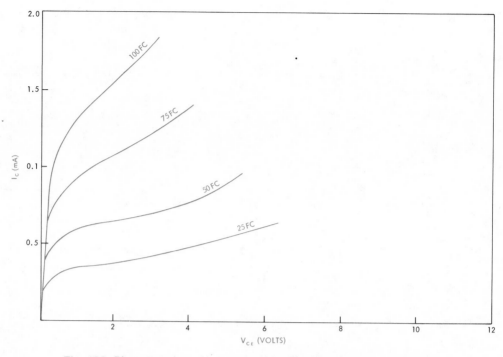

Fig. 102. *Phototransistor V-A curves showing non-linear operation.*

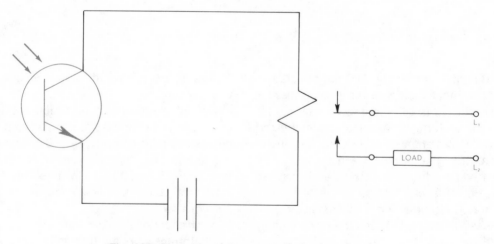

Fig. 103. *Phototransistor-controlled relay circuit.*

Fig. 103 shows a simple phototransistor-controlled relay circuit. Radiant energy striking the semiconductor creates a carrier current which is the equivalent of conventional base current. This current causes the phototransistor to conduct. Thus, the

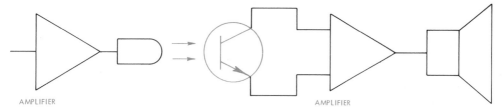

Fig. 104. *Phototransistor as optical sensor in light-beam communications system.*

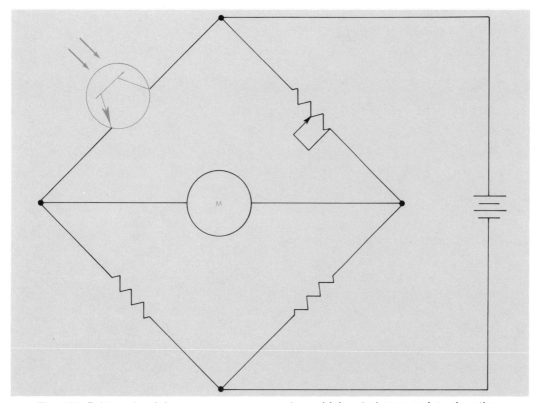

Fig. 105. *Bridge circuit improves accuracy and sensitivity of phototransistor function.*

phototransistor acts as an optical switch, connecting the relay to the power supply.

A phototransistor is shown in Fig. 104 as a receiving device in a radiant-beam communications system. Output from the amplifier modulates the radiant beam which is focused on the phototransistor. By transistor action variations in the radiation are reproduced in the collector current. The output of the phototransistor is amplified and applied to the speaker.

To eliminate phototransistor "dark current" effects and measure small currents, the bridge circuit in Fig. 105 can be used. To cancel the dark-current error, the bridge is balanced while the phototransistor is "dark." When radiated, the phototransistor conducts, decreasing the resistance of this leg of the bridge. The resulting imbalance causes a flow of current through the meter. The meter can be calibrated in units suited to the purpose for which the phototransistor is used as the transducer.

Unit 6

section 7

Light-Activated SCR (LASCR)

The conventional silicon controlled rectifier is triggered by a gate signal. However, because silicon is photosensitive, responding to both visual and infrared radiation (Fig. 88), it is used in a *light-activated* form of controlled rectifier—the LASCR. (The "light" referred to in the following discussion of the LASCR is considered to be the incandescent radiation of a tungsten lamp—normally containing both visual and infrared radiation.)

In addition to radiant activation, the LASCR can be triggered into conduction by an electrical gate signal, as in the conventional SCR. It is a high-gain device which uses small amounts of radiant energy to control much larger amounts of electrical energy. A typical commercial model is shown in Fig. 106.

Fig. 106. *Light-activated SCR (LASCR). (Courtesy of General Electric Co.)*

Construction of LASCR

The light-activated SCR and the conventional form are similar in construction except that the LASCR has a window to allow light to activate the silicon. Construction of an LASCR is illustrated in Fig. 107. It consists of three PN junctions plus anode, cathode, and gate terminals. The window transmits light to the J_2 junction area.

Operation of LASCR

When radiation strikes the silicon in the area of junction J_2, electron-hole pairs are formed as in other light-activated devices. With a potential across the unit, these carriers increase the gate current to a level which triggers the LASCR into conduction. Except for light-activation this device operates in essentially the same manner as the conventional silicon controlled rectifier.

The effect of light energy striking the silicon is known as *irradiance*. The amount necessary to trigger an LASCR is called the *effective irradiance* (H_{ET}). The same factors affect H_{ET} that affect the trigger current in an SCR. Increases in temperature or voltage reduce the irradiance required for triggering. Resistor R_g in Fig. 108 is usually essential to the proper operation of an LASCR. It limits leakage current to a value below that required to trigger the unit into conduction. It is also a factor in setting the level of irradiance required for triggering—increases in R_g reduce H_{ET}.

LASCR Applications

In applications where light is the control signal, an LASCR is comparable to a low-power SCR controlled by an electrical signal. A combination of LASCR and lamp is the equivalent of an electromechanical relay. It completely isolates output from input and has good current capacity. In addition, the LASCR has a number of advantages: fast response, long life, no contact wear or bounce, and small size.

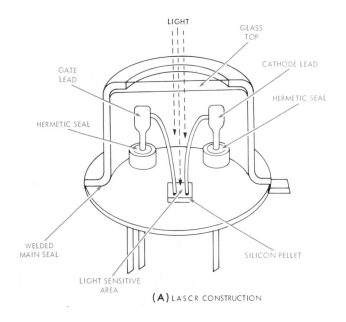

(A) LASCR CONSTRUCTION

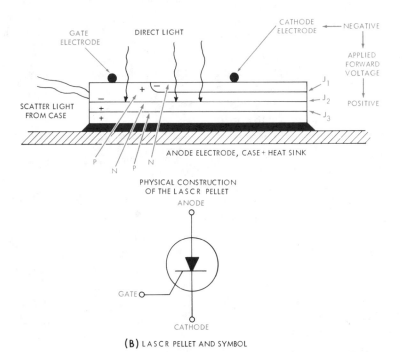

(B) LASCR PELLET AND SYMBOL

Fig. 107. *Construction of light-activated SCR (LASCR). (Courtesy of General Electric Co.)*

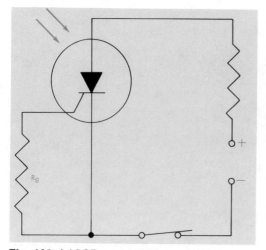

Fig. 108. *LASCR as a latching relay.*

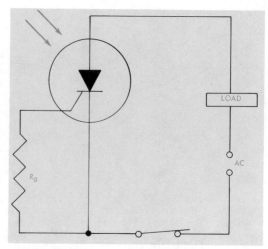

Fig. 109. *With ac power source the LASCR does not latch.*

In Fig. 108 the LASCR acts as a latching relay. When the lighting level is below a certain value the LASCR acts as an open switch in series with the load. The full supply voltage appears across the LASCR. Increased illumination triggers conduction, LASCR resistance decreases from maximum to minimum and the voltage across the LASCR drops to about one volt. Essentially the full supply voltage is across the load during conduction. Thus, the LASCR acts as a light-controlled switch. "Latching" occurs because, if the light is decreased or removed after the LASCR fires, the LASCR (like the SCR) continues to conduct. De-energization of the load is accomplished by opening the line switch.

A similar lamp-LASCR combination is shown in Fig. 109, connected to an ac supply. As in Fig. 108, when the LASCR is dark it acts as an open switch and no current flows through the load. When the LASCR is illuminated and the anode is positive the LASCR triggers on and load current flows. On the half-cycles when the

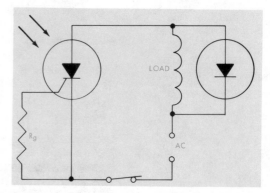

Fig. 110. *Commutating diode improves operation.*

anode is negative the LASCR cannot conduct, although it is illuminated. Because of the alternating action in this circuit, latching does not occur.

If the load is inductive (relay, solenoid, etc.) a diode can be connected as shown in Fig. 110. On conducting half-cycles the diode is reverse-biased and does not conduct. Normal current flows through the

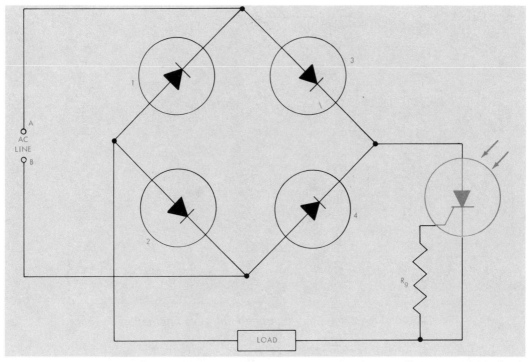

Fig. 111. *LASCR and bridge rectifier provide light-controlled full-wave direct current to load.*

load. On non-conducting half-cycles the collapsing field of the load forward-biases the diode. The diode conducts and a current flows through both diode and load. Thus, direct current flows through the load during both half-cycles of the applied ac voltage. If the load is a motor the result is smoother torque; if it is a relay, possible "chatter" is reduced or eliminated.

A bridge rectifier is used in Fig. 111 to provide light-controlled direct current through a load. When the LASCR is illuminated and line terminal A is negative, conduction occurs through diode 1, the load, the LASCR, and diode 4. During the alternate half-cyle, conduction is through diode 2, the load, the LASCR, and diode 3. Thus, the LASCR is conducting at all times

and the load is carrying full-wave direct current.

To provide light-controlled full-wave alternating current through a load, the circuit in Fig. 112 can be used. During the half-cycle when terminal B is negative, electron flow is through diode 2, the LASCR, diode 3, and the load. During the half-cycle when terminal A is negative electron flow is through the load, diode 1, the LASCR, and diode 4, to terminal B.

The circuit in Fig. 113 can also be used to provide controlled alternating current to a load. Here the inverse-parallel arrangement allows each LASCR to conduct during one half-cycle. When terminal B is positive LASCR 1 conducts; when terminal B is negative LASCR 2 conducts. Thus current

403

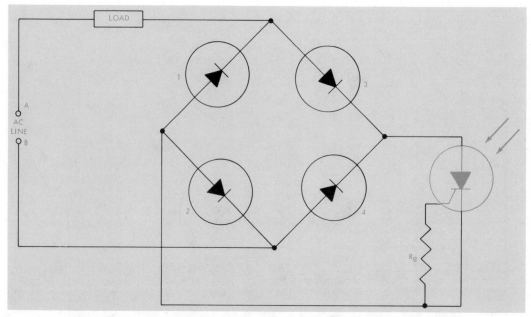

Fig. 112. *Load receiving light-controlled full-wave alternating current.*

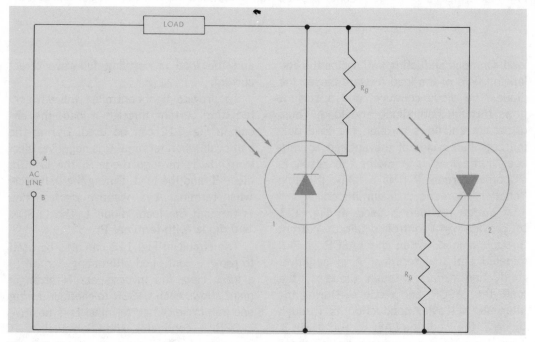

Fig. 113. *Inverse-parallel arrangement provides LASCR-controlled alternating current to load.*

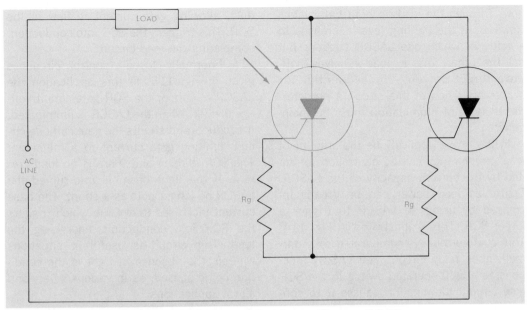

Fig. 114. *LASCR control of "normally-open" SCR.*

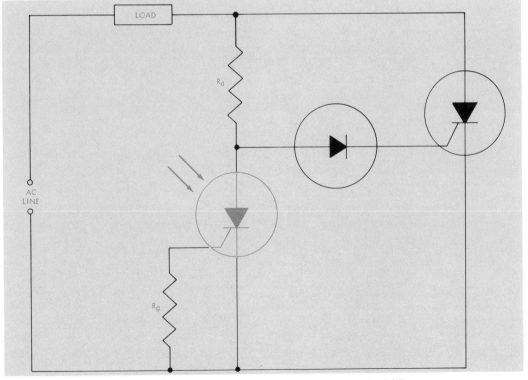

Fig. 115. *LASCR control of "normally-closed" SCR.*

flows through the load on both half-cycles. However, if the lighting level decreases to a value at which one LASCR triggers but not the other, the ac load receives half-wave direct current. Consequently, for proper operation of this circuit a predetermined level of illumination must be maintained.

In the above applications the amount of load power which can be controlled is limited by the current capacity of the LASCR. Controlled load power can be greatly increased by using an LASCR to trigger a larger SCR. This is illustrated in Fig. 114. This configuration is comparable to a normally-open relay circuit. The LASCR functions as a light-operated switch in the SCR gate circuit. Illumination causes it to conduct, allowing gate current to flow in the SCR. This triggers the SCR into conduction, completing the load circuit.

A "normally-closed" control circuit is given in Fig. 115. In this application the LASCR is part of the SCR gate-circuit voltage divider. When the LASCR is illuminated, it conducts and shunts the gate-cathode circuit, limiting gate current to a minimum. The SCR is open and there is no load current. If the light beam is interrupted the LASCR no longer acts as a shunt. The base current increases to a value which triggers the SCR into conduction, energizing the load. This circuit is useful in situations wherein the absence of light is the condition being sensed, as in various safety and alarm applications.

Unit 6

section 8

Laboratory Procedures

The laboratory procedures outlined in this Section assume that the student has access to the devices and equipment listed for each experiment, is familiar with basic circuits and circuit diagrams, and performs the work under the supervision of an instructor.

Some of the devices and circuits require 120 V ac. Adequate precautions should be observed.

Phototube: Basic Operation

Purpose: To study the response of a phototube to incandescent radiation.

Devices and Equipment: Phototube, 1P39A; power supply, 0-150 V dc; microammeter, 0-10 μA; resistor, 10 megohm, 1/4 W; light meter; light source, incandescent, variable.

Procedure:
1. Study specifications and ratings of 1P39 phototube.
2. Wire circuit as shown in Fig. 116. Have wiring approved.
3. Place phototube in darkened area.
4. Increase applied voltage to 100 V. Record current. (Observe rated maximum.)
5. Set applied voltage at zero. Apply low value of illumination to phototube.
6. Increase voltage to 140 V in 20 V steps. Record corresponding currents. (Observe rated maximum.)
7. Calculate and record resistor and phototube voltages.
8. Set supply voltage at 60 V. Increase illumination gradually and record effect on current. (Observe rated maximum.)

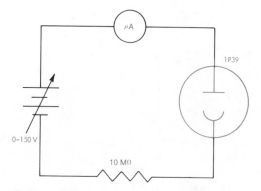

Fig. 116. *Experimental basic phototube circuit.*

9. Repeat step 8 at 80 V and 100 V.
10. Darken phototube. Set supply voltage at 150 V. Gradually illuminate phototube and record effect on current. (Observe rated maximum.)
11. Write a statement explaining effects in steps 8 and 9.

Photovoltaic Cell: Basic Operation

Purpose: To study operation of a photovoltaic cell under various conditions: (A) open circuit; (B) short circuit; (C) maximum power transfer.

Devices and Equipment: Photovoltaic cell (International Rectifier S1MC, S3MC, S4MC, S5MC, S0520E11, Vactec R5LB, R10LB, Texas Instruments LS222, LS223); light meter; light source, incandescent, variable; milliammeter; microammeter; millivoltmeter; VTVM; resistors—50Ω, 560Ω, 2200Ω, 10 kΩ, 27 kΩ, 39 kΩ, 120 kΩ, ¼-½ W.

Note: *Current meter selection depends on short-circuit current value of selected photovoltaic cell. Although true short-circuit operation requires a load of zero ohms, effective short-circuit operation can gener-*

ally be achieved with relatively low-resistance loads (a few hundred ohms). Effective short-circuit operation occurs when the load voltage is 20% or less of the cell voltage. True open-circuit operation requires an infinite load resistance. Effective open-circuit operation is possible with high-resistance loads across which at least 80% of the cell voltage appears.

Procedure:

Part A

1. Study specifications of selected photovoltaic cell.
2. Connect cell to millivoltmeter or VTVM. Darken cell area.
3. Increase illumination in steps from a practical minimum (a few footcandles) to a maximum value (500 footcandles or more). Record illumination levels and corresponding voltage readings.
4. With a load greater than 10,000 ohms check effective open-circuit operation.
5. Plot open-circuit voltage as a function of illumination.

Part B

1. Connect milliammeter or microammeter to photovoltaic cell. Darken cell area.
2. Increase illumination in steps from a practical minimum to a practical maximum. Record illumination levels and corresponding current readings.
3. Connect a 50 ohm resistance in series with cell and meter. Repeat step 2.
4. Replace 50 ohm resistance with larger values and repeat step 2.
5. Plot current as a function of illumination for several values of load resistance.

Part C

1. Determine optimum conditions (load re-

sistance, etc.) for maximum power transfer.

2. Connect calculated load resistance and current meter to photovoltaic cell.
3. Illuminate cell and record load voltage and current.
4. Calculate load power.
5. Repeat steps 3 and 4 using somewhat larger and smaller ($\pm$20%-30%) load resistances.
6. Compare power values.

Photovoltaic Cell Application: Sensitive-Relay Operation

Purpose: To study application of photovoltaic cells as relay energy source.

Devices and Equipment: Several photovoltaic cells (International Rectifier S series); relay, dc, sensitive, 25-50 ohms, 10-25 mA; milliammeter; light meter; light source, incandescent, variable; relay load and load source.

Procedure:

1. Wire circuit as shown in Fig. 117. Start with two cells and a low-resistance, low-current relay. Have wiring approved.
2. Illuminate cells and record pull-in illumination level and current.
3. Increase number of cells and check operation.
4. Wire series-parallel cell array and check operation.
5. Write a statement describing advantages and disadvantages of photovoltaic cells as relay power sources.

Photovoltaic Cell Application: Transistor-Relay Control

Purpose: To study application of a photo-

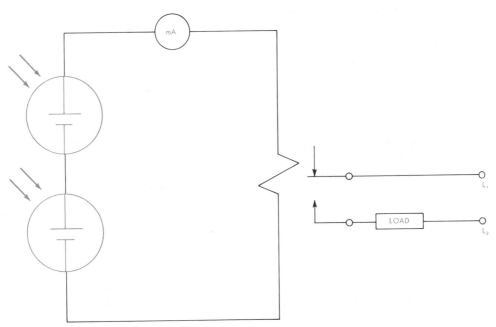

Fig. 117. *Photovoltaic cells as energy source for sensitive-relay operation.*

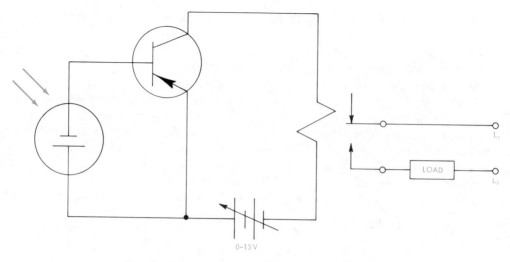

Fig. 118. *Photovoltaic cell as transistor trigger.*

voltaic cell as a trigger source for a transistor-relay combination.

Devices and Equipment: Photovoltaic cell (International Rectifier S series); relay, plate type, 2,500 ohms (Potter and Brumfield LB type or equivalent); transistor, 2N188A, 2N109, 2N407, or equivalent; power supply 0-15 V dc; light meter; light source, incandescent, variable; relay load and load source; VTVM.

Procedure:

1. Wire circuit as shown in Fig. 118. Have wiring approved.
2. Test operation of circuit using various levels of illumination and supply voltage. Record corresponding values.
3. Write a statement describing operation of the circuit under various conditions.

Photoconductor: Basic Operation

Purpose: To investigate the response of a photoconductor to a range of light intensity.

Devices and Equipment: Photoconductive cell (General Electric GE-X6, Vactec VT-100 series, Clairex 500 series, Clairex 5M series, RCA 7163); ohmmeter; light meter; light source, incandescent, variable.

Procedure:

1. Study specifications of selected photoconductive cell.
2. Connect cell to ohmmeter. Set cell and light meter in darkened area.
3. Apply minimum light to cell and meter. Record light level and cell resistance.
4. Step-increase the illumination and record corresponding light levels and resistance readings.
   Option: Repeat procedure using other photoconductive cells.
5. Plot photoconductor resistance as a function of light intensity.
6. Write a statement describing the linearity (or non-linearity of the resistance-light relationship.

Photoconductor Application: Relay Control

Purpose: To study the application of a photoconductive cell as a relay control.

Devices and Equipment: Photoconductive cell (GE-X6 or equivalent); relay, plate type, 5,000 ohms (Sigma LB 22, Potter and Brumfield LB5, or equivalent); power supply, 0-15 V dc; light meter; light source, incandescent, variable; relay load and load source; VTVM.

Procedure:

1. Study specifications and ratings of selected devices.
2. Wire circuit as shown in Fig. 119. Have wiring approved.
3. Set photocell in darkened area. Set supply voltage at 10 volts.
4. At a low light level measure and record cell voltage and coil voltage.
5. Increase illumination until relay operates. Record light level and voltages.
6. Adjust illumination and supply voltage to produce rated voltage across relay coil. Test operation.

7. Write a statement describing the effectiveness of a photoconductive cell as a relay-control device.

Option: To increase sensitivity of photoconductor-relay combination, add a transistor amplifier stage.

Photodiode: Basic Operation

Purpose: To study basic operation of a photodiode.

Devices and Equipment: Photodiode (1N77A, 1N2175, Texas Instruments T1XL80, or equivalent); power supply, low-voltage, dc; VTVM; microammeter; light source, incandescent, variable; lightmeter.

Procedure:

1. Study specifications and ratings of selected photodiode.
2. Wire circuit as shown in Fig. 120. Have wiring approved.
3. Set supply voltage at zero and apply low value of illumination.
4. Increase supply voltage in steps and record corresponding values of diode cur-

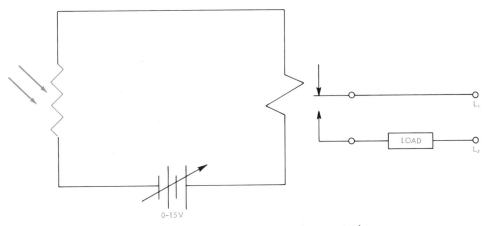

Fig. 119. *Photoconductor as relay control.*

411

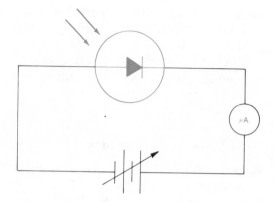

Fig. 120. *Experimental basic photodiode circuit.*

rent. Do not exceed rated voltage and power maximums.

5. Increase illumination level and repeat step 4.
6. Repeat step 4 for two or three additional illumination levels.
7. Plot diode current as a function of applied voltage for several values of illumination.
8. Write a statement describing diode current as a function of applied voltage and illumination.

Photodiode: Operation with Load

Purpose: to study operation of a photodiode with a load.

Devices and Equipment: Photodiode (1N77A, 1N2175, Texas Instruments T1XL80, or equivalent); power supply, low voltage, dc; VTVM; microammeter; light meter; light source, incandescent, variable; load resistance.

Procedure:

1. Determine a suitable load resistance by calculating and plotting a load line. Use characteristic curves from preceding experiment or published device data.

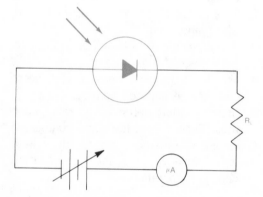

Fig. 121. *Experimental photodiode-load circuit.*

2. Wire circuit as shown in Fig. 121. Have wiring approved.
3. Set supply voltage at load-line maximum. Set illumination at a low level (from characteristic curves).
4. Record diode voltage, load voltage and current (Q-point values).
5. Repeat step 4 using other curve values of illumination.
6. Check recorded values of voltage and current against those in load-line plot. *Option:* Calculate and plot a second load

line. Install calculated resistance and test circuit operation.

7. Select an operating point on a load line at an illumination level. Assume variation (increase and decrease) in illumination. Show graphically the resulting parameter variations.

Photodiode Application: Transistor-Relay Trigger

Purpose: To study application of a photodiode as a transistor-triggering device.

Devices and Equipment: Photodiode (1N77A, 1N2175, Texas Instruments T1XL80 or equivalent); transistor, 2N188A, 2N109, 2N407, or equivalent; relay, 5-10 kΩ (Potter and Brumfield LB type or equivalent); power supply, 0-24 V, dc; VTVM; milliammeter; light meter; relay load and source; light source, incandescent, variable;

resistor, ½ W—equal to relay resistance; resistor, 51 kΩ, ½ W.

Procedure:

1. Study specifications and ratings of selected devices.
2. Wire circuit as shown in Fig. 122. Connect VTVM across relay coil. Have wiring approved.
3. Apply 20 volts dc and increase illumination gradually. Record relay pull-in voltage and current.
4. At increased illumination levels decrease supply voltage and check operation of circuit.
5. Replace relay with approximately equal resistance.
6. Apply 20 V dc and measure output (across resistance) at several illumination levels.

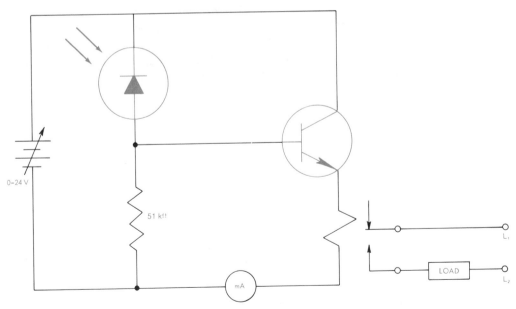

Fig. 122. *Photodiode as transistor trigger.*

7. Describe two applications of the circuit in step 6.

Phototransistor: Basic Operation

Purpose: To study basic operation of a phototransistor.

Devices and Equipment: Phototransistor (General Electric L14A502, L15A600, L15, Texas Instruments TIL81); power supply, 0-24 V dc; VTVM; milliammeter; light meter; light source, incandescent, variable; resistor, 10 kΩ, ½ W.

Procedure:

1. Study specifications and ratings of selected phototransistor.
2. Wire circuit as shown in Fig. 123. Have wiring approved.
3. Set voltage at zero and apply low value of illumination.
4. Increase supply voltage in steps and record corresponding values of collector voltage and current. Do not exceed maximum ratings of transistor.
5. Increase illumination level and repeat step 4.
6. Repeat step 4 for two or three additional illumination levels.

7. Plot collector current as a function of collector voltage for several values of illumination.
8. Write a statement describing collector-load current as a function of collector voltage and illumination.

Phototransistor: Operation with Load

Purpose: To study operation of a phototransistor with a load.

Devices and Equipment: Phototransistor (General Electric L14A502, L15A600, L15, Texas Instruments TIL81); power supply, 0-24 V dc; VTVM; milliammeter; light meter; light source, incandescent, variable; load resistor.

Procedure:

1. Determine a suitable load resistance by calculating and plotting a load line. Use characteristic curves from previous experiment or published device data.
2. Wire circuit as shown in Fig. 124. Have wiring approved.
3. Set supply voltage at load-line maximum. Set illumination at low level (from characteristic curves).

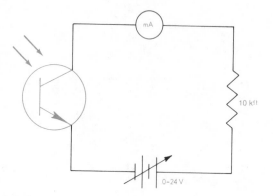

Fig. 123. *Experimental basic phototransistor circuit.*

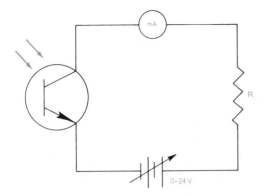

Fig. 124. *Experimental phototransistor-load circuit.*

4. Record collector voltage, load voltage and current (Q-point values).
5. Repeat step 4 using other characteristic-curve values of illumination.
6. Check recorded voltage and current values against those in load-line plot. *Option:* Calculate and plot a second load line. Install calculated load resistance and check circuit operation.
7. Select an operating point on a load line at an illumination level. Assume variation (increase and decrease) in illumination. Show graphically the resulting parameter variations.

LASCR: Basic Operation (DC)

Purpose: To study operation of an LASCR (light-activated silicon controlled rectifier) in a simple circuit.

Devices and Equipment: LASCR (General Electric L8/L9 series, GE-X2A, or equivalent); power supply, low voltage, dc; VTVM; milliammeter, 0-200 mA, dc; light meter; light source, incandescent, variable; resistors, several 10 kΩ-62 kΩ, ½ W; lamp, No. 40 or 47.

Note: *Manufacturer recommends 56 kΩ gate-to-cathode resistor for GE-X2A and L8/L9 series.*

Procedure:
1. Study specifications and ratings of selected LASCR.
2. Wire circuit as shown in Fig. 125. Have wiring approved.
3. Place LASCR in darkened area. Set supply voltage at 8 volts.
4. Increase illumination until LASCR fires. Record current, LASCR voltage, lamp voltage and brightness.
5. Connect jumper anode-to-cathode and record effect.
6. Remove jumper. Reverse supply-voltage polarity and record effect. Return to original polarity.
7. Replace 56 kΩ resistor with other values, such as 10 kΩ, 18 kΩ, 27 kΩ, 39 kΩ, 47 kΩ, 62 kΩ, and record illumination levels required to trigger the LASCR.
8. Plot level of illumination necessary for triggering as a function of the gate-to-cathode resistance.

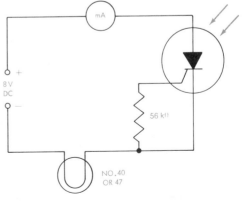

Fig. 125. *Experimental dc LASCR circuit.*

415

LASCR: Basic Operation (AC)

Purpose: To study operation of an LASCR as a light-controlled rectifier.

Devices and Equipment: LASCR (General Electric L8/L9 series, GE-X2A, or equivalent); ac supply, 6-8 V; milliammeter, dc; oscilloscope; VTVM; light meter; light source, incandescent, variable; resistor, 56 kΩ, ½ W.

Procedure:

1. Study specifications and ratings of selected LASCR.
2. Wire circuit as shown in Fig. 126. Connect oscilloscope across lamp. Have wiring approved.
3. Apply 6-8 volts to circuit and illuminate LASCR.
4. Record load and LASCR voltages.
5. Record scope patterns and currents at several illumination levels.
6. Write a statement describing operation of an LASCR as a light-controlled rectifier.

LASCR Application: Latching Relay

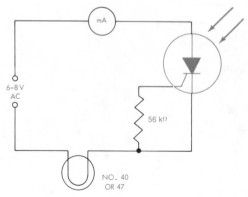

Fig. 126. *LASCR as light-controlled rectifier.*

Purpose: To observe operation of an LASCR as a latching relay.

Devices and Equipment: LASCR (General Electric L8/L9 series, GE-X2A, or equivalent); light source, incandescent, variable; load and load supply, dc; ammeter, dc; light meter; switch, SPST; resistor, 56 kΩ, ½ W.

Procedure:

1. Select dc load and supply which result in current less than rated maximum of LASCR.
2. Wire circuit as shown in Fig. 127. Have wiring approved.
3. Apply potentials and close switch to trigger LASCR. Record effect at load.
4. Open switch and record effect.
5. With correct voltage applied to load determine minimum illumination required to trigger LASCR.
6. Change load and check circuit operation.
7. Write a statement describing a practical application of this circuit.

LASCR as AC Control

Purpose: To observe control of an ac load with inverse-parallel LASCR's.

Devices and Equipment: Two LASCR's (General Electric L8/L9 series, GE-X2A, or equivalent); light source, incandescent, variable; load and load supply, ac; VTVM; oscilloscope; 2 resistors, 56 kΩ, ½ W.

Procedure:

1. Select ac supply and load which result in currents and voltages below rated maximums of LASCR.
2. Wire circuit as shown in Fig. 128. Connect scope across load. Have wiring approved.
3. Darken one LASCR. Apply potentials and illuminate second LASCR. Record load voltage and waveform.

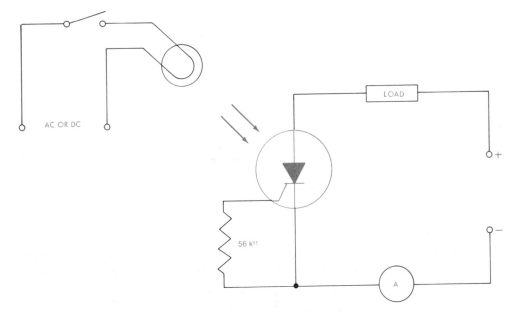

Fig. 127. *LASCR as latching relay.*

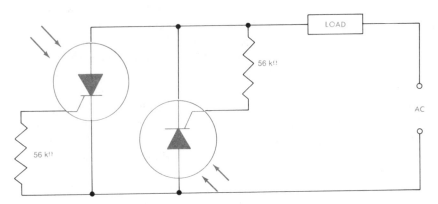

Fig. 128. *LASCR's as ac switch.*

4. Darken second LASCR, illuminate first. Apply potentials. Record load voltage and waveform.
5. Illuminate both LASCRs gradually and note triggering at scope.
6. Adjust illumination for maximum on-time. Record load voltage and waveform.
7. Write a statement evaluating back-to-back LASCR's as ac control devices.

Try writing out the answer
to each question before look-
ing up the answer.

Review Questions

1. Express the wavelength range of human vision in terms of microns and angstroms.
2. What is an advantage of a modulated light beam?
3. List some features of SSL's which make them appropriate for a variety of applications.
4. Why are indirect-gap materials less efficient than direct-gap materials as optical emitters?
5. What is the effect of temperature on the output of an SSL?
6. What effect does the addition of silicon have on GaAs emission?
7. What are some advantages of GaP over GaAsP?
8. Describe the construction of a vacuum phototube.
9. Why are alkali metals used as photocathode coatings?
10. List some characteristics of vacuum phototubes which make them useful photoelectric devices.
11. How does the response of a gas-filled phototube to an increasing anode voltage differ from that of a vacuum phototube?
12. How does the non-linearity of the gas-filled phototube affect its application?
13. What needs are met by the multiplier phototube?
14. Why is silicon preferred to selenium for use in solar cells?
15. Why are solar-cell banks usually series-parallel arrays?
16. What are some advantages of photoconductive cells over photoemissive devices?
17. How does illumination lower the resistance of photoconductive materials?
18. For what applications are typical photoconductive cells not suitable?
19. What is the approximate spectral-response range of germanium?
20. List some properties of photodiodes which make them useful in a variety of applications.
21. For what purposes are phototransistor base leads used?
22. What is an advantage of the phototransistor over the photodiode?
23. What is meant by the effective irradiance of an LASCR?
24. Why does latching not occur in the circuit of Fig. 109?
25. What precaution should be observed when the circuit in Fig. 113 is utilized?

Cover this page with a piece
of paper until you are sure
of the answer.

Answers to
Review Questions

1. The wavelength range of human vision expressed in microns is 0.4 to 0.75 microns; expressed in angstroms it is 4000 to 7500 angstroms.

2. A modulated light beam can be used to advantage in applications where ambient light interferes with the sensing of a constant light beam.

3. Among the features of SSL's which make them appropriate for a variety of applications are: high reliability, short response time, small size, light weight, low power dissipation, and low impedance.

4. Indirect-gap materials are less efficient than direct-gap materials as optical emitters because more energy is lost in indirect-gap materials during the recombination process. This is due to electrons being trapped momentarily at energy levels in the forbidden gap.

5. SSL output is inversely proportional to operating temperature. The output of a typical SSL, such as the General Electric SSL-12, decreases 25% for each 25°C increase in temperature. An opposite effect occurs with a decrease in temperature.

6. When silicon is added to GaAs peak-emission wavelength is shifted from 9000 Å to 9400 Å.

7. Gallium phosphide is more efficient and operates at lower current than gallium arsenide phosphide.

8. A typical vacuum phototube consists of an evacuated glass envelope containing a rod-like anode and a coated, half-cylinder cathode.

9. Alkali metals are used as photocathode coatings because they have comparatively low photoelectric work functions —that is, they emit electrons more easily than other materials when exposed to light.

10. Vacuum phototubes have linear response, good dynamic response at high frequencies, and good stability.

11. In a gas-filled phototube the current increases rapidly as the anode voltage increases; in a vacuum phototube an increase in anode voltage above some low value does not increase the current.

12. Because of its non-linearity the gas phototube is not used to measure illumination. However, it is useful for detection purposes.

13. The multiplier phototube can be used to amplify low-level radiant signals with good fidelity and provide output to low-impedance loads.

14. Silicon is several times more efficient

than selenium in conversion of radiant energy to electrical output.

15. Solar-cell banks are usually series-parallel arrays in order to meet voltage (series) and current (parallel) requirements.

16. Photoconductive cells are smaller, more rugged, more easily installed, and thousands of times more sensitive than photoemissive devices.

17. Illumination raises the energy level of valence electrons in photoconductive materials to the conduction level, effectively lowering the resistance of such materials.

18. Photoconductive cells are not suitable for applications which require relatively high rates of response.

19. The spectral-response range of germanium extends from about 0.3 micron (3000 angstroms) to about 1.8 microns (18,000 angstroms).

20. Photodiodes are suitable for a variety of applications because they are small and rugged, have fast response, good linearity, and long life.

21. Phototransistor base leads are used in setting operating points and providing temperature stabilization.

22. The phototransistor provides amplification in addition to photo-detection, whereas the photodiode does not amplify.

23. The effective irradiance of an LASCR is the amount required to trigger the LASCR into conduction.

24. Latching does not occur in the circuit of Fig. 109 because ac voltage is applied to the anode.

25. The lighting level should be sufficient to assure triggering of both LASCR's. Triggering of only one LASCR creates pulsating direct current in the ac load.